Custom edition containing material from:

Student Study Guide and Solutions Manual

to accompany **College Physics** Fourth Edition

Wilson/Buffa

BO LOU

Taken from:

Student Study Guide and Solutions Manual for College Physics, Fourth Edition
by Bo Lou

A Pearson Education Company
Upper Saddle River, New Jersey 07458

This special edition published in cooperation with Pearson Custom Publishing

Printed in the United States of America

10 9 8 7 6 5 4 3 2

Please visit our web site at www.pearsoncustom.com

ISBN 0–536–63047–X

BA 993078

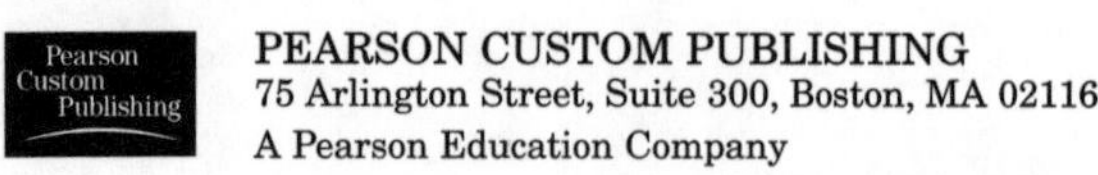

PEARSON CUSTOM PUBLISHING
75 Arlington Street, Suite 300, Boston, MA 02116
A Pearson Education Company

Table of Contents

Preface

This **Study and Guide and Student Solutions Manual** for **College Physics**, fourth edition, was prepared to help students gain a greater understanding of the principles of their introductory physics courses. Most of us learn by summary and examples, and this manual has been organized along these lines. For each chapter you will find:

- **Chapter Objectives**
  states the learning goals for the chapter. The objectives tell you what you should know upon completion of chapter study. Your instructor may omit some topics.

- **Key Terms**
  lists the key terms for the chapter. The definitions and/or explanations of the most important key terms can be found in the next section.

- **Chapter Summary and Discussion**
  outlines the important concepts and provide a brief overview of the major chapter contents. Extra worked out examples are included to further strengthen the concepts and principles. This review allows you to check the thoroughness of your study and serves as a last minute quick review (about 30 minutes) before quizzes or tests. Common students' mistakes and misconceptions are noted.

- **Mathematical Summary**
  lists the important mathematical equations in the chapter. The purpose is for self-review. You should be identify each symbol in an equation and explain what relationship the equation describes. The equation number in the text is included for reference. A last glance of this section is helpful before taking a test or quiz.

- **Solutions to Selected Exercises and Paired/Trio Exercises**
  provides the worked out solutions of the even-numbered annotated (red dot) end-of-chapter text exercises. The paired/trio exercises are similar in nature. You should try to work out the even-numbered paired/trio exercise independently and then check your work with solutions in this manual. After working the odd-numbered exercise of a pair/trio, you can check your answer in the Answers to Odd-Numbered Exercises at the back of the text. Solutions for some additional end-of-the-chapter exercises are also included.

- **Practice Quiz**

  consists of multiple choice questions and problems of the most fundamental concepts and problem solving skills in the chapter. This allows you to self-check your understanding and knowledge of the chapter. The answers to the quizzes are also given.

As you can see, this manual provides a through review for each chapter. The conscientious student can make good use of the various sections to assist in understanding and mastering the course contents and preparing for exams. I certainly hope you find this manual helpful in your learning.

ACKNOWLEDGMENT

I would like to thank the following people and organizations for their enormous help and support.

First to the authors, Jerry D. Wilson and Anthony J. Buffa, for their meticulous checking of my work and numerous constructive and helpful comments and discussions.

To John Kinard and Jerry Wilson for their solutions manual of the second edition Wilson book. Some of the solutions are still from their work.

To the editors of Prentice Hall, Paul corey, Alison Reeves, Karen Karlin, Wendy Rivers, and Liz Kell, for their guidance, and Gillian Kieff for assistance.

To Carolyn Gauntt for proof-reading this manual.

Last but not the least, to my family, Lingfei and Alina, for their essential and generous support and love. I dedicate this manual to them.

Bo Lou, Ph.D., Professor of Physics (http://instruction.ferris.edu/loub)
Department of Physical Sciences
Ferris State University
Big Rapids, MI 49307

CHAPTER 1

Units and Problem Solving

I. Chapter Objectives

Upon completion of this chapter, you should be able to:

1. distinguish standard units and system of units.
2. describe the SI and specify the references for the three main base quantities of this system.
3. use common metric prefixes and nonstandard metric units.
4. explain the advantage of and apply dimensional analysis and unit analysis.
5. explain conversion factor relationships and apply them in converting units within a system or from one system of units to another.
6. determine the number of significant figures in a numerical value and report the proper number of significant figures after performing simple calculations.
7. establish a problem-solving procedure and apply it to typical problems.

II. Key Terms

Upon completion of this chapter, you should be able to define and/or explain the following key terms:

standard unit	**fps system**
system of units	**liter (L)**
International System of Units (SI)	**dimensional analysis**
SI base units	**unit analysis**
SI derived units	**density (ρ)**
meter (m)	**conversion factor**
kilogram (kg)	**exact number**
second (s)	**measured number**
mks system	**significant figures (sf).**
cgs system	

The definitions and/or explanations of the most important key terms can be found in the following section: **III. Chapter Summary and Discussion.**

III. Chapter Summary and Discussion

1. International System of Units (SI) (Sections 1.1 – 1.3)

Objects and phenomena are measured and described using **standard units**, a group of which makes up a **system of units.**

(1) The International System of Units (SI), or the metric system, has only seven base quantities (see Table 1.1). The base units for the base quantities length, mass, and time are the **meter** (m), the **kilogram** (kg), and the **second** (s), respectively. A derived quantity (unit) is a combination of the base quantity (units). For example, the units of the derived quantity speed, **meters per second**, are a combination of **meter** and **second**. There are many derived units.

(2) The metric system is a base–10 (decimal) system, which is very convenient in changing measurements from one unit to another. Metric multiples are designated by prefixes, the most common of which are **kilo**–(1000), **centi**–(1/100), and **milli**–(1/1000). For example, a centimeter is 1/100 of a meter, etc. A complete list of the metric prefixes is given in Table 1.2. A unit of volume or capacity is the **liter** (L), and 1 L = 1000 mL = 1000 cm^3 (cubic centimeters).

2. Dimensional Analysis (Section 1.4)

The fundamental or base quantities, such as length, mass, and time are called **dimensions**. These are commonly expressed by bracketed symbols [L], [M], and [T], respectively. **Dimensional analysis** is a procedure by which the dimensional correctness of an equation may be checked. Both sides of an equation must not only be equal in numerical value, but also in dimension; and dimensions can be treated like algebraic quantities. Units, instead of dimensional symbols, may be used in **unit analysis.**

Dimensional analysis can be used to

(1) check whether an equation is **dimensionally correct**, i.e., if an equation has the same dimension (unit) on both sides.

(2) find out dimension or units of derived quantities.

Example 1.1: Check whether the equation $x = at^2$ is dimensionally correct, where x is length, a is acceleration, and t is time interval.

Solution:

The dimensions and units of x, a, and t, are [L], m; $\frac{[L]}{[T]^2}$, m/s^2; and [T], s; respectively.

Dimensional analysis: Dimension of left side of the equation is [L].

Dimension of right side of the equation is $\frac{[L]}{[T]^2} \times [T]^2 = [L]$.

So the dimension of the left side is equal to the dimension of the right side and the equation is dimensionally correct. Note: *dimensionally correct does not necessarily mean the equation is correct.* For example, the "equation," 2 tables = 3 tables, is dimensionally correct, but not numerically correct.

Unit analysis: Units of the left side are m.

Units of the right side are $(\text{m/s}^2)(\text{s})^2 = \text{m}$.

So the units of the left side are equal to the units of the right side and the equation is dimensionally correct.

Example 1.2: Einstein's famous energy–mass equivalence states that the energy a mass has is equal to its mass times the speed of light squared. Determine the dimension and units of energy.

Solution:

Since energy is equal to mass times speed squared, the dimension (units) of energy must be equal to the dimension (units) of mass times the dimension (units) of speed squared.

So the dimension of energy is $[M] \times \left(\frac{[L]}{[T]}\right)^2 = \frac{[M]\cdot[L]^2}{[T]^2}$,

and the units of energy are $\text{kg} \times (\text{m/s})^2 = \text{kg}\cdot\text{m}^2/\text{s}^2$, which is called joule (J).

---

3. Conversions of Units (Section 1.5)

A quantity may be expressed in other units through the use of **conversion factors** such as (1 mi/1609 m) or (1609 m/1 mi). Note that any conversion factor is equal to 1 (because 1 mi = 1609 m, for example) and so they can be multiplied or divided to any quantity without altering the quantity. The appropriate form of a conversion factor is easily determined by dimensional (unit) analysis.

Example 1.3: A jogger walks 3200 meters everyday. What is this distance in miles?

Solution:

Here we need to convert meters to miles. We can accomplish this by using the conversion factor (1 mi/1609 m). The result units will be m × (mi/m) = mi. We do not multiply (1609 m/1 mi) because the result units would be m × (m/mi) = m^2/mi.

$$(3200 \text{ m}) \times 1 = (3200 \text{ m}) \times \frac{1 \text{ mi}}{1609 \text{ m}} = 1.99 \text{ mi} \approx 2.0 \text{ mi}. \quad \left(\text{here } \frac{1 \text{ mi}}{1609 \text{ m}} = 1\right)$$

Note the cancellation of the units m.

We can also use the conversion factor (1609 m/1 mi). Then we have to divide 3200 m by (1609 m/1 mi) in order to get mi. $\frac{3200 \text{ m}}{(1609 \text{ m})/(1 \text{ mi})} \approx 2.0 \text{ mi}$. Note that unit cancellation tells you if you get the desired result unit.

Example 1.4: A car travels with a speed of 25 m/s. What is this speed in mi/h (miles per hour)?

Solution:

Here we need to convert meters to miles *and* seconds to hours. We can use the conversion factor (1 mi/1609 m) to convert meters to miles and (3600 s/1 h) to convert 1/s to 1/h.
[Why can't we multiply by (1 h/3600 s)?]

$$(25 \text{ m/s}) \times 1 \times 1 = (25 \text{ m/s}) \times \frac{1 \text{ mi}}{1609 \text{ m}} \times \frac{3600 \text{ s}}{1 \text{ h}} = 56 \text{ mi/h}.$$

We can also use the direct conversion (1 mi/h = 0.447 m/s).

$$(25 \text{ m/s}) \times \frac{1 \text{ mi/h}}{0.447 \text{ m/s}} = 56 \text{ mi/h}.$$

---

4. Significant Figures (Section 1.6)

The number of **significant figures** (sf) in a quantity is the number of reliably known digits it contains. For example, the quantity 15.2 m has 3 sf, 0.052 kg has 2 sf, and 3.0 m/s has 2 sf. In general,

- *the final result of a multiplication and/or division should have the same number of significant figures as the quantity with the least number of significant figures used in the calculation*, and
- *the final result of an addition and/or subtraction should have the same number of decimal places as the quantity with the least number of decimal places used in the calculation.*

The proper number of figures or digits is obtained by rounding off a result.

Example 1.5: Perform the following operations:

(a) $0.586 \times 3.4 =$

(b) $13.90 \div 0.580 =$

(c) $(13.59 \times 4.86) \div 2.1 =$

(d) $4.8\times10^{5} \div 4.0\times10^{-3} =$

(e) $(3.2\times10^{8})(4.0\times10^{4}) =$

Solution:

The final result of the multiplication and/or division should have the same number of significant figures as the quantity with the least number of significant figures.

(a) $0.586 \times 3.4 = 2.0$.

(b) $13.90 \div 0.580 = 24.0$.

(c) $13.59 \times 4.86 \div 2.1 = 31$.

(d) $4.8\times10^{5} \div 4.0\times10^{-3} = 1.2\times10^{8}$.

(e) $(3.2\times10^{8})(4.0\times10^{4}) = 1.3\times10^{13}$.

Example 1.6: Perform the following operations:

(a) $23.1 + 45 + 0.68 + 100 =$

(b) $157 - 5.689 + 2 =$

(c) $23.5 + 0.567 + 0.85 =$

(d) $4.69\times10^{-6} - 2.5\times10^{-5} =$

(e) $8.9\times10^{4} + 2.5\times10^{5} =$

Solution:

The final result of the addition and/or subtraction should have the same number of decimal places as the quantity with the least number of decimal places.

(a) $23.1 + 45 + 0.68 + 100 = 169$.

(b) $157 - 5.689 + 2 = 153$.

(c) $23.5 + 0.567 + 0.85 = 24.9$.

(d) $4.69\times10^{-6} - 2.5\times10^{-5} = 0.469\times10^{-5} - 2.5\times10^{-5} = -2.0\times10^{-5}$.

(e) $8.9\times10^{4} + 2.5\times10^{5} = 8.9\times10^{4} + 25\times10^{4} = 34\times10^{4} = 3.4\times10^{5}$.

5. Problem Solving (Section 1.7)

Problem solving is a skill that has to be learned and accumulated gradually over a period of time. You can not learn this skill in a lecture or overnight. It takes practice, lots of practice, and the exact procedure you adopt will probably be unique to you. The point is to develop one that works for you. However, there are some suggested problem solving procedures that can be followed.

(1) *Say it in words.*
Read the problem carefully and analyze it. Write down the given data and what you are to find.

(2) *Say it in pictures.*
Draw a diagram, if appropriate, as an aid in visualizing and analyzing the physical situation of the problem.

(3) *Say it in equations.*
Determine which equation(s) are applicable to this situation and how they can be used to get from the information given to what is to be found.

(4) *Simplify the equations.*
Simplifying mathematical expressions as much as possible through algebraic manipulations before inserting actual numbers.

(5) *Check the units.*
check units before doing calculations.

(6) Insert numbers and calculate; check significant figures.
substitute given quantities into equation(s) and perform calculations. Report the result with proper units and the proper number of significant figures.

(7) *Check the answer: is it reasonable?*
Consider whether the result is reasonable.

The details of these procedures can be found on page 21 and 22 in the text.

Example 1.7: Starting from city A, an airplane flies 250 miles east to city B, then 300 miles north to city C, and finally 700 miles west to city D. What is the distance from city A to city D?

Solution: Given: the distances and directions of each trip.
Find: the distance from city A to D.

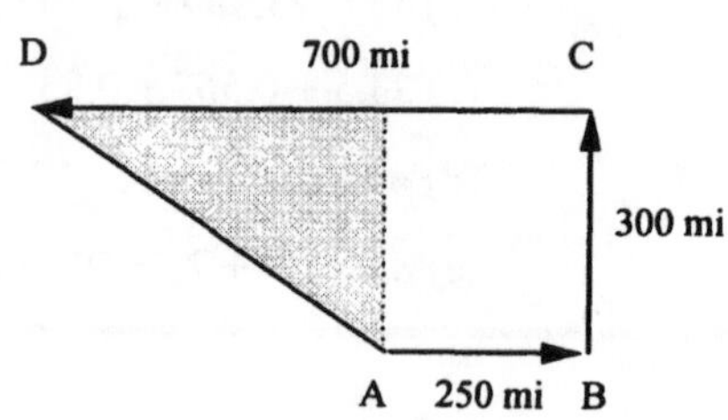

Following the problem statement, we draw a diagram. It is easy to see that the distance from A to D is the hypotenuse of the shaded right-angle triangle. The sides perpendicular to each other are 300 mi and (700 mi − 250 mi) = 450 mi.

To find the hypotenuse of a right-angle triangle, we use Pythagorean theorem:

$c^2 = a^2 + b^2$, where a and b are the sides perpendicular to each other and c is the hypotenuse.

$$c = \sqrt{a^2 + b^2} = \sqrt{(300 \text{ mi})^2 + (450 \text{ mi})^2} = 541 \text{ mi}.$$

Obviously, the units, miles, are right; the answer, 541, is reasonable; and the number of significant figures, 3, in the final result, is the same as the least number of significant figures between 300 mi and 450 mi. These checking make us feel confident that we did the right calculations.

Example 1.8: The density of the metal aluminum is 2700 kg/m^3. Find the mass of a solid aluminum cylinder of radius 10 cm and height 1.0 ft.

Solution: Given: the dimensions of the cylinder and the density of aluminum.

Find: the mass of the aluminum.

First we find the volume of the cylinder. Be aware of the different units in the problem; so we first convert all cylinder dimensions to meters.

$$r = 10 \text{ cm } (1 \text{ m}/100 \text{ cm}) = 0.10 \text{ m}, \quad h = 1.0 \text{ ft } (0.3048 \text{ m/ft}) = 0.3048 \text{ m}.$$

The volume of a cylinder is base area times height = $\pi r^2 h = \pi(0.10 \text{ m})^2 (0.3048 \text{ m}) = 9.58 \times 10^{-3} \text{ m}^3$.

Next we find the mass of the cylinder.

From $\rho = \dfrac{m}{V}$, multiplying V on both sides yields $m = \rho V$.

So $m = (2700 \text{ kg/m}^3)(9.58 \times 10^{-3} \text{ m}^3) = 26 \text{ kg}$.

IV. Mathematical Summary

Density	$\rho = \dfrac{m}{V} \left(\dfrac{\text{mass}}{\text{volume}}\right)$ (1.1)	Defines density in terms of mass and volume.

V. Solutions of Selected Exercises and Paired/Trio Exercises

6. (a) Two *Different* ounces are used. One is for volume measurement and another for weight measurement.

(b) Again, two different pound units are used. Avoirdupois lb = 16 oz and troy lb = 12 oz.

12. The dimension of the left side of the equation is $[L]$.

The dimension of the right side of the equation is $[L] + \frac{[L]}{[T]} \times [T] = [L] + [L]$.

So the dimension of the left side is equal to the dimension of the right side and the equation is dimensionally correct.

18. From $x = \frac{gt^2}{2}$, we have $g = \frac{2x}{t^2}$.

So the units of g are the units of x divided by the units of t^2, that is $\boxed{\text{m/s}^2}$.

24. (a) Since $F = ma$, newton = (kg)(m/s^2) = $\boxed{\text{kg}\cdot\text{m/s}^2}$.

(b) $\boxed{\text{Yes}}$.

From $F = m\frac{v^2}{r}$, the units of force F are $(\text{kg}) \times \frac{(\text{m}/\text{s})^2}{\text{m}} = \text{kg}\cdot\text{m}/\text{s}^2$.

34. (a) $0.5 \text{ gal} = (0.5 \text{ gal}) \times \frac{3.785 \text{ L}}{1 \text{ gal}} = 1.89 \text{ L}$. $2 \text{ L} - 1.89 \text{ L} = 0.11 \text{ L}$.

So $\boxed{\text{2 L by 0.11 L more}}$.

(b) $16 \text{ oz} = (1 \text{ pt}) \times \frac{946 \text{ mL}}{2 \text{ pt}} = 473 \text{ mL}$. $500 \text{ mL} - 473 \text{ mL} = 27 \text{ mL}$.

So $\boxed{\text{500 mL}}$ gives the most for your money and you get $\boxed{\text{27 mL more}}$.

38. Using the $\frac{1 \text{ mi}}{1609 \text{ m}}$ and $\frac{3600 \text{ s}}{1 \text{ h}}$ conversion factors.

$$15 \text{ m/s} = (15 \text{ m/s}) \times 1 \times 1 = (15 \text{ m/s}) \times \frac{1 \text{ mi}}{1609 \text{ m}} \times \frac{3600 \text{ s}}{1 \text{ h}} = 34 \text{ mi/h}.$$

So it travels $\boxed{\text{34 mi}}$ in one hour.

40. (a) represents the greatest speed.

46. (a) $x = (19 \text{ in.}) \cos 37° = 15.2 \text{ in.}$

$y = (19 \text{ in.}) \sin 37° = 11.4 \text{ in.}$

So the area $= xy = (15.2 \text{ in.})(11.4 \text{ in.}) = \boxed{1.7 \times 10^2 \text{ in.}^2}$.

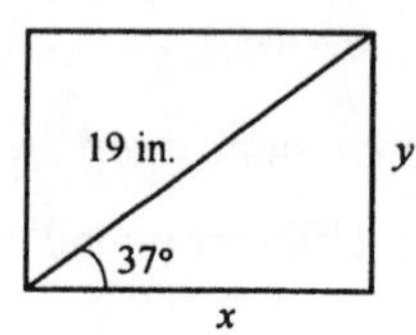

(b) Using the $\dfrac{2.54\text{ cm}}{1\text{ in.}}$ conversion factor.

$$1.7 \times 10^2\text{ in.}^2 = (1.7 \times 10^2\text{ in.}^2) \times 1 = (1.7 \times 10^2\text{ in.}^2) \times \left(\frac{2.54\text{ cm}}{1\text{ in.}}\right)^2 = \boxed{1.1 \times 10^3\text{ cm}^2}.$$

The conversion factor is squared because we are converting in.^{2} to cm^2.

48. (a) Using the $\dfrac{1\text{ kg}}{1000\text{ g}}$ and $\dfrac{100\text{ cm}}{1\text{ m}}$ conversion factors.

$$13.6\text{ g/cm}^3 = (13.6\text{ g/cm}^3) \times 1 \times 1 = (13.6\text{ g/cm}^3) \times \frac{1\text{ kg}}{1000\text{ g}} \times \left(\frac{100\text{ cm}}{1\text{ m}}\right)^3 = \boxed{1.36 \times 10^4\text{ kg/m}^3}.$$

The conversion factor $\dfrac{100\text{ cm}}{1\text{ m}}$ is cubed because we are converting cm^3 to m^3.

(b) $\rho = \dfrac{m}{V}$, ☞ $m = \rho V = (13.6\text{ g/cm}^3)(0.250\text{ L}) \times \dfrac{1000\text{ cm}^3}{1\text{ L}} = 3.40 \times 10^3\text{ g} = \boxed{3.40\text{ kg}}$.

54. The last digit is estimated so the smallest division is the third decimal place, that is $\boxed{0.001\text{ m or }1\text{ mm}}$.

62. From $V = a^3$, we have $a = \sqrt[3]{V} = \sqrt[3]{2.5 \times 10^2\text{ cm}^3} = \boxed{6.3\text{ cm}}$.

63. The area is the sum of that of the top, the bottom, and the side. The side of the can is a rectangle with a length equal to the circumference and width equal to the height of the can.

$$A = \frac{\pi d^2}{4} + \frac{\pi d^2}{4} + Ch = \frac{\pi d^2}{4} + \frac{\pi d^2}{4} + (\pi d)h$$

$$= \frac{\pi(12.559\text{ cm})^2}{4} + \frac{\pi(12.559\text{ cm})^2}{4} + \pi(12.559\text{ cm})(5.62\text{ cm}) = \boxed{470\text{ cm}^2}.$$

68. $\rho = \dfrac{m}{V} = \dfrac{6.0 \times 10^{25}\text{ kg}}{1.1 \times 10^{21}\text{ m}^3} = \boxed{5.5 \times 10^3\text{ kg/m}^3}$.

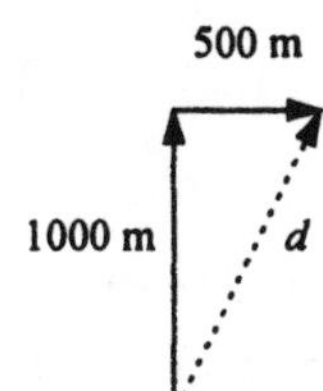

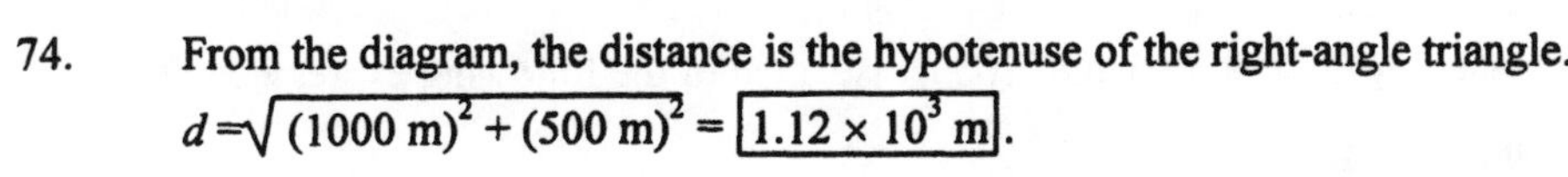

74. From the diagram, the distance is the hypotenuse of the right-angle triangle.
$d = \sqrt{(1000\text{ m})^2 + (500\text{ m})^2} = \boxed{1.12 \times 10^3\text{ m}}$.

81. By drawing a perpendicular line from the island to the shore, the distance from the island to the shore is $d = x \tan 30° = (50\text{ m} - x)\tan 40° = (50\text{ m})\tan 40° - x\tan 40°$.

Solving, $x = \dfrac{(50\text{ m})\tan 40^\circ}{\tan 30^\circ + \tan 40^\circ} = 29.6\text{ m}$.

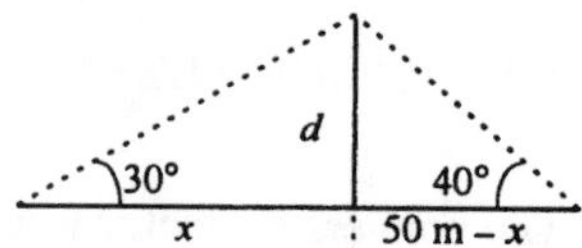

Therefore $d = (29.6\text{ m})\tan 30° = \boxed{17\text{ m}}$.

94. By drawing a diagram of the situation, we can see that the distance is the hypotenuse of the shaded right-angle triangle.

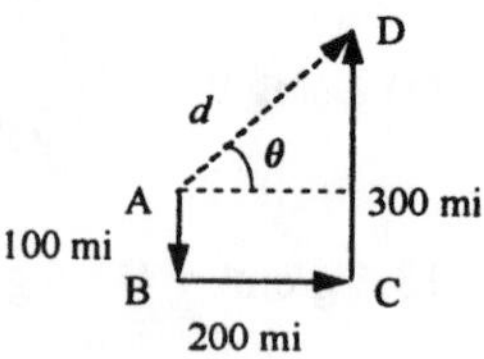

$d = \sqrt{(200\text{ mi})^2 + (300\text{ mi} - 100\text{ mi})^2} = \boxed{283\text{ mi}}$.

$\tan\theta = \dfrac{300\text{ mi} - 100\text{ mi}}{200\text{ mi}} = 1.0$.

So $\theta = \tan^{-1}(1.0) = \boxed{45° \text{ north of east}}$.

VI. Practice Quiz

1. In the SI, the base units for length, mass, and time are
(a) meters, grams, seconds. (b) kilometers, kilograms, seconds.
(c) centimeters, kilograms, seconds. (d) meters, kilograms, seconds.
(e) kilometers, grams, seconds.

2. If v has units of m/s and t has the units of s. What are the units of the quantity t/v?
(a) m (b) s^2/m (c) s/m (d) s/m^2 (e) s

3. Which one of the following has the same dimension as time?
(x is length, v is velocity, and a is acceleration)
(a) $\dfrac{x}{a}$ (b) $\sqrt{\dfrac{2x}{a}}$ (c) $\sqrt{\dfrac{v}{x}}$ (d) vx (e) xa

4. Which one of the following is *not* equivalent to 2.50 miles?
(a) 1.32×10^4 ft (b) 1.58×10^5 in. (c) 4.02×10^3 km (d) 4.02×10^5 cm (e) 4.40×10^3 yd

5. When (3.51×10^4) is multiplied by (4.00×10^2), the product is which of the following expressed to the correct number of significant figures?
(a) 1.40×10^7 (b) 1.4×10^7 (c) 1×10^7 (d) 88 (e) 87.8

6. The density of water is 1.0×10^3 kg/m^3. Find the mass of water needed to fill a 2.0 L soft drink bottle.

(a) 0.020 kg (b) 0.20 kg (c) 2.0 kg (d) 20 kg (e) 200 kg

7. The area of a room floor is 25 ft^2. How many m^2 are there on the floor?

(a) 7.6 m^2 (b) 2.3 m^2 (c) 82 m^2 (d) 2.6×10^2 m^2 (e) none of these

8. An aluminum cube has a mass of 30 kg. What is the length of each side of the cube? (the density of aluminum is 2.7×10^3 kg/m^3)

(a) 0.011 m (b) 0.11 m (c) 1.4×10^{-6} m (d) 0.022 m (e) 0.22 m

9. A person stands 35.0 m from a flag pole. With a protractor at eye-level, he finds that the angle the top of the flag pole makes with the horizontal is 25.0°. How high is the flag pole? (the distance from his feet to his eyes is 1.70 m)

(a) 14.8 m (b) 16.3 m (c) 16.5 m (d) 18.0 m (e) 75.1 m

10. A rectangular garden measures 15 m long and 13.7 m wide. What is the length of a diagonal from one corner of the garden to the other?

(a) 29 m (b) 1.0 m (c) 18 m (d) 4.1×10^2 m (e) 20 m

Answers to Practice Quiz:

1. d 2. b 3. b 4. c 5. a 6. c 7. b 8. d 9. d 10. e

CHAPTER 2

Kinematics: Description of Motion

I. Chapter Objectives

Upon completion of this chapter, you should be able to:

1. define distance and calculate speed, and explain what is meant by a scalar quantity.
2. define displacement and calculate velocity, and explain the difference between scalar and vector quantities.
3. explain the relationship between velocity and acceleration and perform graphical analyses of acceleration.
4. explain the constant acceleration kinematic equations and apply them to physical situations.
5. use the kinetic equations to analyze free fall.

II. Key Terms

Upon completion of this chapter, you should be able to define and/or explain the following key terms:

mechanics
kinematics
dynamics
motion
distance
scalar (quantity)
speed
average speed
instantaneous speed
displacement
vector (quantity)
velocity
average velocity
instantaneous velocity
acceleration
average acceleration
instantaneous acceleration
acceleration due to gravity
free fall.

The definitions and/or explanations of the most important key terms can be found in the following section: **III. Chapter Summary and Discussion.**

III. Chapter Summary and Discussion

1. Distance and Speed; Displacement and Velocity (Sections 2.1 – 2.2)

Motion is related to change of position. The length traveled in changing position may be expressed in terms of **distance**, the actual path length between two points. Distance is a scalar quantity, which has only a magnitude with no direction. The direct straight line pointing from the initial point to the final point is called **displacement** (change in position). Displacement only measures the change in position, not the details involved in the change in position. Displacement is a vector quantity, which has both magnitude and direction. In the Figure shown, an object goes from point A to point C by following paths AB and BC. The distance traced is 3.0 m + 4.0 m = 7.0 m, and the displacement is 5.0 m in the direction of the arrow.

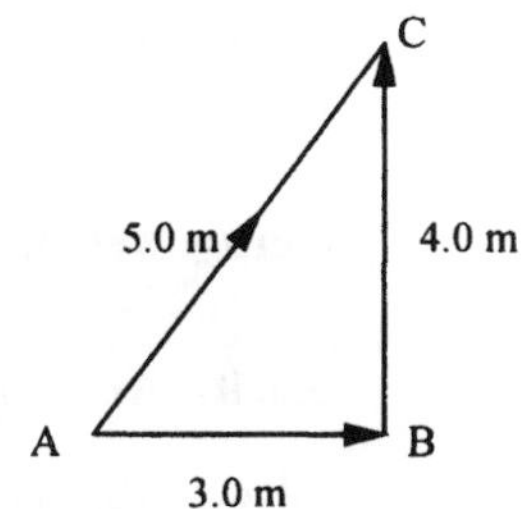

For motion in one dimension along the x axis, the displacement between two points, $\mathbf{x}_1$ and $\mathbf{x}_2$, is simply the vector subtraction between $\mathbf{x}_1$ and $\mathbf{x}_2$. $\Delta\mathbf{x} = \mathbf{x}_2 - \mathbf{x}_1$, where the Greek letter Δ (delta) is used to represent a change or difference in a quantity. For example, if an object moves from a point at $x_1 = 2.0$ m to another point at $x_2 = 4.0$ m, its displacement is $\Delta\mathbf{x} = 4.0\text{ m} - 2.0\text{ m} = +2.0$ m. The positive sign here indicated the direction of the displacement as in the positive x axis. However, if the motion is reversed, then $\Delta\mathbf{x} = 2.0\text{ m} - 4.0\text{ m} = -2.0$ m (what is the meaning of the negative sign here?).

Example 2.1: In a soccer game, a midfielder kicks the ball back 10 yards to a goalkeeper. The goalkeeper then kicks the ball straight up the field 50 yards to a forward. What is the distance traveled by the soccer ball? What is the displacement of the soccer ball?

Solution:

Sketch a diagram of the situation. For clarity, the arrows are laterally displaced.

It is obvious from the diagram that the soccer ball traveled 10 yards first and then 50 yards. So the *distance traveled* is 10 yards + 50 yards = 60 yards.

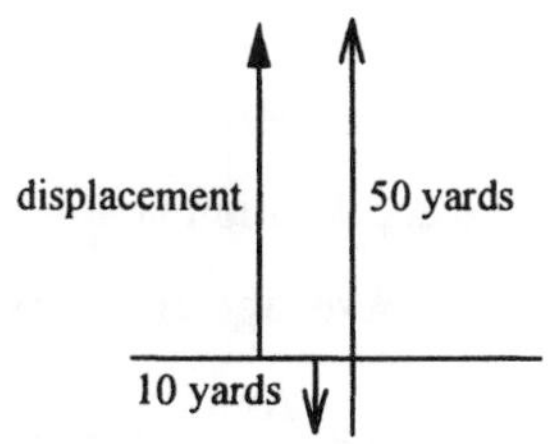

Displacement is the straight line from the initial point to the final point. The ball displaced only 50 yards − 10 yards = 40 yards **straight up the field**.

Try to solve this problem without the diagram. You will find it is very difficult to do. That is why you are encouraged to try to draw a diagram to help solve a problem.

In describing motion, the rate of change of position may be expressed in terms of speed and velocity.

Average speed is defined as the distance traveled divided by the time interval to travel that distance.

$avg.\ sp. = \frac{d}{t}$, where *avg. sp.* is average speed, d is distance traveled, and t is time interval (change in time).

Instantaneous speed is the speed at a particular time instant (t is infinitesimally small or close to zero). Since distance is a scalar quantity with no direction, so are average speed and instantaneous speed. Both tell us only how fast objects are moving.

Average velocity is defined as *displacement* divided by the time interval, $\bar{\mathbf{v}} = \frac{\Delta \mathbf{x}}{\Delta t}$, where $\bar{\mathbf{v}}$ is average velocity, $\Delta \mathbf{x}$ is displacement (change in position), and Δt is time interval. (Direction of displacement indicated by sign, + or – for one-dimensional motion.) **Instantaneous velocity, v**, is the velocity (magnitude and direction) at a particular instant of time (Δt is close to zero). Since displacement is a vector quantity, so are average velocity and instantaneous velocity. Both tell us not only how fast, but in which directions objects are moving. (Direction of velocity indicated by sign, + or – for one-dimensional motion.) The SI units of speed and velocity are m/s.

Example 2.2: If the play described in Example 2.1 lasts 5.0 s, what is the average speed of the soccer ball? What is the average velocity of the soccer ball?

Solution:

Average speed: $avg.\ sp. = \frac{d}{t} = \frac{60\ \text{yd}}{5.0\ \text{s}} = 12\ \text{yd/s}.$

Average velocity: $\bar{\mathbf{v}} = \frac{\Delta \mathbf{x}}{\Delta t} = \frac{40\ \text{yd straight up the field}}{5.0\ \text{s}} = 8.0\ \text{yd/s straight up the field}$

---

2. Acceleration (Section 2.3)

Acceleration is the rate of change of velocity of time. Note: it is *velocity* (a vector), not speed (a scalar). Hence acceleration is also a vector.

Average acceleration is defined as the change in velocity divided by the time interval to make the change,

$\bar{\mathbf{a}} = \frac{\Delta \mathbf{v}}{\Delta t} = \frac{\mathbf{v} - \mathbf{v}_o}{t - t_o}$, where $\bar{\mathbf{a}}$ is average acceleration, $\Delta \mathbf{v}$ is change in velocity, and Δt is time interval.

Instantaneous acceleration is the acceleration at a particular instant of time (Δt is close to zero). As noted, velocity is a vector quantity, so are average acceleration and instantaneous acceleration. The SI units of acceleration are m/s/s or m/s^2.

A common misconception about velocity and acceleration has to do with their directions. Since velocity has both magnitude and direction, a change in either magnitude (speed) and/or direction will result in a change in velocity, therefore an acceleration. We can accelerate objects either by speeding them up or down (change magnitude) and/or by changing their directions of travel. We often call the gas pedal of a car an accelerator. Can we call the brake pedal an accelerator? Can we call the steering wheel an accelerator? The answers are yes for both questions. (Why?)

For motion in one-dimension, when the velocity and acceleration of an object are in the same direction (they have the same directional signs), the velocity increases and the object speeds up (acceleration). When the velocity and acceleration are in opposite directions, the velocity decreases and the object slows down (deceleration). The Learn BY Drawing on page 42 in the textbook graphically illustrates this point.

Example 2.3: An object moving to the right has a decrease in velocity from 5.0 m/s to 1.0 m/s in 2.0 s. What is the average acceleration? What does your result mean?

Solution: Given: $v_o = +5.0$ m/s, $v = +1.0$ m/s, $t = 2.0$ s.

Find: $\bar{a}$.

According to the definition of average acceleration,

$$\bar{a} = \frac{\Delta v}{\Delta t} = \frac{v - v_o}{t} = \frac{+1.0 \text{ m/s} - (+5.0 \text{ m/s})}{2.0 \text{ s}} = \frac{-4.0 \text{ m/s}}{2.0 \text{ s}} = -2.0 \text{ m/s}^2.$$

The negative sign means the acceleration is opposite to velocity (deceleration). The result means that the object *decreases* its velocity by 2.0 m/s every s or 2.0 m/s^2.

---

3. Graphical Interpretation (Sections 2.2 - 2.3)

Graphical analysis is often helpful in understanding motion and its related quantities. In algebra, we learned that if $y = mx + b$, m is the slope of the graph y vs. x. If we take $t_o = 0$, then $\bar{a} = \frac{v - v_o}{t - t_o} = \frac{v - v_o}{t}$, or $v = v_o + \bar{a}\,t$. That is, the slope of a velocity vs. time graph gives the average acceleration.

In general, on a position versus time graph, we can extract the average velocity by finding the slope of a line connecting two points. Instantaneous velocity is equal to the slope of a straight line tangent to the curve at a specific point. For a velocity versus time graph, the average acceleration is the slope of a straight line connecting two points and instantaneous acceleration is the slope of a straight line tangent to the curve at a specific point. The area under the curve in a v vs. t gives displacement and the area under the curve in a vs. t graph yields velocity.

Example 2.8: The graph represents the position of a particle as a function of time.

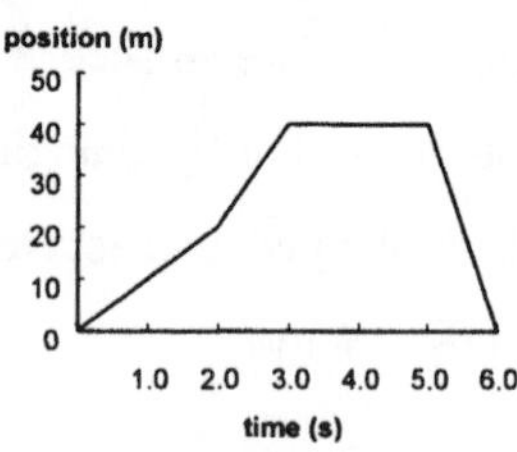

(a) What is the velocity at 1.0 s?

(b) What is the velocity at 2.5 s?

(c) What is the velocity at 4.0 s?

(d) What is the average velocity from 0 to 4.0 s?

(e) What is the average velocity for the 6.0 s interval?

Solution:

(a) Velocity is the slope of the line. $v = \dfrac{\Delta x}{\Delta t} = \dfrac{20\text{ m} - 0\text{ m}}{2.0\text{ s} - 0\text{ s}} = 10\text{ m/s}.$

(b) Velocity is the slope of the line. $v = \dfrac{\Delta x}{\Delta t} = \dfrac{40\text{ m} - 20\text{ m}}{3.0\text{ s} - 2.0\text{ s}} = 20\text{ m/s}.$

(c) The slope of the line is zero and so $v = 0$.

(d) $\bar{v} = \dfrac{\Delta x}{\Delta t} = \dfrac{40\text{ m} - 0\text{ m}}{4.0\text{ s} - 0\text{ s}} = 10\text{ m/s}.$

(e) $\bar{v} = \dfrac{\Delta x}{\Delta t} = \dfrac{0\text{ m} - 0\text{ m}}{6.0\text{ s} - 0\text{ s}} = 0\text{ m/s}.$

Example 2.9: The graph represents the velocity of a particle as a function of time.

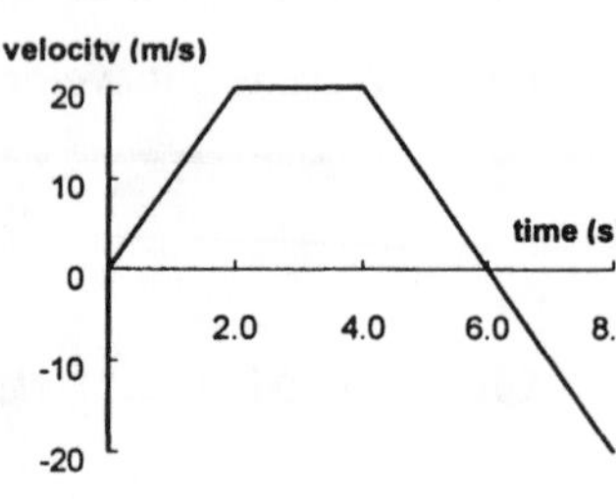

(a) What is the acceleration at 1.0 s?

(b) What is the acceleration at 3.0 s?

(c) What is the average acceleration between 0 and 5.0 s?

(d) What is the average acceleration for the 8.0 s interval?

(e) What is the displacement for the 8.0 s interval?

Solution:

(a) Acceleration is the slope of the line. $a = \dfrac{\Delta v}{\Delta t} = \dfrac{20\text{ m/s} - 0\text{ m/s}}{2.0\text{ s} - 0\text{ s}} = 10\text{ m/s}^2.$

(b) The slope of the line is zero and $a = 0$.

(c) $\bar{a} = \dfrac{\Delta v}{\Delta t} = \dfrac{10\text{ m/s} - 0\text{ m/s}}{5.0\text{ s} - 0\text{ s}} = 2.0\text{ m/s}^2.$

(d) $a = \frac{\Delta v}{\Delta t} = \frac{-20 \text{ m/s} - 0 \text{ m/s}}{8.0 \text{ s} - 0 \text{ s}} = -2.5 \text{ m/s}^2$.

(e) The net area equals the displacement.

The area of a rectangle is length × width and the area of a triangle is $\frac{1}{2}$× base × height.

$\Delta x_{0\text{-}2} = \frac{1}{2}(2.0 \text{ s} - 0 \text{ s})(20 \text{ m/s}) = 20 \text{ m}$; $\Delta x_{2\text{-}4} = (4.0 \text{ s} - 2.0 \text{ s})(20 \text{ m/s}) = 40 \text{ m}$;

$\Delta x_{4\text{-}6} = \frac{1}{2}(6.0 \text{ s} - 4.0 \text{ s})(20 \text{ m/s}) = 20 \text{ m}$; $\Delta x_{6\text{-}8} = \frac{1}{2}(8.0 \text{ s} - 6.0 \text{ s})(-20 \text{ m/s}) = -20 \text{ m}$.

So $\Delta x = 20 \text{ m} + 40 \text{ m} + 20 \text{ m} + (-20 \text{ m}) = 60 \text{ m}$.

---

4. Kinematic Equations (Section 2.4)

Our discussion is restricted to **motions with constant accelerations**. In a motion with constant acceleration, the acceleration is not changing with time or it is a constant. However, the constant could be zero, a negative or a positive non-zero constant. Zero acceleration simply means the velocity is a constant (no acceleration). For positive velocity, a negative acceleration means deceleration (speed decrease) and a positive acceleration means acceleration (speed increase). For negative velocity, a negative acceleration means acceleration (speed increase) and a positive acceleration means deceleration (speed decrease).

The symbols used in the kinematic are: v_o, initial velocity; v, final velocity; a, acceleration; x, displacement; t, time interval. Be aware that the terms initial and final are relative. The end of one event is always the beginning of another. There are three general equations and two algebraic combinations of these equations that provide calculation convenience.

$x = \bar{v}t$	displacement = average velocity × times interval,
$\bar{v} = \frac{v + v_o}{2}$,	average velocity = (final velocity + initial velocity)/2,
$v = v_o + at$,	final velocity = initial velocity + acceleration × time interval,
$x = v_o t + \frac{1}{2}at^2$,	displacement = initial velocity × time interval + $\frac{1}{2}$ × acceleration × time interval squared,
$v^2 = v_o^2 + 2ax$,	final velocity squared = initial velocity squared + 2 × acceleration × displacement.

Among the five equations listed, the last three can be used to solve the majority of kinematic problems. Which equation should you select in solving a particular problem? The equation you select must have the unknown quantity in it and everything else must be given, because we can only solve for one unknown in one equation.

Example 2.4: An object starts from rest and accelerates with a constant acceleration of 5.0 m/s². Find its velocity and displacement at a time of 3.4 s.

Solution: Given: $v_o = 0$ (starts from rest), $a = 5.0$ m/s^2, $t = 3.4$ s.

Find: v and x.

From $v = v_o + at$, we have $v = 0 + (5.0 \text{ m/s}^2)(3.4 \text{ s}) = 17$ m/s.

Also $x = v_o t + \frac{1}{2}at^2 = (0)(3.4 \text{ s}) + \frac{1}{2}(5.0 \text{ m/s}^2)(3.4 \text{ s})^2 = 29$ m.

Both velocity and displacement are in the direction of the motion.

Example 2.5: An automobile accelerates uniformly from rest to 25 m/s while traveling 100 m. What is the acceleration of the automobile?

Solution: Given: $v_o = 0$ (rest), $v = 25$ m/s, $x = 100$ m.

Find: a.

Since $v^2 = v_o{}^2 + 2ax$, $a = \dfrac{v^2 - v_o^2}{2x} = \dfrac{(25 \text{ m/s})^2 - (0)^2}{2(100 \text{ m})} = 3.1 \text{ m/s}^2$

Since a is positive, it is in the direction of the velocity or motion.

---

5. Free Fall (Section 2.5)

Objects in motion solely under the influence of gravity are said to be in **free fall**. A free fall does not necessarily mean a falling object. A vertically rising object is also said to be in free fall. The magnitude of **acceleration due to gravity** is often expressed with a symbol g. Near the surface of the Earth, the acceleration due to gravity is $g = 9.80$ m/s^2 (downward) and near the surface of the Moon, it is $g = 1.7$ m/s^2.

Note that g itself is a positive quantity, 9.80 m/s^2. If you use the upward direction as your positive reference direction, then we say the acceleration due to gravity is $-g$ = –9./80 m/s^2 (downward 9.80 m/s^2). However, if you use the downward direction as your positive reference direction, then the acceleration due to gravity is $+g$ = +9./80 m/s^2 (still downward 9.80 m/s^2).

Since free fall is in the vertical direction and we often choose the upward direction as the $+y$ axis, we replace the x's by y's and a's by $-g$'s in the kinematic equation. The results are

$$y = \bar{v}t, \quad \bar{v} = \frac{v + v_o}{2}, \quad v = v_o - gt, \quad y = v_o t - \tfrac{1}{2}gt^2, \quad v^2 = v_o{}^2 - 2gy, \text{ where } g = 9.80 \text{ m/s}^2.$$

Example 2.6: A ball is thrown upward with an initial velocity near the surface of the Earth. When it reaches the highest point

(a) its velocity is zero and its acceleration is non-zero,

(b) its velocity is zero and its acceleration is zero,

(c) its velocity is non-zero and its acceleration is zero,

(d) its velocity is non-zero and its acceleration is non-zero.

Solution:

The answer is (a) , not (b) as you might think. The velocity has to change its direction at the highest point (goes from positive to negative) and so it is zero. However, the acceleration is not zero there. The acceleration is a constant 9.80 m/s^2 downward, independent of velocity. Stop and think, what if both the velocity and acceleration are zero? Will the ball fall down after it reaches the highest point?

Example 2.7: A ball is thrown upward with an initial velocity of 10.0 m/s from the top of a 50.0 m tall building.

(a) With what velocity will the ball strike the ground?

(b) How long does it take the ball to strike the ground?

Solution: Given: $y = -50.0$ m (displacement), $v_o = +10.0$ m/s.

Find: (a) t (b) v.

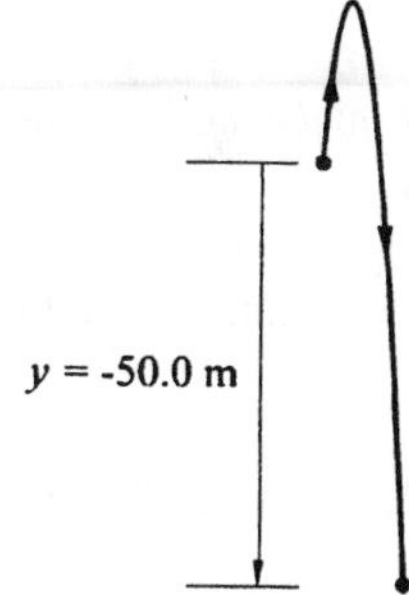

The y in the kinematic equations stands for displacement from the launch point, not distance. When the ball strikes the ground, it will displace −50.0 m, or 50 m below the launch point.

(a) $v^2 = v_o^2 - 2gy = (+10.0 \text{ m/s})^2 - 2(9.80 \text{ m/s}^2)(-50.0 \text{ m}) = 1.08 \times 10^3 \text{ m}^2/\text{s}^2$.

So $v = \sqrt{1.08 \times 10^3 \text{ m}^2/\text{s}^2} = \pm 32.9 \text{ m/s}$.

The positive answer is discarded since the ball is falling when it lands (moving downward).

Therefore $v = -32.9$ m/s.

(b) From $v = v_o - gt$, we have

$$t = \frac{v_o - v}{g} = \frac{(+10.0 \text{ m/s} - (-32.9 \text{ m/s}))}{9.80 \text{ m/s}^2} = \frac{42.9 \text{ m/s}}{9.80 \text{ m/s}^2} = 4.38 \text{ s}.$$

Try to solve this problem without using the overall displacement concept. You could break it into two phases. First, you would have to find out how high the ball goes, then secondly determine the velocity when it strikes the ground, and the total time it is in the air.

IV. Mathematical Summary

Average speed	$avg.\ sp. = \frac{d}{t}$ (2.2)	Defines average speed.
Average velocity	$\bar{v} = \frac{\Delta x}{\Delta t}$ (2.3)	Defines average velocity.
Kinematic equation 1	$x = \bar{v}t$ (2.4)	Relates displacement with average velocity and time.
Kinematic equation 2	$\bar{v} = \frac{v + v_o}{2}$ (2.8)	Defines average velocity for motion with constant acceleration.
Kinematic equation 3	$v = v_o + at$ (2.7)	Relates final velocity with initial velocity, acceleration, and time (constant acceleration only).
Kinematic equation 4	$x = v_o t + \frac{1}{2}at^2$ (2.9)	Relates displacement with initial velocity, acceleration, and time (constant acceleration only).
Kinematic equation 5	$v^2 = v_o^{\ 2} + 2ax$ (2.10)	Relates final velocity with initial velocity, acceleration, and displacement (constant acceleration only).
Equation 1 (free fall)	$y = \bar{v}t$ (2.4')	Relates displacement with average velocity and time.
Equation 2 (free fall)	$\bar{v} = \frac{v + v_o}{2}$ (2.8')	Defines average velocity.
Equation 3 (free fall)	$v = v_o - gt$ (2.7')	Relates final velocity with initial velocity, acceleration, and time.
Equation 4 (free fall)	$y = v_o t - \frac{1}{2}gt^2$ (2.9')	Relates displacement with initial velocity, acceleration, and time.
Equation 5 (free fall)	$v^2 = v_o^{\ 2} - 2gy$ (2.10')	Relates final velocity with initial velocity, acceleration, and displacement.

V. Solutions of Selected Exercises and Paired/Trio Exercises

8. Displacement is the change in position. After half a lap, the car is at the opposite end of a diameter. So the magnitude of the displacement is $\boxed{300\ \text{m}}$.

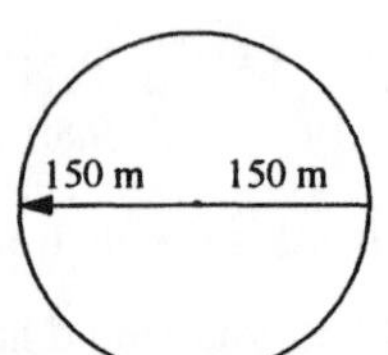

12. (a) First trip: $avg.\ sp. = \frac{d}{t} = \frac{150 \text{ km}}{2.5 \text{ h}} = \boxed{60 \text{ km/h}}$.

Return trip: $avg.\ sp. = \frac{150 \text{ km}}{2.0 \text{ h}} = \boxed{75 \text{ km/h}}$.

(b) Total trip: $avg.\ sp. = \frac{150 \text{ km} + 150 \text{ km}}{2.5 \text{ h} + 2.0 \text{ h}} = \boxed{67 \text{ km/h}}$.

15. Draw a diagram of the situation.

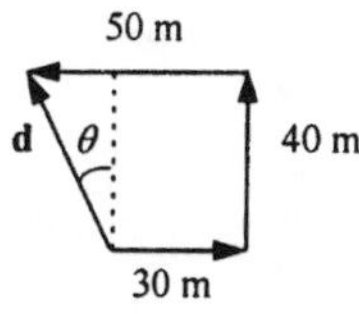

$d = \sqrt{(40 \text{ m})^2 + (50\text{m} - 30 \text{ m})^2} = \boxed{45 \text{ m}}$.

$\theta = \tan^{-1}\left(\frac{50 \text{ m} - 30 \text{ m}}{40 \text{ m}}\right) = \boxed{27° \text{ west of north}}$.

16. (a) $avg.\ sp. = \frac{d}{t} = \frac{2(10 \text{ m})}{2.4 \text{ s}} = \boxed{8.3 \text{ m/s}}$.

(b) Since the ball is caught at the initial height, the displacement is zero.

So the average velocity is $\boxed{\text{zero}}$.

20. (a) From the definition of average velocity, $\bar{v} = \frac{\Delta x}{\Delta t}$, we have

$\bar{v}_{AB} = \frac{1.0 \text{ m} - 1.0 \text{ m}}{1.0 \text{ s} - 0} = \boxed{0}$; $\bar{v}_{BC} = \frac{7.0 \text{ m} - 1.0 \text{ m}}{3.0 \text{ s} - 1.0 \text{ s}} = \boxed{3.0 \text{ m/s}}$;

$\bar{v}_{CD} = \frac{9.0 \text{ m} - 7.0 \text{ m}}{4.5 \text{ s} - 3.0 \text{ s}} = \boxed{1.3 \text{ m/s}}$; $\bar{v}_{DE} = \frac{7.0 \text{ m} - 9.0 \text{ m}}{6.0 \text{ s} - 4.5 \text{ s}} = \boxed{-1.3 \text{ m/s}}$;

$\bar{v}_{EF} = \frac{2.0 \text{ m} - 7.0 \text{ m}}{9.0 \text{ s} - 6.0 \text{ s}} = \boxed{-1.7 \text{ m/s}}$; $\bar{v}_{FG} = \frac{2.0 \text{ m} - 2.0 \text{ m}}{11.0 \text{ s} - 9.0 \text{ s}} = \boxed{0}$;

$\bar{v}_{BG} = \frac{2.0 \text{ m} - 1.0 \text{ m}}{11.0 \text{ s} - 1.0 \text{ s}} = \boxed{0.10 \text{ m/s}}$.

(b) $\boxed{\text{The motion of BC, CD, and DE are not uniform}}$ since they are not straight lines.

(c) The object changes its direction of motion at point D. So it has to stop momentarily $v = \boxed{0}$.

26. To the runner on right, the runner on left is running at a velocity of $+4.50 \text{ m/s} - (-3.50 \text{ m/s}) = +8.00 \text{ m/s}$.

So it takes $\Delta t = \frac{\Delta x}{\bar{v}} = \frac{100 \text{ m}}{8.00 \text{ m/s}} = \boxed{12.5 \text{ s}}$.

They meet at $(4.50 \text{ m/s})(12.5 \text{ s}) = \boxed{56.3 \text{ m from the initial position of the runner on left}}$.

28. (d). Any change in either magnitude or direction results in a change in velocity. The brakes and gear shift change the magnitude and the steering wheel and changes the direction.

34. $60 \text{ mi/h} = (60 \text{ mi/h}) \times \dfrac{1609 \text{ m}}{1 \text{ mi}} \times \dfrac{1 \text{ h}}{3600 \text{ s}} = 26.8 \text{ m/s}.$

$$\bar{a} = \frac{\Delta v}{\Delta t} = \frac{26.8 \text{ m/s} - 0}{3.9 \text{ s}} = \boxed{6.9 \text{ m/s}^2}$$

40. (a) $\bar{a}_{0\text{-}1.0 \text{ s}} = \dfrac{\Delta v}{\Delta t} = \dfrac{0-0}{1.0 \text{ s} - 0} = \boxed{0};$

$$\bar{a}_{1.0 \text{ s-}3.0 \text{ s}} = \frac{8.0 \text{ m/s} - 0}{3.0 \text{ s} - 1.0 \text{ s}} = \boxed{4.0 \text{ m/s}^2};$$

$$\bar{a}_{3.0 \text{ s-}8.0 \text{ s}} = \frac{-12 \text{ m/s} - 8.0 \text{ m/s}}{8.0 \text{ s} - 3.0 \text{ s}} = \boxed{-4.0 \text{ m/s}^2};$$

$$\bar{a}_{8.0 \text{ s-}9.0 \text{ s}} = \frac{-4 \text{ m/s} - (-12.0 \text{ m/s})}{9.0 \text{ s} - 8.0 \text{ s}} = \boxed{8.0 \text{ m/s}^2};$$

$$\bar{a}_{9.0 \text{ s-}13.0 \text{ s}} = \frac{-4.0 \text{ m/s} - 4.0 \text{ m/s}}{13.0 \text{ s} - 9.0 \text{ s}} = \boxed{0}.$$

(b) $\boxed{\text{Constant velocity of } -4.0 \text{ m/s}}$.

46. Given: $v_o = 0$, $a = 2.0 \text{ m/s}^2$, $t = 5.00$ s. Find: v and x.

(a) $v = v_o + at = 0 + (2.0 \text{ m/s}^2)(5.0 \text{ s}) = \boxed{10 \text{ m/s}}$.

(b) $x = v_o t + \frac{1}{2}at^2 = 0 + \frac{1}{2}(2.0 \text{ m/s}^2)(5.0 \text{ s})^2 = \boxed{25 \text{ m}}$.

48. $\boxed{-3.1 \text{ m/s}^2}$.

50. Given: $v_o = 0$, $v = 560 \text{ km/h} = 155.6 \text{ m/s}$, $x = 400$ m. Find: t.

$x = \bar{v}t = \dfrac{v_o + v}{2}\,t$, ☞ $t = \dfrac{2x}{v_o + v} = \dfrac{2(400 \text{ m})}{0 + 155.6 \text{ m/s}} = \boxed{5.14 \text{ s}}$.

54. Given: $v_o = 330 \text{ m/s}$, $v = 0$, $x = 30 \text{ cm} = 0.30$ m. Find: a.

$v^2 = v_o^2 + 2ax$, ☞ $a = \dfrac{v^2 - v_o^2}{2x} = \dfrac{(0)^2 - (330 \text{ m/s})^2}{2(0.30 \text{ m})} = -\boxed{1.8 \times 10^5 \text{ m/s}^2}$.

The negative sign here indicates that the acceleration vector is in opposite direction of velocity.

56. $\boxed{2.0 \times 10^2 \text{ m/s}^2}$.

58. $40 \text{ km/h} = (40 \text{ km/h}) \times \dfrac{1000 \text{ m}}{1 \text{ km}} \times \dfrac{1 \text{ h}}{3600 \text{ s}} = 11.11 \text{ m/s}.$

During reaction, the car travels $d = (11.11 \text{ m/s})(0.25 \text{ s}) = 2.78 \text{ m}$. So the car really has only $13 \text{ m} - 2.78 \text{ m} = 10.2 \text{ m}$ to come to rest. Let's calculate the stopping distance of the car.

Given: $v_o = 11.1 \text{ m/s}$, $v = 0$, $a = -8.0 \text{ m/s}^2$. Find: x.

$$v^2 = v_o^2 + 2ax, \quad ☞ \quad x = \frac{v^2 - v_o^2}{2a} = \frac{0 - (11.1 \text{ m/s})^2}{2(-8.0 \text{ m/s}^2)} = 7.70 \text{ m}.$$

Therefore it takes the car only $2.78 \text{ m} + 7.70 \text{ m} = \boxed{10.5 \text{ m} < 13 \text{ m}}$ to stop.

$\boxed{\text{Yes}}$, the car will stop before hitting the child.

66. (c). It accelerates at 9.80 m/s^2 so it increases its speed by 9.80 m/s in each second.

70. (a) A straight line, slope = $-g$. (b) A parabola.

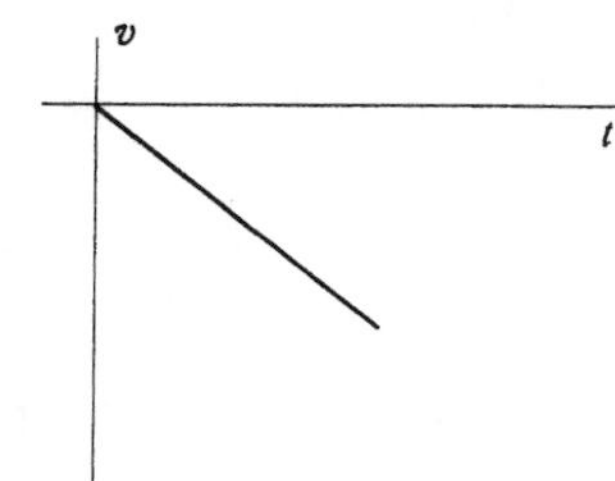

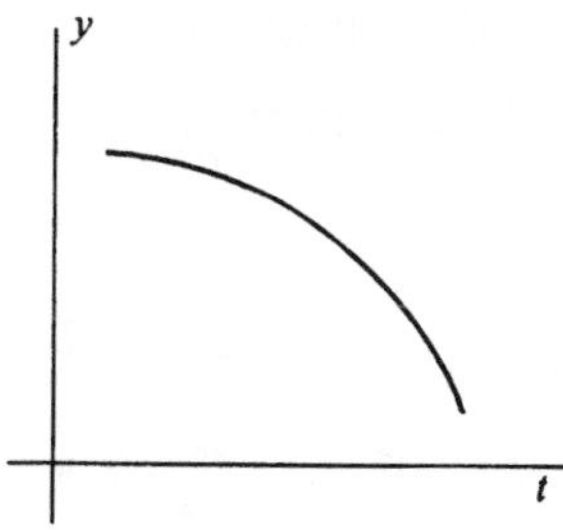

74. Given: $v_o = 15 \text{ m/s}$, $v = 0$ (maximum height). Find: y.

$$v^2 = v_o^2 - 2gy, \quad ☞ \quad y = \frac{v_o^2 - v^2}{2g} = \frac{(15 \text{ m/s})^2 - (0)^2}{2(9.80 \text{ m/s}^2)} = \boxed{11 \text{ m}}.$$

76. (a) Given: $v_o = 21 \text{ m/s}$, $t = 3.0 \text{ s}$. Find: y.

$$y = v_o t - \tfrac{1}{2}gt^2 = (21 \text{ m/s})(3.0 \text{ s}) - \tfrac{1}{2}(9.80 \text{ m/s}^2)(3.0 \text{ s})^2 = \boxed{19 \text{ m}}.$$

(b) $12 \text{ m} = (21 \text{ m/s})t - \tfrac{1}{2}(9.80 \text{ m/s}^2)t^2$, or $4.90t^2 - 21t + 12 = 0$.

Solving the quadratic equation, $t = \boxed{0.68 \text{ s (on the way up) or } 3.6 \text{ s (on the way down)}}$.

86. (a) Given: $v_o = 12.50 \text{ m/s}$ (ascending), $y = -60.0 \text{ m}$. Find: t.

$y = v_o t - \tfrac{1}{2}gt^2$, ☞ $-60.0 \text{ m} = (12.50 \text{ m/s})t - (4.90 \text{ m/s}^2)t^2$.

Reduce to a quadratic equation: $4.90t^2 - 12.50t - 60.0 = 0$.

Solving, $t = \boxed{5.00 \text{ s}}$ or -2.45 s which is physically meaningless.

(b) $v = v_o - gt = 12.50 \text{ m/s} - (9.80 \text{ m/s}^2)(5.00 \text{ s}) = -36.5 \text{ m/s} = \boxed{36.5 \text{ m/s downward}}$.

89. (a) Since 25.0 m is a distance, we need to find the maximum height first.

Given: $v_o = 7.25$ m/s, $v = 0$. Find: y.

$$v^2 = v_o^2 - 2gy, \quad ☞ \quad y = \frac{v_o^2 - v^2}{2g} = \frac{(7.25 \text{ m/s})^2 - 0}{2(9.80 \text{ m/s}^2)} = 2.68 \text{ m}.$$

So if it has traveled a distance of 25.0 m, it has traveled

25.0 m – 2.68 m = 22.3 m downward after reaching maximum height.

So the displacement is $y = -(22.3 \text{ m} - 2.68 \text{ m}) = -19.6$ m.

Now $v^2 = v_o^2 - 2gy = (7.25 \text{ m/s})^2 - 2(9.80 \text{ m/s}^2)(-19.6 \text{ m})$

$= 4.37 \times 10^2 \text{ m}^2/\text{s}^2$. So $v = -\sqrt{v^2} = \boxed{-20.9 \text{ m/s}}$.

2.68 m

22.3 m

y = -19.6 m

(b) $v = v_o - gt$, ☞ $t = \frac{v_o - v}{g} = \frac{7.25 \text{ m/s} - (-20.9 \text{ m/s})}{9.80 \text{ m/s}^2} = \boxed{2.87 \text{ s}}$.

95. From the definition of displacement,

$d = \sqrt{(50 \text{ m})^2 + (50 \text{ m})^2} = \boxed{71 \text{ m}}$.

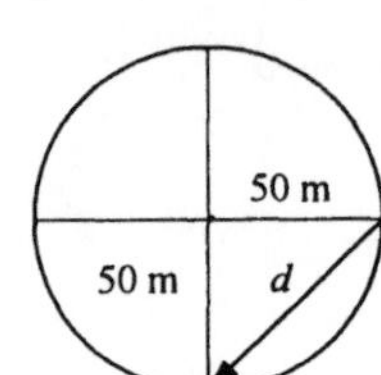

101. (a) Given: $v_o = 15$ m/s, $y = -25$ m. Find: v.

$v^2 = v_o^2 - 2gy = (15 \text{ m/s})^2 - 2(9.80 \text{ m/s}^2)(-25 \text{ m}) = 715 \text{ m}^2/\text{s}^2$.

So $v = -\sqrt{715 \text{ m}^2/\text{s}^2} = -\boxed{27 \text{ m/s}}$

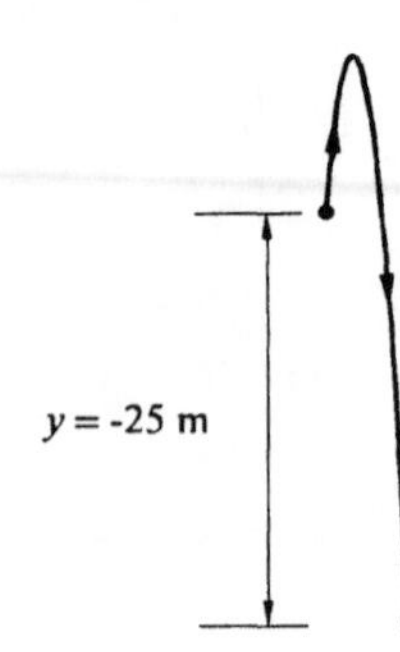

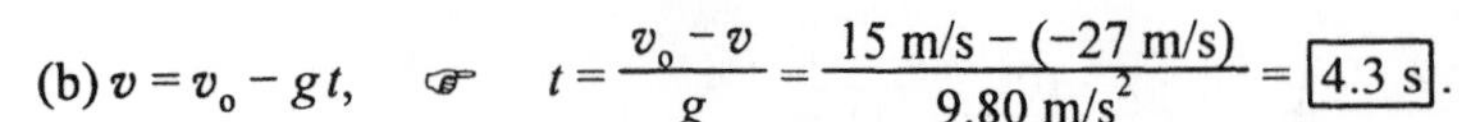

(b) $v = v_o - gt$, ☞ $t = \frac{v_o - v}{g} = \frac{15 \text{ m/s} - (-27 \text{ m/s})}{9.80 \text{ m/s}^2} = \boxed{4.3 \text{ s}}$.

VI. Practice Quiz

1. If you run a full lap around a circular track of radius 25 m in 100 s, the magnitude of your average velocity is

(a) zero. (b) 0.20 m/s. (c) 0.50 m/s. (d) 1.0 m/s. (e) 3.14 m/s.

2. An object moving in the +x axis experiences an acceleration of +5.0 m/s^2. This means the object is

(a) traveling 5.0 m in every second.

(b) traveling at 5.0 m/s in every second.

(c) changing its velocity by 5.0 m/s.

(d) increasing its velocity by 5.0 m/s in every second.

3. A car starts from rest and travels 100 m in 5.0 s. What is the magnitude of the constant acceleration.

(a) zero (b) 5.0 m/s^2 (c) 8.0 m/s^2 (d) 10 m/s^2 (e) 40 m/s^2

4. An object is thrown straight up. When it is at the highest point

(a) both its velocity and acceleration are zero.

(b) neither its velocity nor its acceleration is zero.

(c) its velocity is zero and its acceleration is not zero.

(d) its velocity is not zero and its acceleration is zero.

5. Human reaction time is usually greater than 0.10 s. If your lab partner holds a ruler between your fingers and releases it without warning, how far can you expect the ruler to fall before you catch it?

(a) at least 3.0 cm (b) at least 4.9 cm (c) at least 6.8 cm (d) at least 9.8 cm (e) at least 11.0 cm

6. Which one of the following quantities is an example of a vector?

(a) distance (b) acceleration (c) speed (d) mass

7. A ball is thrown vertically upward with a speed v. An identical second ball is thrown upward with a speed $2v$ (twice as fast). What is the ratio of the height of the second ball to that of the first ball? (How many times higher does the second ball go than the first ball?)

(a) 4:1 (b) 2:1 (c) 1.7:1 (d) 1.4:1 (e) 1:1

8. A car starts from rest and accelerates for 4.0 m/s^2 for 5.0 s, then maintains that velocity for 10 s and then decelerates at the rate of 2.0 m/s^2 for 4.0 s. What is the final speed of the car?

(a) 20 m/s (b) 16 m/s (c) 12 m/s (d) 10 m/s (e) 8.0 m/s

9. An object moves 5.0 m north and then 3.0 m east. Find both the distance traveled and the magnitude of the displacement.

(a) 8.0 m; 5.8 m (b) 5.8 m; 8.0 m (c) 8.0 m; 4.0 m (d) 4.0 m; 8.0 m (e) 5.8 m, 34 m

10. A car with a speed of 25.0 m/s brakes to a stop. If the maximum deceleration of the car is 10.0 m/s^2, what is the minimum stopping distance?

(a) 0.032 m (b) 0.80 m (c) 1.3 m (d) 31 m (e) 6.3×10^2 m

Answers to Practice Quiz:

1. a 2. d 3. c 4. c 5. b 6. b 7. a 8. c 9. a 10. d

CHAPTER 3

Motion in Two Dimensions

I. Chapter Objectives

Upon completion of this chapter, you should be able to:

1. analyze motion in terms of its components and apply the kinematic equations to components of motion.
2. add and subtract vectors graphically and analytically.
3. determine relative velocities through vector addition and subtraction.
4. analyze projectile motion to find position, time of flight, and range.

II. Key Terms

Upon completion of this chapter, you should be able to define and/or explain the following key terms:

components of motion	**unit vector**
vector addition (subtraction)	**component form**
triangle method	**analytical component method**
parallelogram method	**relative velocity**
polygon method	**projectile motion**
component method	**parabola**
magnitude-angle form	**range**

The definitions and/or explanations of the most important key terms can be found in the following section: **III. Chapter Summary and Discussion.**

III. Chapter Summary and Discussion

1. Components of Motion (Section 3.1)

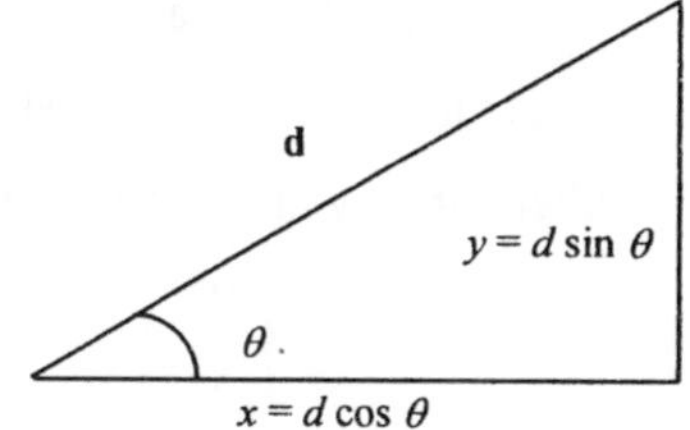

Motion in two dimensions, or curvilinear motion, is motion in which an object moves in a plane which can be described by a rectangular coordinate system. To analyze such motion, quantities are usually resolved into rectangular **components**. The diagram on the right shows the displacement vector being resolved into $x = d\cos\theta$ and $y = d\sin\theta$, the rectangular coordinates. Similarly, velocity and acceleration vectors, **v** and **a**, are resolved into $v_x = v\cos\theta$, $v_y = v\sin\theta$, and $a_x = a\cos\theta$, $a_y = a\sin\theta$, their horizontal and vertical components, respectively.

Note: the angle θ used in the above calculations is the angle relative to the x axis.

Once the displacement, velocity, and acceleration vectors are resolved into their respective components, we can apply the kinematic equations from Chapter 2 to the motion in the x and y directions. For example:

$$v_x = v_{xo} + a_x t, \quad v_y = v_{yo} + a_y t, \quad x = v_{xo} t + \tfrac{1}{2} a_x t^2, \quad y = v_{yo} t + \tfrac{1}{2} a_y t^2, \quad \text{etc.}$$

The key to success in solving two dimensional motion is to resolve the motion in components. Remember to treat the components as independent, i.e., a_x has nothing to do with a_y, etc. However, the time in all the equations is the same, providing a common link. Always think about resolving vectors into components when working problems in two dimensions.

Example 3.1: An airplane is moving at 250 mi/h in a direction of 35° N of E. Find the components of the plane's velocity in the eastward and northward directions.

Solution: Given: **v** = 250 mi/h in a direction of 35° N of E,

or, v = 250 mi/h and θ = 35°.

Find: v_x and v_y.

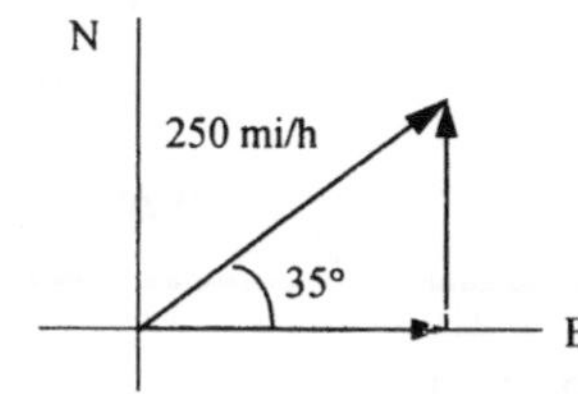

$v_x = v\cos\theta$ = (250 mi/h) cos 35° = 205 mi/h,

$v_y = v\sin\theta$ = (250 mi/h) sin 35° = 143 mi/h.

Example 3.2: A boat travels with a speed of 5.0 m/s in a straight path on a still lake. Suddenly, a steady wind pushes the boat perpendicularly to its straight line path with a speed of 3.0 m/s for 5.0 s. Relative to its position just when the wind started to blow, where is the boat at the end of this time?

Solution: Given: $v_{xo} = 5.0$ m/s, $a_x = 0$, $v_{yo} = 3.0$ m/s, $a_y = 0$, $t = 5.0$ s.

Find: x and y.

Both motions are motion with constant velocity. Choose the straight path of the boat as x axis and the direction of wind as the y axis.

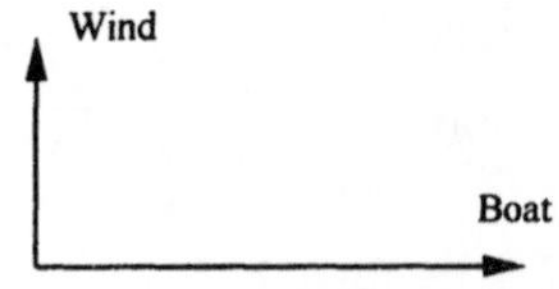

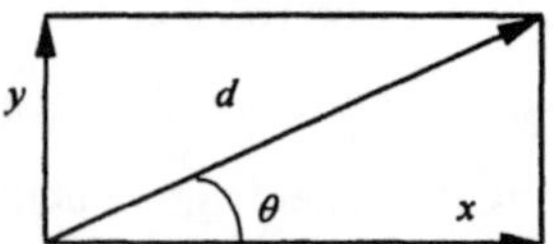

$x = v_{xo}\,t + \frac{1}{2}a_x t^2 = (5.0 \text{ m/s})(5.0 \text{ s}) + 0 = 25 \text{ m},$

$y = v_{yo}\,t + \frac{1}{2}a_y t^2 = (3.0 \text{ m/s})(5.0 \text{ s}) + 0 = 15 \text{ m}.$

Or $d = \sqrt{x^2 + y^2} = \sqrt{(25 \text{ m})^2 + (15 \text{ m})^2} = 29 \text{ m},$

And $\theta = \tan^{-1}\frac{y}{x} = \frac{15 \text{ m}}{25 \text{ m}} = 31°.$

---

2. Vector Addition and Subtraction (Section 3.2)

Vector addition can be done graphically with the triangle method or the parallelogram method for two vectors and the polygon method for more than two vectors. **Vector subtraction** is a special case of vector addition because **A** − **B** = **A** + (−**B**), and a negative vector is defined as a vector having the same magnitude but opposite in direction to the positive vector. For example, the negative vector of a velocity vector at 45 m/s north is simply 45 m/s south. When adding or subtracting vectors graphically, a convenient scale must be used.

Example 3.3: Two vectors **A** and **B** are given. Show

(a) **A** + **B** with the triangle method.

(b) **A** + **B** with the parallelogram method.

(c) **A** − **B** with the triangle method.

(d) **A** − **B** with the parallelogram method.

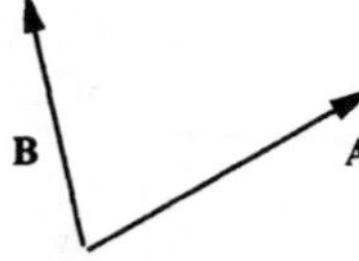

Solution: (a)

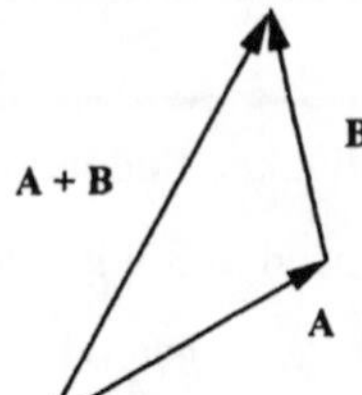

(b)

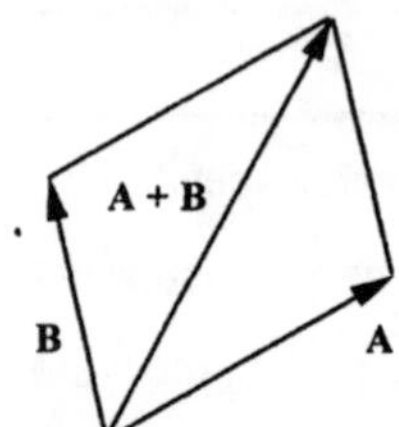

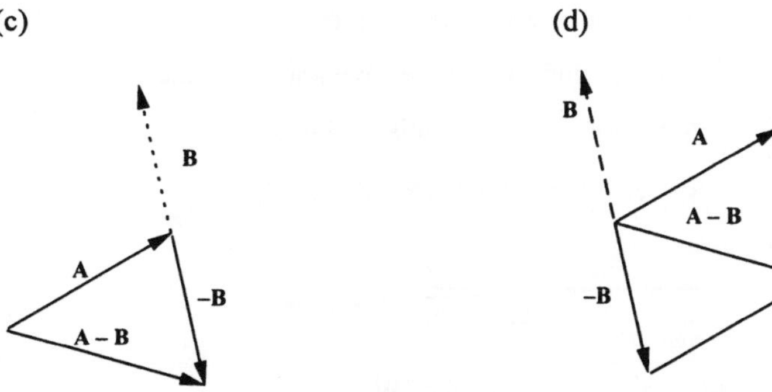

Vector addition is conveniently done by the **analytical component method**. The recommended procedure is as follows:

(1) Resolve the vectors to be added into their x and y components. Include directional signs (plus or minus) in the components.

(2) Add, algebraically, all the x components together and all the y components together to get the x and y components of the resultant vector.

(3) Express the resultant vector using (a) the component form, e.g., $\mathbf{A} = A_x\,\hat{\mathbf{x}} + A_y\,\hat{\mathbf{y}}$, or

(b) in magnitude-angle form, e.g., $A = \sqrt{A_x^2 + A_y^2}$,

$\theta = \tan^{-1}\dfrac{A_y}{A_x}$ (relative to x axis).

A detailed treatment of this procedure can be found on page 75 to 76 in the textbook.

Example 3.4: Find the resultant velocity of the sum of

(i) $\mathbf{v}_1 = 35$ m/s 30° N of E; (ii) $\mathbf{v}_2 = 55$ m/s 45° N of W.

Solution:

(1) Resolve the vectors to be added into their x and y components.

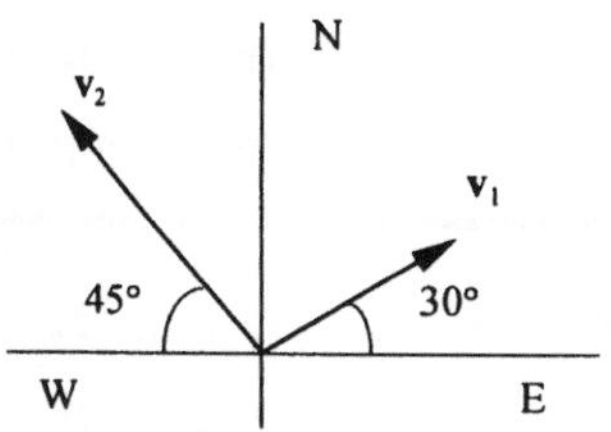

$v_{1x} = v_1 \cos 30° = (35\text{ m/s}) \cos 30° = 30.3$ m/s,

$v_{1y} = (35\text{ m/s}) \sin 30° = 17.5$ m/s.

$v_{2x} = -\,v_2 \cos 45° = (55\text{ m/s}) \cos 45° = -38.9$ m/s, ($-x$ direction)

$v_{2y} = (55\text{ m/s}) \sin 45° = 38.9$ m/s.

(2) Add components.

$v_x = v_{1x} + v_{2x} = 30.3\text{ m/s} + (-38.9\text{ m/s}) = -8.6$ m/s,

$v_y = v_{1y} + v_{2y} = 17.5\text{ m/s} + 38.9\text{ m/s} = 56.4$ m/s.

(3) Express the resultant vector.

First we draw the resultant velocity vector based on the components obtained in the previous procedure. We know that the x-component is –8.6 m/s and the y-component is 56.4 m/s.

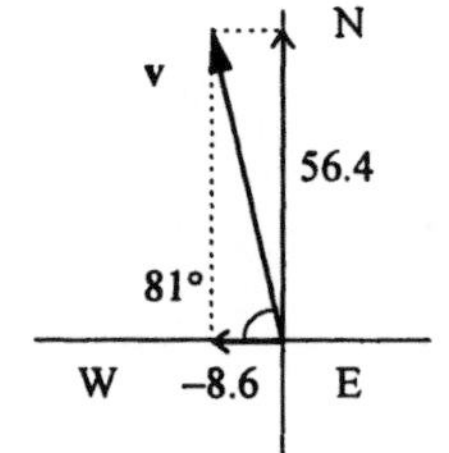

In component form: $\mathbf{v} = \mathbf{v}_1 + \mathbf{v}_2 = -8.6 \text{ m/s } \hat{\mathbf{x}} + 56 \text{ m/s } \hat{\mathbf{y}}$;

In magnitude-angle form:

$$v = \sqrt{v_x^2 + v_y^2} = \sqrt{(-8.6 \text{ m/s})^2 + (56.4 \text{ m/s})^2} = 57 \text{ m/s},$$

and $\theta = \tan^{-1}\frac{v_y}{v_x} = \tan^{-1}\frac{56.4 \text{ m/s}}{-8.6 \text{ m/s}} = 81° \text{ N of W}.$

Note: Once you have the components for the resultant [at the end of step (2)], you need to draw a diagram like the one above to determine the angle and in which quadrant the vector is. It is very difficult for you to determine the location of the vector without the diagram.

---

3. Relative Velocity (Section 3.3)

Physical phenomena can be observed from different **frames of reference**. The velocity of a ball tossed by a passenger in a moving car will be measured differently by a passenger on the car than by an observer on the Earth. As a matter of fact, any velocity we measure is **relative**. The velocity of a moving car is measured relative to the ground, and the revolving motion of our Earth around the Sun is relative to the Sun, etc. Relative velocity can be determined with vector addition or subtraction. The symbols used in relative velocity such as $\mathbf{v}_{cg}$ (where c stands for car and g stands for ground) means the velocity of *a car relative to the ground.*

Example 3.5: A river has a current with a velocity of 1.0 m/s south. A boat, whose speed in still water is 5.0 m/s, is directed east across the 100 m wide river.

(a) How long does it take the boat to reach the opposite shore?

(b) How far downstream will the boat land?

(c) What is the velocity of the boat relative to the shore?

Solution: Given: $v_{rs} = 1.0$ m/s, $v_{br} = 5.0$ m/s, $y = 100$ m.

Find: (a) t (b) x (c) $\mathbf{v}_{bs}$.

We use the following subscripts:

r = river, b = boat, s = shore.

We chose the coordinate system as shown.

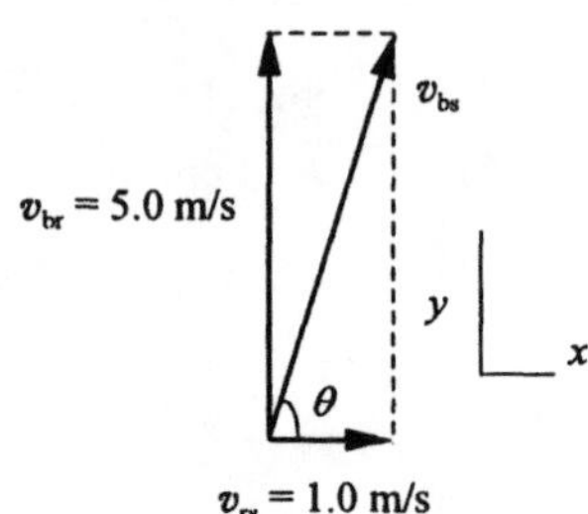

(a) From the concept of components of motion, the time it takes the boat to reach the opposite shore is simply $t = \frac{y}{v_{br}} = \frac{100 \text{ m}}{5.0 \text{ m/s}} = 20 \text{ s}$.

(b) $x = v_{rs}\,t = (1.0 \text{ m/s})(20 \text{ s}) = 20 \text{ m}$.

(c) The velocity of the boat *relative to shore* is the vector sum of the velocity of the boat *relative to the river* and the velocity of the river *relative to the shore* (current). $\mathbf{v}_{bs} = \mathbf{v}_{br} + \mathbf{v}_{rs}$.

Note: The pattern of the subscripts are helpful in problem solving. On the right side of the equation, the two inner subscripts are the same (r). The outer subscripts (b and s) are sequentially the same as those for the relative velocity on the left side of the equation. This pattern is a good check to see if you write the relative velocity equation correctly!

$$v_{bs} = \sqrt{v_{br}^2 + v_{rs}^2} = \sqrt{(5.0 \text{ m/s})^2 + (1.0 \text{ m/s})^2} = 5.1 \text{ m/s},$$

$$\theta = \tan^{-1}\left(\frac{5.0 \text{ m/s}}{1.0 \text{ m/s}}\right) = 79° \text{ measured from shoreline.}$$

The velocity of the *boat relative to the shore* (or an observer standing on the shore) is 5.1 m/s in a direction of 79° measured from the shoreline.

Example 3.6: If the person on the boat in the previous example (Example 3.5) wants to travel directly across the river,

(a) what angle upstream must the boat be directed?

(b) with what speed will the boat cross the river?

(c) how long will it take the boat to reach the opposite shore?

Solution:

To travel directly across the river, the velocity of the boat *relative to the shore* must be directly across the river. The vector form of the relative velocity equation in Example 3.5,

$\mathbf{v}_{bs} = \mathbf{v}_{br} + \mathbf{v}_{rs}$ is still valid.

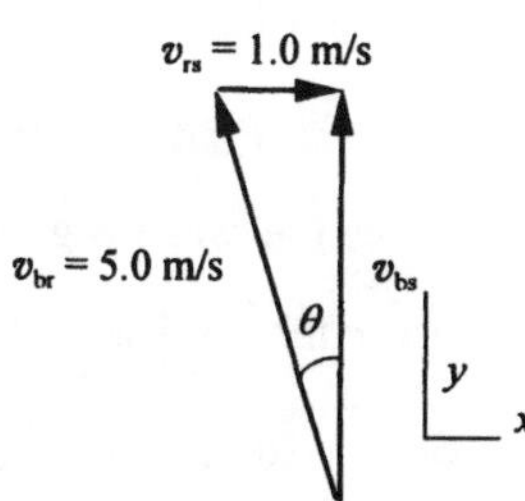

(a) $\theta = \sin^{-1}\frac{v_{rs}}{v_{br}} = \sin^{-1}\frac{1.0 \text{ m/s}}{5.0 \text{ m/s}} = 12°$ upstream from a line straight across the river.

(b) From the triangle in the diagram, we have $v_{bs}^2 + v_{rs}^2 = v_{br}^2$,

so $v_{bs} = \sqrt{v_{br}^2 - v_{rs}^2} = \sqrt{(5.0 \text{ m/s})^2 - (1.0 \text{ m/s})^2} = 4.9 \text{ m/s}$.

(c) The time is then $t = \frac{y}{v_{bs}} = \frac{100 \text{ m}}{4.9 \text{ m/s}} = 20 \text{ s}$.

---

4. Projectile Motion (Section 3.4)

Projectile motion is motion in two dimensions, horizontal and vertical, with the vertical motion under the action of gravity only (downward), Since the action of gravity is in the vertical direction, the horizontal motion has zero acceleration, if air resistance is ignored. The vertical motion is a free fall and so the acceleration is the acceleration due to gravity, $a_y = -g = -9.80$ m/s^2, if the upward direction is chosen positive. This two-dimensional motion is analyzed using components, that is, the horizontal quantities are independent of the vertical quantities and vice versa. However, the time of flight, the time the projectile spends in the air, is the common quantity for both the horizontal and vertical motions.

Applying the general kinematic equations in component form to projectile motion ($a_x = 0$ and $a_y = -g$ with the upward direction chosen positive), we have $v_x = v_{xo}$, $v_y = v_{yo} - gt$, $x = v_{xo}\,t$, $y = v_{yo}\,t - \frac{1}{2}gt^2$, etc. Again, the key to success in solving projectile motion is to resolve the motion into components, treat the components as independent, and use the same time of flight for both motions. Always think about resolving vectors into components. Usually, the time of flight is something you have to find first, since it is a common quantity for both motions and acts as a linkage between the two motions.

Example 3.7: A package is dropped from an airplane traveling with a constant horizontal speed of 120 m/s at an altitude of 500 m. What is the horizontal distance the package travels before hitting the ground (range)?

Solution: Given: horizontal motion (taken in the x direction) $v_{xo} = 120$ m/s, vertical motion (up as positive) $v_{yo} = 0$, $y = -500$ m.

y $v_o = v_{xo}$ x
500 m
Range

Find: x (range).

Since the range is given by $x = v_{xo}\,t$, we have to find the time of flight t first.

From the vertical motion, we use $y = v_{yo}\,t - \frac{1}{2}gt^2$.

So $-500 \text{ m} = 0 - \frac{1}{2}(9.80 \text{ m/s}^2)t^2$, solving, $t = 10.1$ s.

Therefore $x = (120 \text{ m/s})(10.1 \text{ s}) = 1.21 \times 10^3 \text{ m} = 1.21$ km.

Note: The quantities such as initial velocities and displacements have to be treated independently. For example, the initial horizontal velocity is 120 m/s and the initial vertical velocity is zero. The 12.0 m/s can *only* be used in the horizontal motion and the 0 m/s can *only* be used in the vertical motion. A common mistake is to mix up these quantities or not treat them as independent.

Example 3.8: A golfer hits a golf ball with a velocity of 35 m/s at an angle of 25 degrees above the horizontal. If the point where the ball is hit and the point where the ball lands are at the same level,

(a) how long is the ball in the air?

(b) what is the range of the ball?

Solution: Given: horizontal motion

$v_{xo} = v_o \cos\theta$

$= (35 \text{ m/s}) \cos 25°$

$= 31.7 \text{ m/s},$

vertical motion

$v_{yo} = v_o \sin\theta$

$= (35 \text{ m/s}) \sin 25°$

$= 14.8 \text{ m/s}.$

Find: (a) t (b) x.

(a) On landing, $y = 0$; and from $y = v_{yo}t - \frac{1}{2}gt^2$, we have $0 = (14.8 \text{ m/s})t - \frac{1}{2}(9.80 \text{ m/s}^2)t^2$.

Solving, $t = 0$ or 3.02 s. The $t = 0$ root corresponds to the position at the start ($x = 0$ and $y = 0$) and the $t = 3.02$ s corresponds to the landing position (x = range and $y = 0$). So the time of flight is 3.0 s, (to two significant figures).

(b) $x = v_{xo}t = (31.7 \text{ m/s})(3.02 \text{ s}) = 96$ m.

Or, using the range equation, we have $x = R = \dfrac{v_o^2 \sin 2\theta}{g} = \dfrac{(35 \text{ m/s})^2 \sin 2(25°)}{9.80 \text{ m/s}^2} = 96 \text{ m}$

IV. Mathematical Summary

Components of initial velocity	$v_{xo} = v \cos\theta$ (3.1a) $v_{yo} = v \sin\theta$ (3.1b)		Relates the x and y components to the magnitude and the angle of the initial velocity. (θ is from x axis)
Components of displacement	$x = v_{xo}t + \frac{1}{2}a_x t^2$ (3.3a) $y = v_{yo}t + \frac{1}{2}a_y t^2$ (3.3b)		Relates the displacement components to initial velocity components, acceleration components and time (constant acceleration only).
Components of velocity	$v_x = v_{xo} + a_x t$ (3.3c) $v_y = v_{yo} + a_y t$ (3.3d)		Relates the velocity components to initial velocity components and acceleration components (constant acceleration only).
Vector Representation	$C = \sqrt{C_x^2 + C_y^2}$, (3.4a) $\theta = \tan^{-1}\left\|\frac{C_y}{C_x}\right\|$ (3.4b)		Magnitude-angle form.
Vector Representation	$\mathbf{C} = C_x \hat{\mathbf{x}} + C_y \hat{\mathbf{y}}$ (3.7)		Component form.

V. Solutions of Selected Exercises and Paired/Trio Exercises

4. Horizontal component: $v_x = v\cos\theta = (35 \text{ m/s}) \cos 37° = \boxed{28 \text{ m/s}}$.

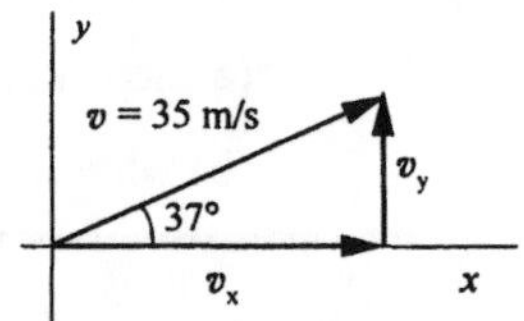

Vertical component: $v_y = v\sin\theta = (35 \text{ m/s}) \sin 37° = \boxed{21 \text{ m/s}}$.

6. $\boxed{\pm 6.3 \text{ m/s}}$.

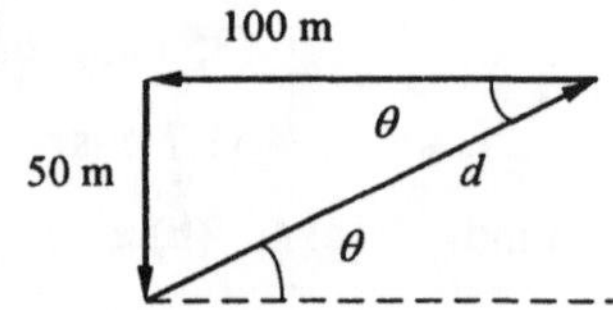

8. The displacement that will bring the student back to the starting point is pointing from the finishing point to the starting point.

$d = \sqrt{(50 \text{ m})^2 + (100 \text{ m})^2} = \boxed{1.1 \times 10^2 \text{ m}}$, $\theta = \tan^{-1}\left(\dfrac{50 \text{ m}}{100 \text{ m}}\right) = \boxed{27° \text{ north of east}}$.

12. From the kinetic equations for components of motion:

$x = v_x t = (0.60 \text{ m/s})(2.5 \text{ s}) = 1.5 \text{ m}$, $y = v_y t = (0.80 \text{ m/s})(2.5 \text{ s}) = 2.0 \text{ m}$.

$d = \sqrt{x^2 + y^2} = \sqrt{(1.5 \text{ m})^2 + (2.0 \text{ m})^2} = \boxed{2.5 \text{ m}}$. $\theta = \tan^{-1}\left(\dfrac{2.0 \text{ m}}{1.5 \text{ m}}\right) = \boxed{53° \text{ above } +x \text{ axis}}$.

18. (c), because the magnitude of the resultant is 1 if the two vectors are opposite and 4 if they are in the same direction.

23. $\boxed{\text{Yes}}$, vector addition is associative.

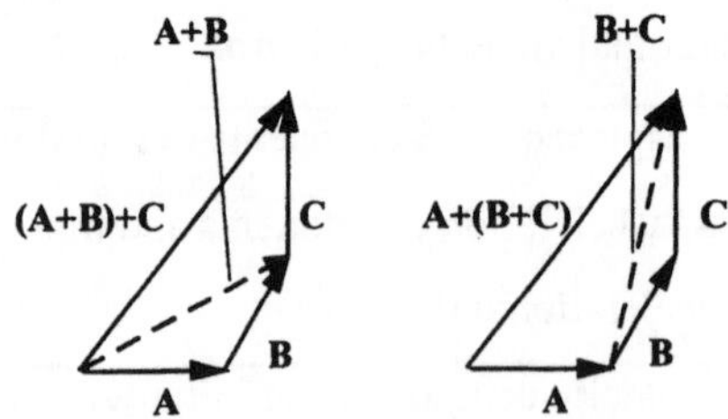

28. (a) See diagram.

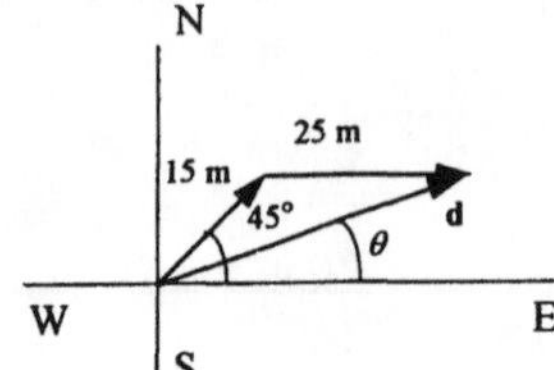

(b) For the 15 m vector: $d_{1x} = (15\text{ m})\cos 45° = 10.6\text{ m}$,

$d_{1y} = (15\text{ m})\sin 45° = 10.6\text{ m}$.

For the 25 m vector: $d_{2x} = 25\text{ m}$, $d_{2y} = 0$.

So $d_x = d_{1x} + d_{2x} = 10.6\text{ m} + 25\text{ m} = 35.6\text{ m}$, $d_y = d_{1y} + d_{2y} = 10.6\text{ m} + 0 = 10.6\text{ m}$.

Therefore $d = \sqrt{(35.6\text{ m})^2 + (10.6\text{ m})^2} = \boxed{37\text{ m}}$

and $\theta = \tan^{-1}\left(\frac{10.6\text{ m}}{35.6\text{ m}}\right) = \boxed{17° \text{ north of east}}$.

30. $\boxed{145\text{ N } 50.1° \text{ north of east}}$.

33. (a) $\mathbf{F}_1 = [(12.0\text{ N})\cos 37°]\,\hat{\mathbf{x}} + [(12.0\text{ N})\sin 37°]\,\hat{\mathbf{y}} = (9.58\text{ N})\,\hat{\mathbf{x}} + (7.22\text{ N})\,\hat{\mathbf{y}}$.

$\mathbf{F}_2 = [-(12.0\text{ N})\cos 37°]\,\hat{\mathbf{x}} + [(12.0\text{ N})\sin 37°]\,\hat{\mathbf{y}} = (-9.58\text{ N})\,\hat{\mathbf{x}} + (7.22\text{ N})\,\hat{\mathbf{y}}$.

So $\mathbf{F}_1 + \mathbf{F}_2 = \boxed{(14.4\text{ N})\,\hat{\mathbf{y}}}$.

(b) $\mathbf{F}_1 = [(12.0\text{ N})\cos 27°]\,\hat{\mathbf{x}} + [(12.0\text{ N})\sin 27°]\,\hat{\mathbf{y}} = (10.7\text{ N})\,\hat{\mathbf{x}} + (5.45\text{ N})\,\hat{\mathbf{y}}$.

So $\mathbf{F}_1 + \mathbf{F}_2 = (1.1\text{ N})\,\hat{\mathbf{x}} + (12.7\text{ N})\,\hat{\mathbf{y}}$. $F_1 + F_2 = \sqrt{(1.1\text{ N})^2 + (12.7\text{ N})^2} = \boxed{12.7\text{ N}}$.

$\theta = \tan^{-1}\left(\frac{12.7\text{ N}}{1.1\text{ N}}\right) = \boxed{85.0° \text{ above } +x \text{ axis}}$

38. From $\mathbf{F}_1 + \mathbf{F}_2 + \mathbf{F}_3 = 0$,

$\mathbf{F}_3 = -\mathbf{F}_1 - \mathbf{F}_2 = -(3.0\text{ N})\,\hat{\mathbf{x}} - (3.0\text{ N})\,\hat{\mathbf{y}} - [(-6.0\text{ N})\,\hat{\mathbf{x}} + (4.5\text{ N})\,\hat{\mathbf{y}}] = (3.0\text{ N})\,\hat{\mathbf{x}} - (1.5\text{ N})\,\hat{\mathbf{y}}$.

So $F_3 = \sqrt{(3.0\text{ N})^2 + (-1.5\text{ N})^2} = \boxed{3.4\text{ N}}$,

and $\theta = \tan^{-1}\left(\frac{-1.5\text{ N}}{3.0\text{ N}}\right) = \boxed{27° \text{ below the } +x \text{ axis}}$.

44. $\mathbf{d}_1 = (60\text{ mi})[(\cos 45°)\,\hat{\mathbf{x}} + (\sin 45°)\,\hat{\mathbf{y}}] = (42.4\text{ mi})\,\hat{\mathbf{x}} + (42.4\text{ mi})\,\hat{\mathbf{y}}$. $\mathbf{d}_2 = (75\text{ mi})\,\hat{\mathbf{y}}$.

$\mathbf{d} = \mathbf{d}_2 - \mathbf{d}_1 = (75\text{ mi})\,\hat{\mathbf{y}} - [(42.4\text{ mi})\,\hat{\mathbf{x}} + (42.4\text{ mi})\,\hat{\mathbf{y}}] = (-42.4\text{ mi})\,\hat{\mathbf{x}} + (32.6\text{ mi})\,\hat{\mathbf{y}}$.

So $d = \sqrt{(-42.4\text{ mi})^2 + (32.6\text{ mi})^2} = 53.48\text{ mi}$.

Therefore $v = \frac{53.48\text{ mi}}{2.0\text{ h}} = \boxed{26.7\text{ mi/h}}$.

$\theta = \tan^{-1}\left(\frac{32.6\text{ mi}}{-42.4\text{ mi}}\right) = \boxed{37.6° \text{ north of west}}$.

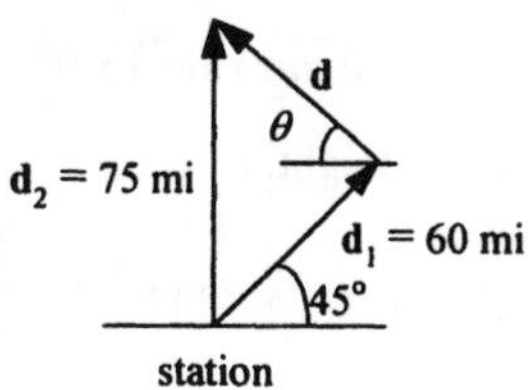

46. $\boxed{23\text{ km } 27° \text{ north of west}}$.

52. Use the following subscripts: t = truck, b = ball, and o = observer.

So $\mathbf{v}_{tg} = 70$ km/h, $\mathbf{v}_{bt} = -15$ km/h.

(a) $\mathbf{v}_{bo} = \mathbf{v}_{bt} + \mathbf{v}_{to} = -15\text{ km/h} + 70\text{ km/h} = \boxed{+55\text{ km/h}}$.

(b) $\mathbf{v}_{bt} = \mathbf{v}_{bo} - \mathbf{v}_{to} = 55\text{ km/h} - 90\text{ km/h} = \boxed{-35\text{ km/h}}$.

58. Use the following subscripts: s = swimmer, c = current, and b = bank.

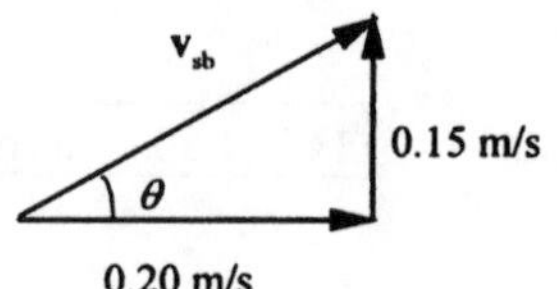

$\mathbf{v}_{sb} = \mathbf{v}_{sc} + \mathbf{v}_{cb}$.

So $v_{sb} = \sqrt{(0.20\text{ m/s})^2 + (0.15\text{ m/s})^2} = \boxed{0.25\text{ m/s}}$.

$\theta = \tan^{-1}\left(\frac{0.15\text{ m/s}}{0.20\text{ m/s}}\right) = \boxed{37°\text{ north of east}}$.

60. (a) $\boxed{0.075\text{ m/s}}$. (b) $\boxed{30°}$

66. The horizontal motion does not affect the vertical motion. The vertical motion of the ball projected horizontally is identical to that of the ball dropped.

70. Given: $v_{xo} = 15$ m/s, $v_{yo} = 0$, $y = -6.0$ m. Find: x.

First we need to find the time of flight from the vertical motion.

From $y = v_{yo}t - \frac{1}{2}gt^2 = 0 - \frac{1}{2}gt^2$, we have $t = \sqrt{-\frac{2y}{g}} = \sqrt{-\frac{2(-6.0\text{ m})}{9.80\text{ m/s}^2}} = 1.11$ s.

$x = v_{xo}t = (15\text{ m/s})(1.11\text{ s}) = \boxed{17\text{ m}}$.

72. $\boxed{7.6\text{ m/s}}$.

78. $v_{xo} = v_o\cos\theta = (20.0\text{ m/s})\cos 15.0° = 19.32$ m/s,

$v_{yo} = v_o\sin\theta = (20.0\text{ m/s})\sin 15.0° = 5.176$ m/s.

(a) At maximum height, $v_y = 0$.

From $v_y^2 = v_{yo}^2 - 2gy$, we have $y = \frac{(5.176\text{ m/s})^2}{2(9.80\text{ m/s}^2)} = \boxed{1.37\text{ m}}$.

(b) At impact, $y = 0$. From $y = v_{yo}t - \frac{1}{2}gt^2$, we have $t = \frac{5.176\text{ m/s}}{\frac{1}{2}(9.80\text{ m/s}^2)} = 1.056$ s.

So $R = x = v_{xo}t = (19.32\text{ m/s})(1.056\text{ s}) = \boxed{20.4\text{ m}}$.

(c) Since the range depends on the initial speed and the angle so the player can either kick the ball harder to increase v_o and/or increase the angle to as close to 45° as possible.

84. The range $R = 15$ m. So $R = \dfrac{v_o^2 \sin 2\theta}{g} = 15$ m.

or $R = \dfrac{(55 \text{ m/s})^2 \sin 2\theta}{9.80 \text{ m/s}^2} = 15$ m. Solving, $\sin 2\theta = 0.0486$.

Therefore $2\theta = \sin^{-1}(0.0486) = 2.79°$, hence $\theta = \boxed{1.4°}$.

89. (a) $\alpha = \tan^{-1}\left(\dfrac{12.0 \text{ m}}{150 \text{ m}}\right) = 45.7°$, so the launch angle $\theta = 4.57° + 10.0° = 14.6°$.

$x = v_{xo}\, t = (v_o \cos\theta) t$, ☞ $t = \dfrac{x}{v_{xo}} = \dfrac{x}{v_o \cos\theta}$,

$y = v_{yo}\, t - \frac{1}{2} g t^2 = v_o \sin\theta \times \dfrac{x}{v_o \cos\theta} - \frac{1}{2} g \left(\dfrac{x}{v_o \cos\theta}\right)^2$

$= x \tan\theta - \dfrac{g x^2}{2 v_o^2 \cos^2\theta}$.

$v_o = \dfrac{x}{\cos\theta}\sqrt{\dfrac{g}{2(x \tan\theta - y)}} = \dfrac{150 \text{ m}}{\cos 14.57°}\sqrt{\dfrac{9.80 \text{ m/s}^2}{2[(150 \text{ m}) \tan 14.57° - 12.0 \text{ m}]}}$

$= \boxed{66.0 \text{ m/s}}$.

(b) $\theta = 4.57° + 10.5° = 15.07°$.

First we need to find the time of flight from the vertical motion.

$12.0 \text{ m} = (66.0 \text{ m/s})(\sin 15.07°)t - (4.90 \text{ m/s}^2)t^2$,

or $4.90\, t^2 - 17.16\, t + 12.0 = 0$. Solving, $t = 0.97$ s or 2.54 s.

The 0.97 s answer is the time it takes to reach 12 m on the way up.

Therefore $x = (66.0 \text{ m/s})(\cos 15.07°)(2.54 \text{ s}) = 162 \text{ m} > 150 \text{ m}$,

$y = (66.0 \text{ m/s})(\sin 15.07°)(2.54 \text{ s}) - (4.90 \text{ m/s}^2)(2.54 \text{ s})^2 = 12.0$ m.

So the shot is $\boxed{\text{too long for the hole}}$.

94. Use the following subscripts: b = boat, w = water, and g = ground.

For the boat to make the trip straight across, v_{bw} must be the hypotenuse of the right-angle triangle. So it must be greater in magnitude than v_{wg}. So if the reverse is true, that is, if $v_{wg} > v_{bw}$, the boat cannot make the trip directly across the river.

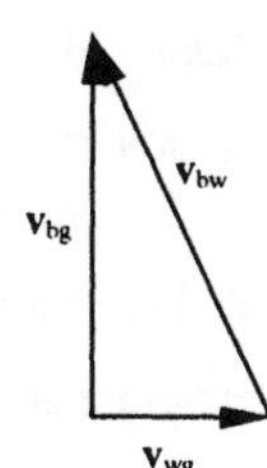

VI. Practice Quiz

1. The resultant of two vectors is greatest when the angle between them is

   (a) 0° (b) 45° (c) 60° (d) 90° (e) 180°

2. If a ball is thrown with a velocity of 25 m/s at an angle of 37° above the horizontal, what is the vertical component of the velocity?

   (a) 25 m/s (b) 20 m/s (c) 18 m/s (d) 15 m/s (e) 10 m/s

3. An object is moving in the x–y plane. The acceleration in the x and y directions are 1.0 m/s^2 and 3.0 m/s^2, respectively. If the object starts from rest, what are its coordinates at t = 4.0 s?

   (a) (8.0 m, 24 m) (b) (24 m, 8.0 m) (c) (4.0 m, 12 m) (d) (12 m, 4.0 m) (e) (8.0 m, 12 m)

4. A boat, whose speed in still water is 8.0 m/s, is directed across a river with a current of 6.0 m/s along the shore. What is the speed of the boat relative to the shore as it crosses the river?

   (a) 2.7 m/s (b) 5.3 m/s (c) 6.0 m/s (d) 8.0 m/s (e) 10 m/s

5. Find the resultant of the following vectors:

   $\mathbf{v}_1$ = 2.0 m/s **x** + 3.0 m/s **y**, $\mathbf{v}_2$ = −4.0 m/s **x** + 7.0 m/s **y**, $\mathbf{v}_3$ = 10 m/s, 37° above the $-x$ axis.

   (a) 19 m/s, 58° above $+x$ axis (b) 19 m/s, 58° above $-x$ axis (c) 19 m/s, 22° above $+x$ axis

   (d) 19 m/s, 22° above $-x$ axis (e) none of the above

6. A stone is thrown horizontally with an initial speed of 8.0 m/s from the edge of a cliff. A stop watch measures the stone's trajectory time from top of cliff to bottom to be 3.4 s. What is the height of the cliff?

   (a) 17 m (b) 27 m (c) 34 m (d) 57 m (e) 1.1×10^2 m

7. An Olympic long-jumper goes into the jump with a speed of 10 m/s at an angle of 30° above the horizontal. How far is the jump?

   (a) 1.0 m (b) 5.0 m (c) 8.8 m (d) 9.8 m (e) 10 m

B ? A

8. The resultant shown in the vector diagram on the right is for

   (a) **A** + **B**. (b) **A** − **B**. (c) **B** + **A**. (d) **B** − **A**. (e) **A** × **B**.

9. You are traveling at +55 mi/h relative to a straight, level road and pass a car traveling at +45 mi/h. The velocity of your car relative to the other car is

   (a) 10 mi/h. (b) −10 mi/h. (c) 65 mi/h. (d) 35 mi/h. (e) 100 mi/h.

10. The football field for your college team is 10 km at 30° north of east from your residence. You first drive 3.0 km north to go to a store. What should be your next displacement so you can go to the football game?

(a) 13 km at 8.9° north of east (b) 8.9 km at 13° north of east (c) 7.0 km at 30° north of east

(d) 7.0 km at 60° north of east (e) 12 km at 43° north of east

Answers to Practice Quiz:

1. a 2. d 3. a 4. e 5. b 6. d 7. c 8. d 9. a 10. b

CHAPTER 4

Force and Motion

I. Chapter Objectives

Upon completion of this chapter, you should be able to:

1. relate force and motion and explain what is meant by a net or unbalanced force.
2. state and explain Newton's first law of motion and describe inertia and its relationship to mass.
3. state and explain Newton's second law of motion, apply it to physical situations, and distinguish weight and mass.
4. state and explain Newton's third law of motion and identify action–reaction force pairs.
5. apply Newton's second law in analyzing various situations, using free-body diagrams, and understand the concept of translational equilibrium.
6. explain the causes of friction and how it is described by using coefficients of friction.

II. Key Terms

Upon completion of this chapter, you should be able to define and/or explain the following key terms:

force
net (unbalanced) force
inertia
Newton's first law of motion (law of inertia)
newton (unit)
Newton's second law of motion
weight
Newton's third law of motion
normal force
free-body diagram
translational equilibrium
condition for translational equilibrium
force of friction
static friction
kinetic (sliding) friction
rolling friction
coefficient of static friction
coefficient of kinetic friction
air resistance
terminal velocity

The definitions and/or explanations of the most important key terms can be found in the following section: **III. Chapter Summary and Discussions.**

III. Chapter Summary and Discussion

1. Force and Net Force (Section 4.1)

Force F is the cause of *acceleration* or change in velocity, and it is the technical term for what we commonly call a push, pull, kick, or shove. Force is a vector quantity (it has both magnitude and direction). There must be a **net force** (unbalanced force) acting on an object for the object to change its velocity (either magnitude and/or direction), or to accelerate.

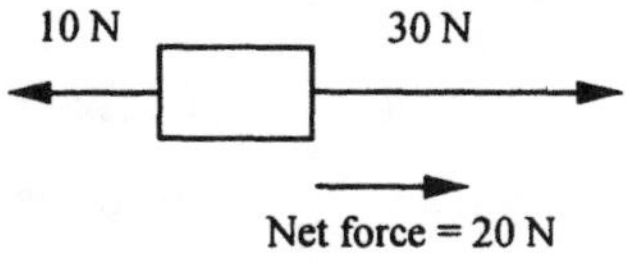

10 N 30 N

Net force = 20 N

Net Force ΣF or $\mathbf{F}_{net}$ is the vector sum, the resultant, or the unbalanced force acting on an object. Here the symbol Σ means "the sum of." **ΣF** means the vector sum of forces. The unit of force in SI is a combination of the fundamental units of mass, length, and time and it is called **newton** (N). 1 N is the net force required to accelerate a mass of 1 kg mass with an acceleration of 1 m/s^2 or, $1 \text{ N} = 1 \text{ kg}\cdot\text{m/s}^2$. For example, as illustrated in the diagram above, two forces, 10 N and 30 N, are acting on an object in opposite directions. There are two forces on the object. However, there is only one net force (the resultant of the vector sum of the two forces) of 20 N (to the right) acting on the object.

Note: The net force is *not* a separate force. It is simply the vector sum of the individual forces.

To analyze the forces acting on an object, you should draw a **free-body diagram** (more on free-body diagram later in Section 4.5). This is done by

(1) Isolating the object of interest (this should be the only object in the diagram).

(2) Drawing all the forces acting on the object as vectors (including directions).

Example 4.1: Draw a free-body diagram of a book sitting on a horizontal desk.

Solution:

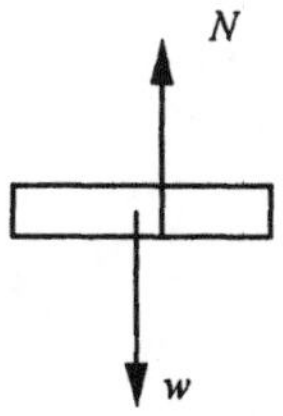

N

w

First we isolate the book and analyze the forces acting on the book. There are two forces acting on the book, the gravitational force (or weight) and the supporting force on the book by the desk. First of all, the gravitational force (an action-at-a-distance force with no physical contact) is always present if we are dealing with objects on the Earth. Secondly, whenever an object makes a physical contact with another object, a force results. Here the book makes a contact with the desk and so there is a supporting force. In most cases, these contact forces are perpendicular to the contact surface and therefore are called **normal forces**. As a follow up to this example, try to draw a free-body diagram of an object sliding freely on a frictionless inclined ramp.

---

2. Newton's Laws of Motion (Sections 4.2 – 4.4)

(1) **Newton's first law** describes the state of motion of an object when there is *no net force* (net force equals zero) acting on the object.

An object at rest will remain at rest and an object in motion will keep moving with constant velocity if the net force on the object is zero.

An object at rest has no change in velocity and so its acceleration is zero. An object moving with constant velocity (same speed and same direction) has no change in velocity and its acceleration is also zero. Therefore, Newton's first law can be summarized in a very simple relation:

If $\Sigma\mathbf{F} = 0$, then $\mathbf{v}$ = constant (zero is just a special case of velocity being constant), or $\mathbf{a} = 0$.

Note: Newton's first law is often called the law of inertia. **Inertia** is the natural tendency of an object to resist acceleration or change in motion, and it is measured quantitatively by its mass.

A common misconception about Newton's first law is that a force is required to keep an object in motion. This is not so. Experiments done on air tracks (where there is negligible friction) show that no force is required to keep an object moving with constant velocity. We get this misconception because friction is always present in our everyday lives. To maintain constant velocity of a moving car, you have to push the accelerator. Does this contradict Newton's first law? No! It is seen clearly in the diagram on the right that the forward force on the car is equal in magnitude and opposite to the backward friction force (air friction plus ground friction) and so they cancel each other, resulting in a zero net force Therefore, there is still no net force and the car moves away with constant velocity.

friction = 100 N

forward force = 100 N

Net force = 0

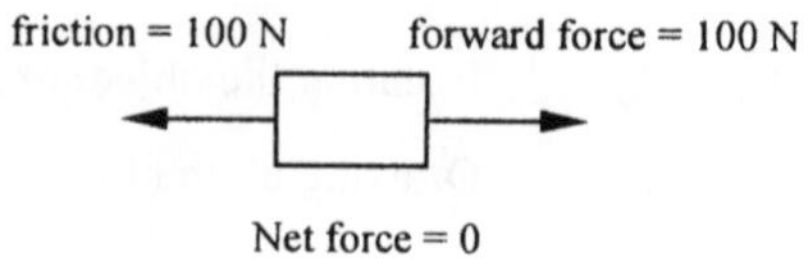

What happens if the *net force is not zero*? Newton's second law describes the relation among force, mass, and acceleration when there is a non-zero net force on an object.

(2) **Newton's second law** states that the acceleration depends on the net force $\Sigma\mathbf{F}$ and on the mass m of the object (note it is net force here, not just force). Mathematically, it is equivalent to

$$\mathbf{a} = \frac{\Sigma\mathbf{F}}{m} \quad \text{or} \quad \Sigma\mathbf{F} = m\,\mathbf{a}.$$

If you think of inertia as the qualitative term for the tendency of a body that resists acceleration, then **mass** (a scalar quantity) is the quantitative measure of inertia. If the mass is large, the acceleration produced by a given net force will be small.

Newton's second law is a vector equation. Note acceleration **a** is in the direction of the net force $\Sigma\mathbf{F}$, not necessarily the direction of velocity **v**. You must include *all* the forces acting on an object to determine the net force, and then the acceleration. However, many times you will find that a force on an object is balanced by an equal and opposite force, such as weight balanced by a normal force. Since these pair of forces cancel each other, you do not need to include them in your calculation.

Example 4.2: A 20-kilogram box sitting on a horizontal surface is pulled by a horizontal force of 5.0 N. A friction force of 3.0 N retards the motion. What is the acceleration of the object?

Solution: Given: $m = 20$ kg, F (pulling) = 5.0 N,

f (friction) = 3.0 N.

Find: a.

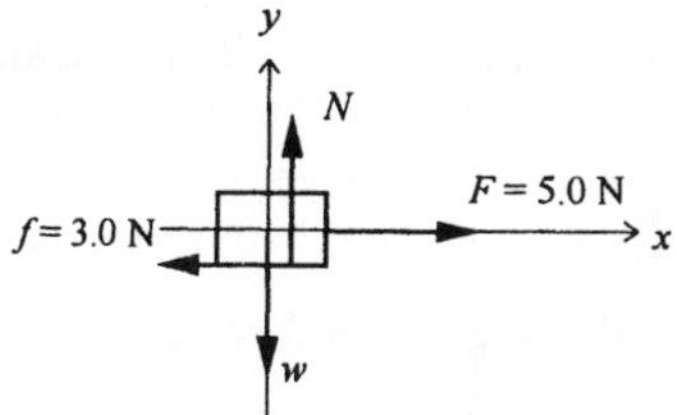

First we draw a free-body diagram of the box. The two vertical forces w, and N are equal and opposite (if they were not, the box would accelerate up or down). So they cancel out or $\Sigma F_y = ma_y = 0$ and we do not need to include them in our calculation. Thus we have only two forces, 5.0 N to the right and 3.0 N to the left, to deal with. The net force in this case is (with F direction taken as positive)

$\Sigma\mathbf{F} = F - f = 5.0\text{ N} - 3.0\text{ N} = 2.0\text{ N}$ (to the right or $+x$).

Hence the acceleration of the object is $\mathbf{a} = \dfrac{\Sigma\mathbf{F}}{m} = \dfrac{2.0\text{ N}}{20\text{ kg}} = 0.10\text{ m/s}^2$ (to the right or $+x$).

If you apply Newton's second law to gravity near the Earth's surface, you get the relation among weight $\mathbf{w}$ (gravitational force), mass m, and gravitational acceleration $\mathbf{g}$: $\mathbf{w} = m\mathbf{g}$.

Example 4.3: Find the weight of a 3.50-kg object.

Solution: Given: $m = 3.50$ kg. Find: w.

We use the relation: $\mathbf{w} = m\mathbf{g} = (3.50\text{ kg})(9.80\text{ m/s}^2\text{ downward}) = 34.3\text{ N downward}$.

Note: Weight and mass are two very different physical quantities. Mass is a measure of the inertia or resistance to change in motion of an object. Mass is a constant for a given object and so it is independent of where the mass is located. For example, a 5.0-kilogram mass on the Earth is still 5.0 kg on the Moon. Weight is the gravitational force acting on an object, and so depends on the acceleration due to gravity and mass. A 5.0-kilogram mass has a weight of $(5.0\text{ kg})(9.80\text{ m/s}^2) = 49$ N on the Earth, $(5.0\text{ kg})(1.67\text{ m/s}^2) = 8.4$ N on the Moon, and *zero* newton in deep space (why?).

(3) **Newton's Third Law** states that if object 1 exerts a force on object 2, then object 2 exerts an equal and opposite force on object 1. In mathematical terms, it can be written as $\mathbf{F}_{12} = -\mathbf{F}_{21}$.

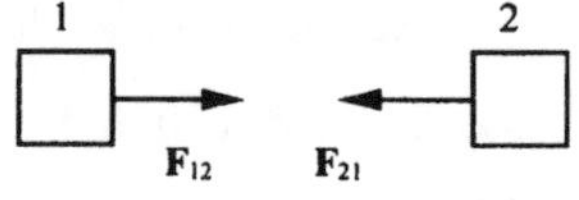

The negative sign in the above relation simply means that $\mathbf{F}_{12}$ is opposite $\mathbf{F}_{21}$. The notation $\mathbf{F}_{12}$ stands for the force on object 1 by object 2.

The force by object 1 is *on* object 2, and the force by object 2 is *on* object 1, and so the two forces are always acting on *two different* objects. Therefore, even though these two forces are equal and opposite, they *do not* cancel out each other because of this fact. If you analyze only object 1 in the diagram, there is only *one* force acting on it and object 1 will accelerate.

Newton's third law is often called action and reaction. The first force, for example, the force by object 1, is called the action force and the second force is then called the reaction force.

There is another misconception concerning the third law. The third law states that the two forces are *equal* no matter what. For example, an egg and a stone collide with each other, the egg breaks and the stone is intact. Since the egg breaks, we often conclude that the force by the stone on the egg is greater than the force by the egg on the stone. This is not so. The forces are always equal. The egg breaks because it is simply easier to break. It takes a smaller force to break the egg than to break the stone.

Example 4.4: A large truck collides head-on with a small car and causes a lot of damage to the small car. Since there is more damage on the small car than on the large truck,

(a) the force on the truck is greater in magnitude than the force on the car,

(b) the force on the truck is equal in magnitude to the force on the car,

(c) the force on the truck is smaller in magnitude than the force on the car,

(d) the force on the truck is in the same direction as the force on the car.

(e) the truck did not slow down during the collision.

Solution:

According to Newton's third law, the answer is (b). Why isn't answer (c) correct since the truck causes more damage on the car? It takes a smaller force to damage a small car than to damage a large truck. When the truck and the car collide, they exert equal in magnitude but opposite in direction forces on each other, say 15 000 N. It may take only 10 000 N to damage the bumper on the car and 20 000 N to damage the bumper on the truck. So the car gets damaged and the truck remains basically undamaged, even though the forces by the car on the truck is the same magnitude as the force on the car by the truck.

(e) is also wrong as the truck *did* slow down from the force by the car is opposite its motion.

---

3. Application of Newton's Laws (Section 4.5)

When it comes to applying Newton's laws to various mechanical systems, there is no short cut to take. You *must* follow a certain set of procedures to analyze and solve the unknown physical quantities. Here is a simplified version of the procedures outlined in the text:

(1) Draw a free-body diagram for each object involved in the analysis.

(2) Select a rectangular coordinate system. The solutions will be much easier if you select the $+x$ axis in the direction of acceleration and the $+y$ axis perpendicular to the x axis.

(3) Resolve all forces not pointing in the x or y directions to their x and y components, respectively.

(4) Add, algebraically, all the x components and y components of the forces, respectively.

(5) Set $\Sigma F_x = ma$ and $\Sigma F_y = 0$ and solve for the unknown quantities.
Since you have chosen the $+x$ axis in the direction of acceleration, the object will not accelerate in the y direction. So its acceleration in the y direction is zero and $\Sigma F_y = ma_y = 0$.

Do these steps read familiar? In essence, these are the same procedures we followed when we added vectors using the component method. Our goal here is to find the net force and then the acceleration. Since force is a vector, it really boils down to add vectors.

Example 4.5: A student pulls a box of books on a smooth horizontal floor with a force of 100 N in a direction of 37° above the horizontal surface. If the mass of the box and the books is 40.0 kg, what is the acceleration of the box and the normal force on the box by the floor?

Solution: Given: $F = 100$ N, $\theta = 37°$, $m = 40.0$ kg.

Find: a and N.

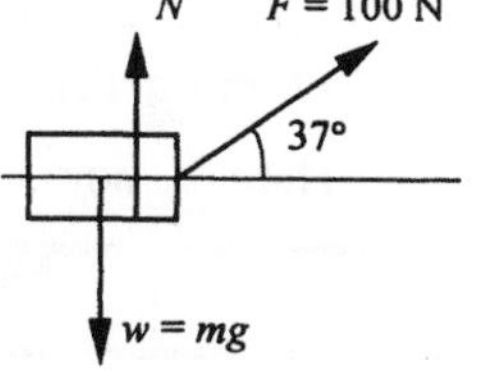

(1) Free-body diagram:

Since the box is on the Earth, it has a weight of $w = mg$ pointing toward the center of the earth (or perpendicular to the horizontal direction). The box is also making physical contacts with the floor and the student. So there will be two contact forces. The contact force with the floor is a normal force and is directed straight upward perpendicular to the contact surface. The force by the student is directed at 37° above the horizontal direction (smooth floor implies negligible friction).

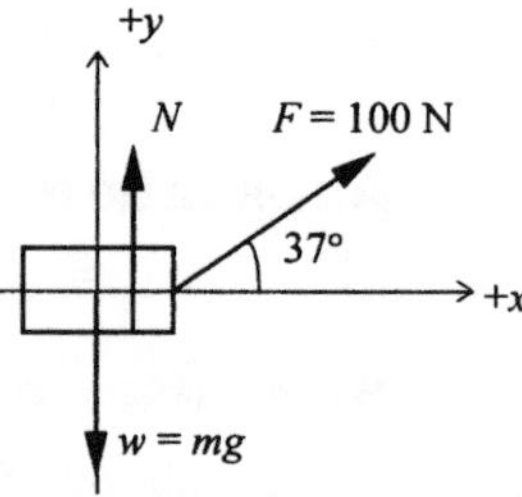

(2) Coordinate system:

Even though the student is pulling at an angle above the horizontal direction, the box will still move or accelerate along the horizontal direction. So we choose the horizontal direction (to the right) as the +*x* axis and the vertical direction (upward) as the +*y* axis.

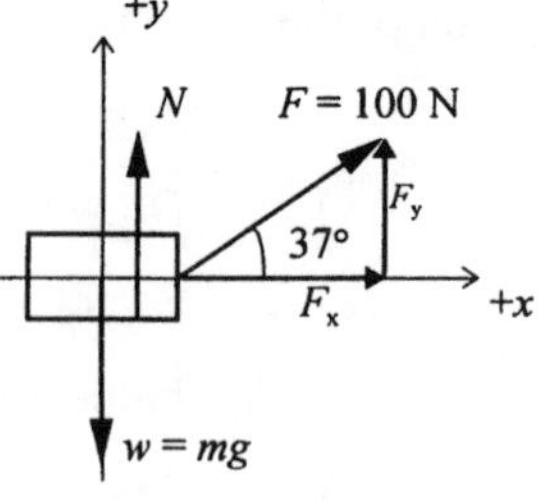

(3) *x* and *y* components:

Among the three forces, only the student's pulling force is not completely along either the *x* or the *y* axis. So we need to find its *x* and *y* components. From trigonometry, we can see that the *x* component is adjacent to the 37° angle and the *y* component is opposite to the 37° angle. Therefore we use cos 37° to calculate the *x* component and sin 37° to calculate the *y* component.

$$F_x = F\cos 37° = (100\text{ N})\cos 37° = 80.0\text{ N},$$

$$F_y = F\sin 37° = (100\text{ N})\sin 37° = 60.0\text{ N}.$$

(4) Adding *x* and *y* components, respectively:

In the *x* direction, there is only one force, the *x* component of the student's pulling force, 80 N. In the *y* direction, there are three forces: the upward normal force *N*, the upward *y* component of the student's pulling force (60 N), and the downward weight of the box and books of

$$w = mg = (40.0\text{ kg})(9.80\text{ m/s}^2) = 392\text{ N}.$$

So $\quad \Sigma F_x = 80.0\text{ N}$ and $\Sigma F_y = N + 60.0\text{ N} - w = N + 60.0\text{ N} - 392\text{ N} = N - 332\text{ N}.$

(5) Setting $\Sigma F_x = ma$ and $\Sigma F_y = 0$ and solving for the unknown quantities:

$$\Sigma F_x = 60.0\text{ N} = ma = (40.0\text{ kg})a. \qquad \text{Eq. (1)}$$

and

$$\Sigma F_y = N - 332\text{ N} = 0. \qquad \text{Eq. (2)}$$

From Eq. (1), we have $a = \dfrac{80.0\text{ N}}{40.0\text{ kg}} = 2.00\text{ m/s}^2.$

From Eq. (2), we have $N = 332$ N.

Here the normal force (332 N) is not equal to the weight of the box and the books (392 N). Why?

Example 4.6: A 5.0-kilogram box, starting from rest, slides down a smooth 37° inclined plane.

(a) Find the acceleration of the mass and the normal force by the inclined plane on the mass.

(b) If the plane is 10 m long, what will be its speed at the bottom of the plane?

Solution: Given: $m = 5{,}0$ kg, $\theta = 37°$, $v_o = 0$, $x = 10$ m.

Find: (a) a and N (b) v.

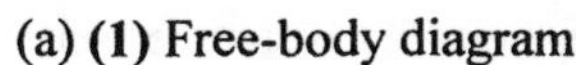

(a) **(1)** Free-body diagram:

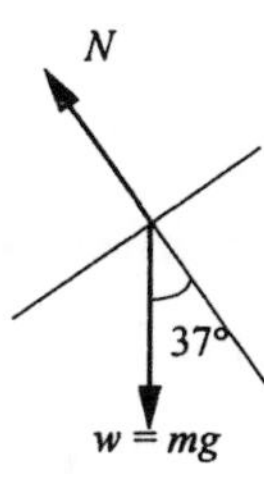

Since the box is on the Earth, it has weight $w = mg$ pointing toward the center of the Earth (or perpendicular to the horizontal direction). The box is also making physical contact with the inclined plane. So there will be a contact force (normal force) perpendicular to the inclined plane.

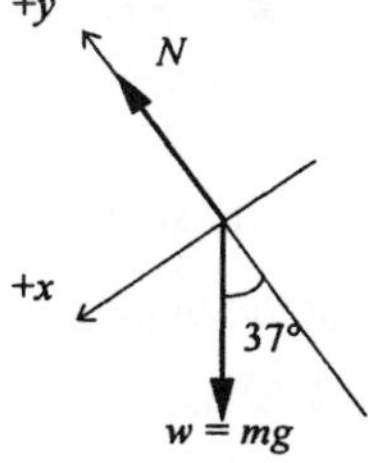

(2) Coordinate system:

Since the mass slides down the inclined plane, we choose the $+x$ axis down the inclined plane and the $+y$ axis perpendicular to the inclined plane.

(3) x and y components:

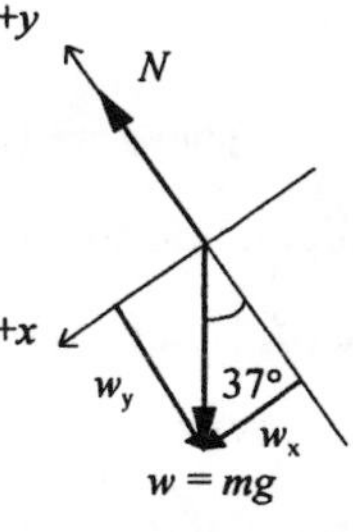

The weight of the mass $w = mg$ is not along either the x axis or the y axis. So we need to find its x and y components. From trigonometry, we can see that the x component is opposite to the 37° angle and the y component is adjacent to the 37° angle.

So $w_x = w \sin 37° = mg \sin 37°$ and $w_y = w \cos 37° = mg \cos 37°$.

(4) Adding x and y components, respectively:

In x direction, there is only one force, w_x.

So $\Sigma F_x = mg \sin 37° = mg \sin 37°$.

In y direction, there are two forces, N and w_y. So $\Sigma F_y = N - mg \cos 37°$.

(5) Setting $\Sigma F_x = ma$ and $\Sigma F_y = 0$ and solving for the unknown quantities:

$$\Sigma F_x = mg \sin 37° = ma. \qquad \text{Eq. (1)}$$

and

$$\Sigma F_y = N - mg \cos 37°. \qquad \text{Eq. (2)}$$

From Eq. (1), we have $a = g \sin 37° = (9.80 \text{ m/s}^2) \sin 37° = 5.9 \text{ m/s}^2$.

From Eq. (2), we have $N = mg \cos 37° = (5.0 \text{ kg})(9.80 \text{ m/s}^2) \cos 37° = 39$ N.

(b) Since velocity is a kinematic quantity, we need to use one of the kinematic equations.

From $v^2 = v_o^2 + 2ax = (0)^2 + 2(5.9 \text{ m/s}^2)(10 \text{ m}) = 118 \text{ m}^2/\text{s}^2$, so $v = 11$ m/s.

If there are *no forces* acting on an object, or if there are *equal and opposite forces* acting on it, the net force on the object *is zero* and the object *will not* accelerate. This state of motion is called **translational equilibrium**. If the system is in equilibrium, we can set $\Sigma \mathbf{F} = 0$, that is, $\Sigma F_x = 0$ and $\Sigma F_y = 0$ in component form, and then solve for unknown quantities.

Translational equilibrium is a special application of Newton's laws (**a** = 0). The problem solving procedure is the same as described in Examples 4.5 and 4.6. The only minor difference is in step **(5)**. Instead of setting $\Sigma F_x = ma$ and $\Sigma F_y = 0$, we set both $\Sigma F_x = 0$ and $\Sigma F_y = 0$, and solving for the unknown quantities.

4. Force of Friction (Section 4.6)

Consider one object in contact with another, such as a book on a desk. Suppose that the desk is stationary and that the book is either *sliding* or *on the verge of sliding* on the desk. There is interaction between the book and the desk based on intermolecular attractions and repulsions. It is convenient, however, to consider the interaction as if it were two independent ones: one perpendicular to the contact surface (the *normal* force mentioned earlier) and another one parallel to the contact surface, which is called *force of friction* or *friction force.*

There are two kinds of friction forces: static friction and kinetic friction. Static friction force ($f_s \leq \mu_s N$) is parallel to the contact surface when there is *no relative motion* between the objects in contact and kinetic friction force ($f_k = \mu_k N$) is also parallel to the contact surface when there is *relative motion* between objects in contact. Here μ_s is called the coefficient of static friction and μ_k the coefficient of kinetic friction. They are basically measures of the strengths of the molecular interactions. N is the normal force.

Kinetic friction force doesn't cause much conceptual difficulty, but static friction force is often misunderstood and therefore incorrectly interpreted. If a book is at rest on a desk and no forces with horizontal components are applied to the book, there is *no* static friction force. However, suppose a small horizontal force is applied to the book but the book still remains at rest, then we must conclude that an equal and opposite force acts on the book to prevent it from moving. This is the static friction force. If the horizontally applied force increases, the static friction force will increase by the same amount until its maximum value is reached ($f_s = \mu_s N$). So the static friction force is *not* a fixed value, but is always equal to the applied force, with an upper limit of $f_s = \mu_s N$.

Another misconception about static friction force is about its direction. Somehow we have the idea that friction force is always opposite to the direction of motion. This is always true only if the friction force is kinetic. Static friction force can be in directions other than opposite to motion. Think about a machine part moving on a conveying belt in a factory and a car turning on a flat surface. What is moving the part and turning the car? It is static friction force. The static friction force is in the direction of motion on the machine part and perpendicular to the direction of motion on the car. Think carefully when you walk the next time. What enables you to walk? In which direction is that force? (Hint: why is it difficult to walk on ice? Is it possible to walk on perfectly smooth surface?)

Example 4.7: The coefficients of static and kinetic frictions between a 3.0-kilogram box and a desk are 0.40, and 0.30, respectively. What is the net force on the box when each of the following horizontal forces is applied to the box? (a) 5.0 N, (b) 10 N, (c) 15 N.

Solution: Given: $\mu_s = 0.40$, $\mu_k = 0.30$, $m = 3.0$ kg. $F = 5.0$ N (a), 10 N (b), 15 N (c).

Find: ΣF (net force) in (a), (b), and (c).

From the discussion about friction forces, we know that if the applied force is greater than the maximum static friction force, the box will accelerate. Since both static and kinetic forces depend on the normal force, we must find it first.

Applying Newton's second law in the vertical direction, $\Sigma F_y = N - w = ma_y = 0$ so the normal force between the box and the desk is $N = w = mg = (3.0 \text{ kg})(9.80 \text{ m/s}^2) = 29.4 \text{ N}$.

The maximum static friction force is then $f_{s\,max} = \mu_s N = 0.40(29.4 \text{ N}) = 11.8 \text{ N}$.

(a) Since the applied force of 5.0 N is smaller than 11.8 N, the maximum static friction force, the object remains at rest and therefore the net force is zero.

(b) The applied force is still smaller than the maximum static friction force and the net force is still zero.

(c) Now the applied force of 15 N is greater than the maximum static friction force, the object will accelerate and there is a relative motion along the contact surface. Therefore we need to replace the static friction force with the kinetic friction force.

$$f_k = \mu_k N = 0.30(29.4 \text{ N}) = 8.82 \text{ N}.$$

Hence the net force is $\Sigma F = 15 \text{ N} - 8.82 \text{ N} = 6.18 \text{ N}$ and the box will accelerate at a rate of

$$a = \frac{\Sigma F}{m} = \frac{6.18 \text{ N}}{3.0 \text{ kg}} = 2.1 \text{ m/s}^2.$$

The direction of the acceleration is in the same direction as the horizontal force.

IV. Mathematical Summary

Newton's second law	$\Sigma \mathbf{F} = m\mathbf{a}$ (4.1) (Note: it is a vector equation)	Relates acceleration with mass and net force when the net force on it is not zero.
Component form of Newton's second law	$\Sigma F_x = ma_x$ (4.3b) $\Sigma F_y = ma_y$ (4.3b)	Relates acceleration with mass and force in a particular direction.
Newton's third law	$\mathbf{F}_{12} = -\mathbf{F}_{21}$	Action and reaction (on different objects).
Weight and mass	$\mathbf{w} = m\mathbf{g}$ (4.2)	Relates weight (gravitational force) with mass and gravitational acceleration.

Translational equilibrium condition	$\Sigma\mathbf{F} = 0$ (4.4) $\Sigma F_x = 0$ and $\Sigma F_y = 0$ (4.5)	The conditions an object must satisfy if it has zero acceleration.
Force of static friction	$f_s \le \mu_s N$ (4.6) $f_{smax} = \mu_s N$ (4.7) (Note: f_s is not a fixed value)	Calculates the static friction force when there is no relative motion along the contact surface.
Force of kinetic friction	$f_k = \mu_k N$ (4.8) (Note: f_k is a fixed value)	Calculates the kinetic friction force when there is a relative motion along the contact surface.

V. Solutions of Selected Exercises and Paired/Trio Exercises

6. The bubble would move $\boxed{\text{forward}}$ in the direction of velocity or acceleration, because the inertia of the liquid will resist the forward acceleration. So the bubble of negligible mass or inertia moves forward relative to the liquid. Then it moves $\boxed{\text{backward}}$ opposite the velocity (or in the direction of acceleration) for the same reason.

(b) The principle is based on the $\boxed{\text{inertia of the liquid}}$.

12. (a) $\mathbf{F}_1 = (3.6\text{ N})[(\cos 74°)\,\hat{\mathbf{x}} - (\sin 74°)\,\hat{\mathbf{y}}] = (0.99\text{ N})\,\hat{\mathbf{x}} - (3.46\text{ N})\,\hat{\mathbf{y}}$.

$\mathbf{F}_2 = (3.6\text{ N})[(-\cos 34°)\,\hat{\mathbf{x}} + (\sin 34°)\,\hat{\mathbf{y}}] = -(2.98\text{ N})\,\hat{\mathbf{x}} + (2.01\text{ N})\,\hat{\mathbf{y}}$.

If $a = 0$, then $\Sigma\mathbf{F} = 0$ from Newton's first law.

$\Sigma\mathbf{F} = \mathbf{F}_1 + \mathbf{F}_2 = -(1.99\text{ N})\,\hat{\mathbf{x}} - (1.45\text{ N})\,\mathbf{y} \neq 0$, so there must be a third force to make $\Sigma\mathbf{F} = 0$.

So $\Sigma\mathbf{F} = \mathbf{F}_1 + \mathbf{F}_2 + \mathbf{F}_3 = 0$, and $\mathbf{F}_3 = -(\mathbf{F}_1 + \mathbf{F}_2) = (1.99\text{ N})\,\hat{\mathbf{x}} + (1.45\text{ N})\,\mathbf{y}$.

$F_3 = \sqrt{(1.99\text{ N})^2 + (1.45\text{ N})^2} = \boxed{2.5\text{ N}}$. $\theta = \tan^{-1}\left(\dfrac{1.45\text{ N}}{1.99\text{ N}}\right) = \boxed{36°\text{ above the }+x\text{ axis}}$.

(b) $\boxed{\text{No}}$, all we can say is that the acceleration is zero. The object could be at rest or moving with constant velocity.

18. From Newton's second law $\Sigma F = ma$, we have $a = \dfrac{\Sigma F}{m} = \dfrac{3.0\text{ N}}{1.5\text{ kg}} = \boxed{2.0\text{ m/s}^2}$.

21. From Newton's second law $\Sigma F = ma = (7.0 \times 10^7\text{ kg})(0.10\text{ m/s}^2) = \boxed{7.0 \times 10^6\text{ N}}$.

26. $150 \text{ lb} = (150 \text{ lb}) \times \dfrac{4.45 \text{ N}}{1 \text{ lb}} = \boxed{668 \text{ N}}$. $m = \dfrac{w}{g} = \dfrac{668 \text{ N}}{9.80 \text{ m/s}^2} = \boxed{68.2 \text{ kg}}$.

29. (a) $m = \dfrac{w}{g} = \dfrac{98 \text{ N}}{9.80 \text{ m/s}^2} = 10 \text{ kg}$. So $a = \dfrac{\Sigma F}{m} = \dfrac{12 \text{ N}}{10 \text{ kg}} = \boxed{1.2 \text{ m/s}^2}$.

(b) For the same object, the mass is still 10 kg. So the acceleration is also the $\boxed{\text{same}}$.

30. The resistive force is opposite the forward force.

From Newton's second law $\Sigma F = ma$, we have $a = \dfrac{\Sigma F}{m} = \dfrac{15 \text{ N} - 8.0 \text{ N}}{1.0 \text{ kg}} = \boxed{7.0 \text{ m/s}^2}$.

34. First we need to find acceleration from kinematics.

$v_o = 90 \text{ km/h} = 25 \text{ m/s}$, $v = 0$, $t = 5.5 \text{ s}$.

So $a = \dfrac{v - v_o}{t} = \dfrac{0 - 25 \text{ m/s}}{5.5 \text{ s}} = -4.56 \text{ m/s}^2$.

Now from Newton's second law $\Sigma F = ma = (60 \text{ kg})(-4.55 \text{ m/s}^2) = -\boxed{2.7 \times 10^2 \text{ N}}$.

The negative sign indicates that the force is opposite the motion or the velocity.

36. $\boxed{69 \text{ N}}$.

38. The answer is (d). (a) is incorrect because the forces are always equal in magnitude. (b) is incorrect because the forces cannot be cancelled as they are on two different bodies. (c) is incorrect because the forces always act on two different bodies.

43. From Newton's second law, the force on the female by the male is

$F = ma = (45 \text{ kg})(2.0 \text{ m/s}^2) = 90 \text{ N}$.

The force on the male by the female is also 90 N according to Newton's third law.

So $a_{\text{male}} = \dfrac{90 \text{ N}}{60 \text{ kg}} = \boxed{1.5 \text{ m/s}^2}$ opposite to hers.

46. (a) The scale reading is equal to the normal force on the person. The net force in the vertical direction is $\Sigma F = w - N = ma = 0$,

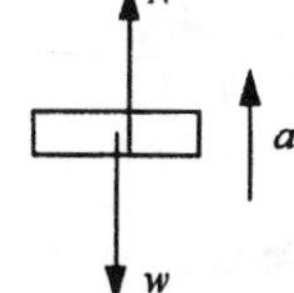

so $N = w = mg = (75.0 \text{ kg})(9.80 \text{ m/s}^2) = \boxed{735 \text{ N}}$.

(b) a is still zero. So $N = \boxed{735 \text{ N}}$.

(c) From $\Sigma F = N - w = ma$,

we have $N = w + ma = mg + ma = m(g + a) = (75.0 \text{ kg})(9.80 \text{ m/s}^2 + 2.00 \text{ m/s}^2) = \boxed{885 \text{ N}}$.

50. (a) Although the boy pulls in a non-horizontal direction, the box still accelerates in the horizontal direction, which is chosen as the $+x$ axis.

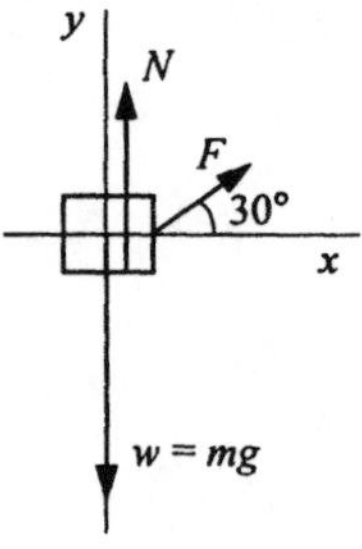

$\Sigma F_x = F\cos 30° = (25\text{ N})\cos 30° = 21.65\text{ N} = ma_x$,

so $\quad a_x = \dfrac{21.65\text{ N}}{30\text{ kg}} = \boxed{0.72\text{ m/s}^2}$.

(b) $\Sigma F_y = N + F\sin 30° - w = ma_y = 0$,

so $\quad N = w - F\sin 30° = (30\text{ kg})(9.80\text{ m/s}^2) - (25\text{ N})\sin 30° = \boxed{2.8\times 10^2\text{ N}}$.

52. (a) The x-component of the weight is the side opposite to the angle θ shown, so sine is used. $\quad \Sigma F_x = mg\sin\theta = ma_x$,

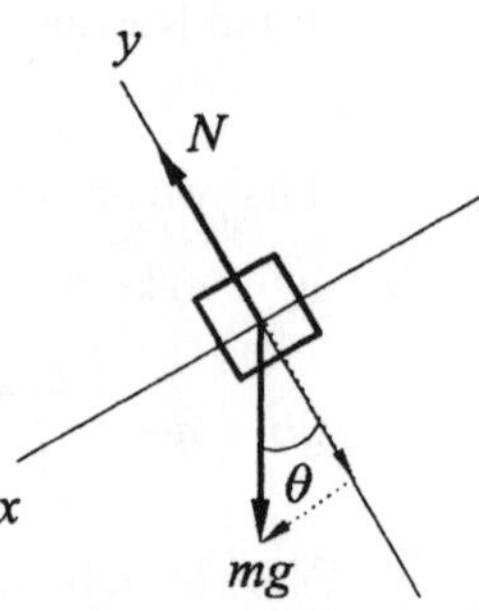

So $\quad a_x = g\sin\theta = (9.80\text{ m/s}^2)\sin 37° = \boxed{5.9\text{ m/s}^2}$.

(b) From $v^2 = v_o^2 + 2ax$, $v = \sqrt{(5.0\text{ m/s})^2 + 2(5.9\text{ m/s}^2)(35\text{ m})} = \boxed{21\text{ m/s}}$.

59. The free-body diagrams of the three objects.

For m_1: $\quad T_1 - m_1 g = m_1 a, \qquad (1)$

For m_3: $\quad T_2 - T_1 = m_3 a, \qquad (2)$

For m_2: $\quad m_2 g - T_2 = m_2 a, \qquad (3)$

(1) + (2) + (3) gives $\quad (m_2 - m_1)g = (m_1 + m_2 + m_3)a$.

Solving, $\quad a = \dfrac{(m_2 - m_1)g}{m_1 + m_2 + m_3}$.

(a) $a = \dfrac{(0.50\text{ kg} - 0.25\text{ kg})(9.80\text{ m/s}^2)}{0.25\text{ kg} + 0.50\text{ kg} + 0.25\text{ kg}} = \boxed{2.5\text{ m/s}^2\text{ to right}}$.

(b) $a = \dfrac{(0.15\text{ kg} - 0.35\text{ kg})(9.80\text{ m/s}^2)}{0.35\text{ kg} + 0.15\text{ kg} + 0.50\text{ kg}} = -2.0\text{ m/s}^2$.

So it is $\boxed{2.0\text{ m/s}^2\text{ to left}}$.

60. From Example 4.6 in textbook (The Atwood machine),

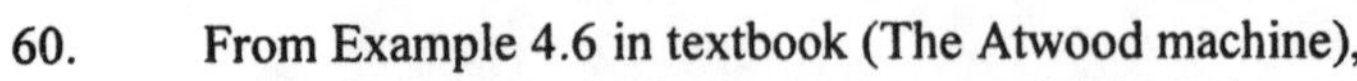

$$a = \frac{(m_2 - m_1)g}{m_1 + m_2} = \frac{(0.25\text{ kg} - 0.20\text{ kg})(9.80\text{ m/s}^2)}{0.25\text{ kg} + 0.20\text{ kg}} = \boxed{1.2\text{ m/s}^2\text{, up}}.$$

64. Both at rest and moving with constant velocity corresponds to zero acceleration, so $a_x = a_y = 0$.

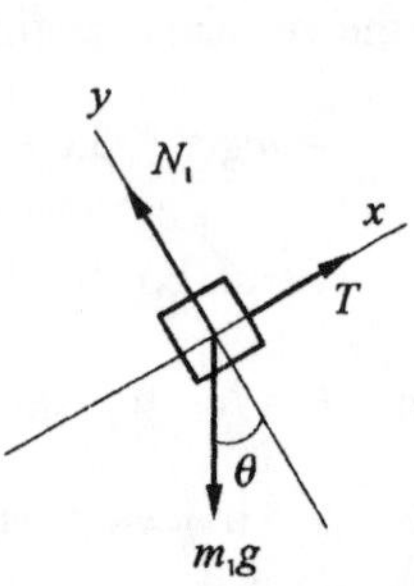

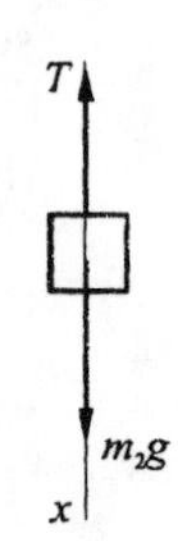

For m_1: $\Sigma F_x = T - m_1 g\sin\theta = m_1 a_x = 0$, that is $T = m_1 g\sin\theta$.

For m_2: $\Sigma F_y = m_2 g - T = m_2 a_y = 0$, or $m_2 g = T = m_1 g\sin\theta$.

Combining the two equations, we have $m_2 = m_1 \sin\theta = (2.0\text{ kg}) \sin 37° = \boxed{1.2\text{ kg}}$.

If both are moving at constant velocity, the answer is the $\boxed{\text{same}}$ 1.2 kg because the acceleration is still zero and the forces must still balance out.

68. (c).

74. (a) From the exercise, we know that 275 N is the maximum static friction force and 195 N is the kinetic friction force.

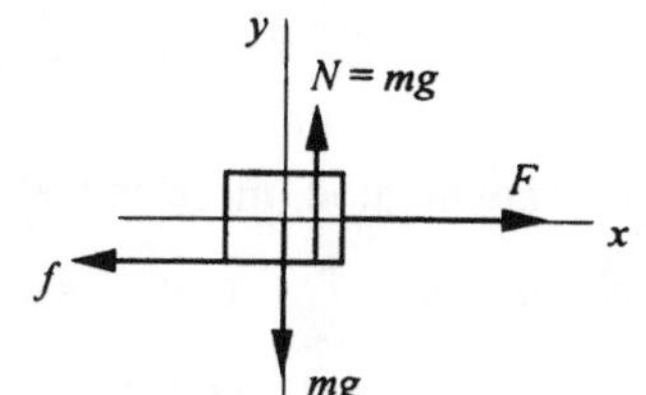

$\Sigma F_y = N - mg = ma_y = 0$, that is $N = mg$.

$\Sigma F_x = F - f_s = ma_x = 0$ (on the verge of moving),

so $f_{smax} = \mu_s N = F$,

or $\mu_s = \dfrac{F}{mg} = \dfrac{275\text{ N}}{(35.0\text{ kg})(9.80\text{ m/s}^2)} = \boxed{0.802}$.

(b) Similarly, $\mu_k = \dfrac{195\text{ N}}{(35.0\text{ kg})(9.80\text{ m/s}^2)} = \boxed{0.569}$.

78. (a) First we need to find acceleration from dynamics and use μ_k from Table 4.1.

$\Sigma F_x = -f_k = -\mu_k mg = ma$, so $\mu_k = -\dfrac{a}{g}$.

Therefore $a = -\mu_k g = -0.85(9.80\text{ m/s}^2) = -8.33\text{ m/s}^2$,

and $v_o = 90\text{ km/h} = 25\text{ m/s}$, $v = 0$.

From the kinematic equation $v^2 = v_o^2 + 2ax$,

we have $x = \dfrac{v^2 - v_o^2}{2a} = \dfrac{0 - (25\text{ m/s})^2}{2(-8.33\text{ m/s}^2)} = \boxed{38\text{ m}}$.

(b) $a = -0.60(9.80\text{ m/s}^2) = -5.88\text{ m/s}^2$. So $x = \dfrac{0 - (25\text{ m/s})^2}{2(-5.88\text{ m/s}^2)} = \boxed{53\text{ m}}$.

82. $\Sigma F_y = N - mg\cos\theta = ma_y = 0$, that is $N = mg\cos\theta$.

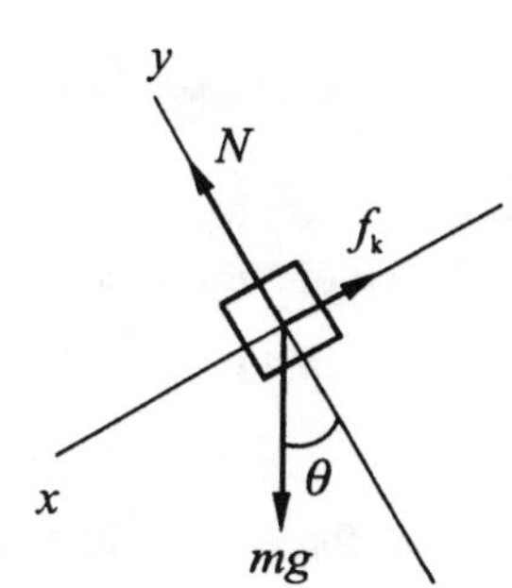

For constant velocity, $a_x = 0$. So $\Sigma F_x = mg\sin\theta - f_k = 0$.

Or $mg\sin\theta = \mu_k N = \mu_k (mg\cos\theta)$.

Therefore $\mu_k = \dfrac{\sin\theta}{\cos\theta} = \boxed{\tan\theta}$.

84. $\theta = \boxed{30°}$ and $\mu_s = \boxed{0.58}$.

89. For m_1: $\Sigma F = T_1 - m_1 g = 0$, (1)

For m_3: $\Sigma F = T_2 - T_1 - f_{smax} = 0$, (2)

For m_2: $\Sigma F = m_2 g - T_2 = 0$, (3)

(1) + (2) + (3) gives $(m_2 - m_1)g - f_s = 0$,

or $(m_2 - m_1)g - \mu_s N_3 = (m_2 - m_1)g - \mu_s m_3 g = 0$.

Solving, $\mu_s = \dfrac{m_2 - m_1}{m_3} = \dfrac{0.50 \text{ kg} - 0.25 \text{ kg}}{0.75 \text{ kg}} = \boxed{0.33}$.

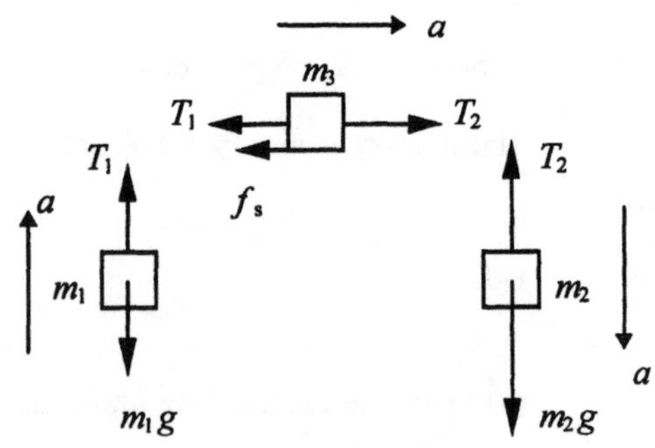

Alternate method (more conceptual).

Since $a = 0$, $T_1 = m_1 g$ and $T_2 = m_2 g$.

So for m_3, $m_2 g - m_1 g - f_s = 0$, or $m_2 g - m_1 g - \mu_s m_3 g = 0$.

Therefore $\mu_s = \dfrac{m_2 - m_1}{m_3}$.

97. $\Sigma F_y = N - mg - F \sin\theta = 0$, so $N = mg + F \sin\theta$.

$\Sigma F_x = F \cos\theta - f_{smax} = 0$,

or $F \cos\theta - \mu_s N = F \cos\theta - \mu_s (mg + F \sin\theta) = 0$.

Therefore $F = \dfrac{\mu_s mg}{\cos\theta - \mu_s \sin\theta}$.

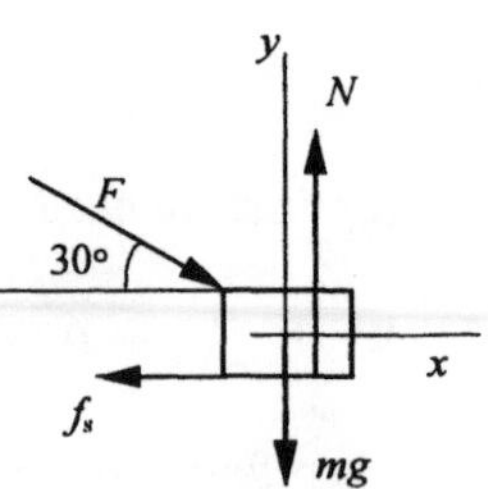

(a) $\mu_s = 0.75$ (Table 4.1), so $F = \dfrac{0.75(5.0 \text{ kg})(9.80 \text{ m/s}^2)}{\cos 30° - (0.75) \sin 30°} = \boxed{75 \text{ N}}$.

(b) $\mu_s = 0.12$, so $F = \dfrac{0.12(5.0 \text{ kg})(9.80 \text{ m/s}^2)}{\cos 30° - (0.12) \sin 30°} = \boxed{7.3 \text{ N}}$.

VI. Practice Quiz

1. Which of Newton's laws of motion *best* explains why motorists should buckle-up?
(a) the first law (b) the second law (c) the third law (d) the law of gravitation

2. A net force F accelerates a mass m with an acceleration a. If the same net force is applied to mass $m/2$, then the acceleration will be
(a) $4a$. (b) $2a$. (c) a. (d) $a/2$. (e) $a/4$.

3. A brick hits a window and breaks the glass. Since the brick breaks the glass,
(a) the force on the brick is greater in magnitude than the force on the glass,
(b) the force on the brick is equal in magnitude to the force on the glass,
(c) the force on the brick is smaller in magnitude than the force on the glass,
(d) the force on the brick is in the same direction as the force on the glass.
(e) the brick did not slow down.

4. An object weighs 100 N on the surface of Earth. What is the mass of this object on the surface of the Moon where the acceleration due to gravity is only 1/6 of that on the Earth?
(a) 1.70 kg (b) 10.2 kg (c) 16.7 kg (d) 58.8 kg (e) 100 kg

5. Two horizontal forces act on a 5.0-kilogram object. One force has a magnitude of 8.0 N and is directed due north. The second force toward the east has a magnitude of 6.0 N. What is the acceleration of the object?
(a) 1.6 m/s^2 due north (b) 1.2 m/s^2 due east (c) 2.0 m/s^2 at 53° N of E (d) 2.0 m/s^2 at 53° E of N

6. A box is placed on a smooth inclined plane with an angle of 20° to the horizontal. If the inclined plane is 5.0-meter long, how long does it take for the mass to reach the bottom of the inclined plane after it is released from rest?
(a) 1.0 s (b) 1.3 s (c) 1.5 s (d) 1.7 s (e) 1.9 s

7. During a hockey game, a hockey puck is given an initial speed of 10 m/s. It slides 50 m on the ice before it stops. What is the coefficient of kinetic friction between the puck and ice?
(a) 0.090 (b) 0.10 (c) 0.11 (d) 0.12 (e) 0.13

8. A person on a scale rides in an elevator. If the mass of the person is 60 kg and the elevator accelerate upward with an acceleration of 4.9 m/s^2, what is the reading on the scale in newtons?
(a) 147 N (b) 294 N (c) 588 N (d) 882 N (e) 1176 N

9. A traffic light of weight 100 N is supported by two ropes as shown in the diagram. What are the tensions in the ropes?
(a) 50 N (b) 63 N
(c) 66 N (d) 83 N
(e) 100 N

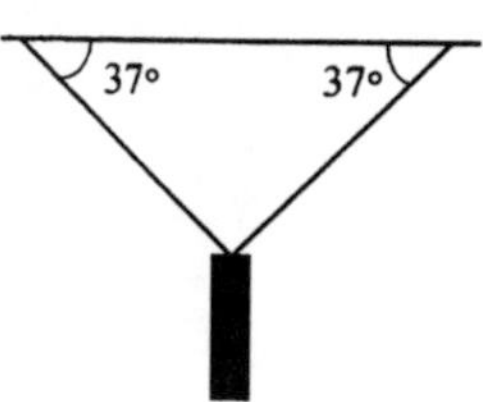

10. Find the magnitudes of the acceleration of the system and the tension in the connecting string. (Neglect friction and mass of the pulley)

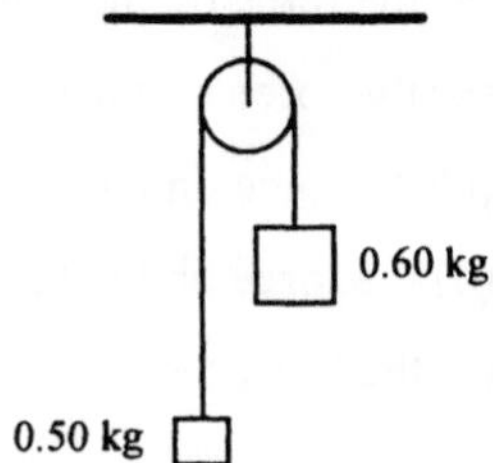

(a) 5.3 m/s^2, 7.5 N
(b) 4.5 m/s^2, 7.1 N
(c) 0.89 m/s^2, 5.3 N
(d) 0.090 m/s^2, 4.9 N
(e) 1.2 m/s^2, 4.3 N.

Answers to Practice Quiz:

1. a 2. b 3. c 4. b 5. c 6. d 7. b 8. d 9. d 10. c

CHAPTER 5

Work and Energy

I. Chapter Objectives

Upon completion of this chapter, you should be able to:

1. define mechanical work and compute the work done in various situations.
2. differentiate work done by constant and variable force and compute the work done by a spring force.
3. explain the work–energy theorem and apply it in solving problems.
4. explain how potential energy depends on position and compute values of gravitational potential energy.
5. distinguish between conservative and nonconservative forces and explain their effects on the conservation of energy.
6. define power and describe mechanical efficiency.

II. Key Terms

Upon completion of this chapter, you should be able to define and/or explain the following key terms:

work
joule (unit)
spring (force) constant
kinetic energy
work-energy theorem
potential energy
gravitational potential energy
law of conservation of total energy
conservative force
nonconservative force
total mechanical energy
conservative system
law of conservation of mechanical energy
power
watt (unit)
horsepower (unit)
efficiency

The definitions and/or explanations of the most important key terms can be found in the following section: **III. Chapter Summary and Discussion**.

III. Chapter Summary and Discussion

1. Work Done by a Constant Force (Section 5.1)

The **work** done by a constant force is $W = (F \cos\theta)\, d$, where F and d are the magnitudes of the force and displacement vectors, respectively, and θ is the angle between these two vectors. Although force and displacement are vectors, work is a scalar quantity. The SI unit of work is N·m, which is called a joule (J).

Note: The angle in the work definition is the *angle between the force vector and the displacement vector*, which is not necessarily the angle from the horizontal.

Graphically, the work done by a force is equal to the area under the curve in a force versus position graph.

Example 5.1 A 500-kilogram elevator is pulled upward by a constant force of 5500 N for a distance of 50.0 m.
(a) Find the work done by the upward force.
(b) Find the work done by the gravitational force.
(c) Find the work done by the net force (the net work done on the elevator).

Solution: Given: $F_{up} = 5500$ N, $w = mg = (500 \text{ kg})(9.80 \text{ m/s}^2) = 4900$ N, $d = 50.0$ m.

Find: (a) W_{up}, (b) W_{grav}, and (c) W_{net}.

(a) The displacement is upward and the upward force is (of course) upward. So the angle between them is zero.

Therefore $W_{up} = (F \cos\theta)\, d = (F_{up} \cos 0°)\, d = (5500 \text{ N})(1)(50.0 \text{ m}) = 2.75 \times 10^5$ J.

(b) The angle between displacement and the gravitational force (weight vector) is 180°.

So $W_{grav} = (w \cos 180°)\, d = (4900 \text{ N})(-1)(50.0 \text{ m}) = -2.45 \times 10^5$ J.

(c) The work done by the net force is equal to the net work done on the elevator.

$W_{net} = W_{up} + W_{grav} = 2.75 \times 10^5 \text{ J} + (-2.45 \times 10^5 \text{ J}) = 3.0 \times 10^4$ J.

Note: W_{net} is also equal to $W_{net} = (F_{net} \cos\theta)\, d$, where $F_{net} = F - w$.

Example 5.2 A force moves an object in the direction of the force. The graph on the right shows the force versus the object's position. Find the net work done when the object moves

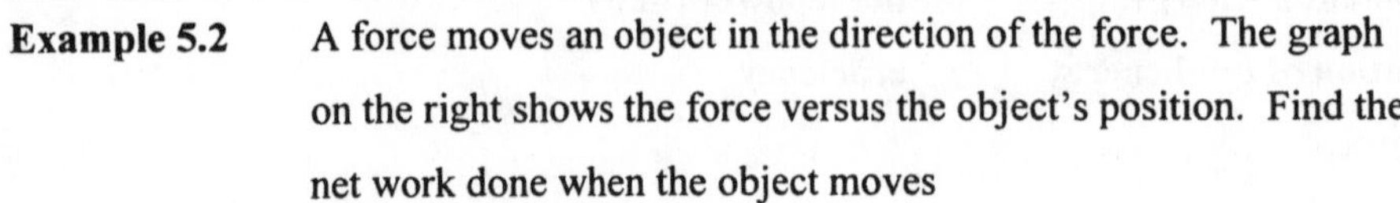

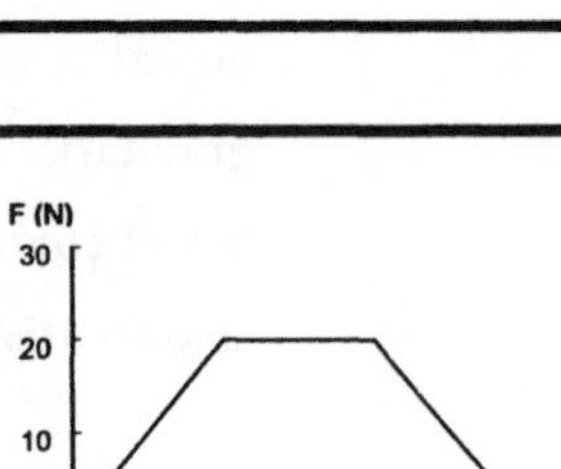

(a) from 0 to 2.0 m.
(b) from 2.0 to 4.0 m.

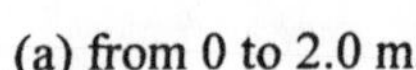

(c) from 4.0 to 6.0 m.
(d) from 0 to 6.0 m.

Solution:

Work done is equal to the area under the curve.

(a) The area under the curve from 0 to 2.0 m is the left triangle. The area of a triangle is $\frac{1}{2}$(base × height).

So $W_{0\text{-}2} = \frac{1}{2}(2.0 \text{ m} - 0)(20 \text{ N}) = 20 \text{ J}.$

(b) The area under the curve from 2.0 m to 4.0 m is the rectangle.

So $W_{2\text{-}4} = (4.0 \text{ m} - 2.0 \text{ m})(20 \text{ N}) = 40 \text{ J}.$

(c) The area under the curve from 4.0 m to 6.0 m is the right triangle.

So $W_{4\text{-}6} = \frac{1}{2}(6.0 \text{ m} - 4.0 \text{ m})(20 \text{ N}) = 20 \text{ J}.$

(d) The area under the curve from 0 to 6.0 m is the sum of the areas of the two triangles and the rectangle.

So $W_{0\text{-}6} = W_{0\text{-}2} + W_{2\text{-}4} + W_{4\text{-}6} = 20 \text{ J} + 40 \text{ J} + 20 \text{ J} = 80 \text{ J}.$

---

2. Work Done by a Variable Force (Section 5.2)

Our discussion of variable force in this section is restricted to spring force described by Hooke's law, $F_s = -kx$ (with $x_o = 0$), where k is a constant called spring constant or force constant which measures the stiffness of a spring, x is the displacement from the spring's unstretched position, and the negative sign indicates that the spring force and the spring displacement are always opposite to each other. Hooke's law is a linear equation, that is, doubling x will also double F_s.

The work done by an external force in stretching or compressing a spring (overcoming the spring force) is $W = \frac{1}{2}kx^2$, where x is the stretch or compression distance. Note that this expression is a quadratic expression, that is, doubling x will also quadruple W.

Example 5.3 A spring of spring constant 20 N/m is to be compressed by 0.10 m.

(a) What is the maximum force required?

(b) What is the work required?

Solution: Given: $k = 20$ N/m and $x = -0.10$ m.

Find: (a) $F_{s(max)}$ (b) W.

(a) From Hooke's law, the maximum force corresponds to the maximum compression.

$F_{s(max)} = -kx = -(20 \text{ N/m})(-0.10 \text{ m}) = 2.0 \text{ N}.$

(b) $W = \frac{1}{2}kx^2 = \frac{1}{2}(20 \text{ N/m})(-0.10 \text{ m})^2 = 0.10 \text{ J}.$

---

3. Work-Energy Theorem: Kinetic Energy (Section 5.3)

Kinetic energy is the energy of motion and it is defined as $K = \frac{1}{2}mv^2$, where m is the mass and v is the velocity of the object. Although velocity is a vector quantity, kinetic energy is a scalar quantity because it depends on the square of velocity. The SI unit of kinetic energy is the joule (J). By combining the definition of work, a kinematic equation, and Newton's second law, we can derive the **work–energy theorem**, which states that the net work done on an object is equal to its change in kinetic energy, i.e., $W_{net} = K - K_o = \Delta K$. In general, work is a measure of energy transfer, and energy is the capacity of doing work.

Example 5.4 An object hits a wall and bounces back with half of its original speed. What is the ratio of the final kinetic energy to the initial kinetic energy?

Solution: Given: $v = \frac{v_o}{2}$. Find: $\frac{K}{K_o}$.

$K_o = \frac{1}{2}mv_o^2$ and $K = \frac{1}{2}mv^2 = \frac{1}{2}m\left(\frac{v_o}{2}\right)^2 = \frac{1}{4}(\frac{1}{2}m\,v_o^2)$. So $\frac{K}{K_o} = \frac{1}{4}$.

Why isn't the result $\frac{1}{2}$?

Since the work–energy theorem is a combination of kinematics and dynamics, it offers a convenient method to solve mechanical problems. Rather than working from kinematics then to dynamics or vice versa, this new theorem can solve these typical "two-step" problems in a single step, as the following example shows.

Example 5.5 The kinetic friction force between a 60.0-kilogram object and a horizontal surface is 50.0 N. If the initial speed of the object is 25.0 m/s, what distance will it slide before coming to a stop?

Solution: Given: $m = 60.0$ kg, $v_o = 25.0$ m/s, $v = 0$, $f_k = 50.0$ N.

Find: d.

The kinetic friction force f_k is the only unbalanced force and the angle between the friction force and the displacement is 180°. With $W_{net} = K - K_o$, we have

$W_{net} = (F\cos\theta)\,d = (f_k \cos 180°)\,d = (50.0\text{ N})(-1)d = K - K_o = \frac{1}{2}mv^2 - \frac{1}{2}mv_o^2$

$= \frac{1}{2}(60.0\text{ kg})(0)^2 - \frac{1}{2}(60.0\text{ kg})(25.0\text{ m/s})^2$. Solving, $d = 3.75 \times 10^2$ m.

Note: This problem can also be solved with dynamics and kinematics. We can first find the acceleration of the object from Newton's second law and then use kinematic equations to find the distance.

---

4. Potential Energy (Section 5.4)

Potential energy is the energy of position. Two forms of potential energy are considered here, **gravitational potential energy** and **elastic (spring) potential energy**. A zero reference point/level is always required in measuring position and potential energy. For example, a question like "how high is that table?" is really meaningless unless we specify a zero reference level, such as the floor, the ground, etc., to measure that height This choice of zero reference point/level is arbitrary, i.e., you can choose anywhere as your zero reference point/level in your calculation. With the zero potential location chosen as the zero reference point/level, the two forms of potential energy can be written as

Gravitational potential energy: $U = mgh$ (with $h_o = 0$)

Elastic potential energy: $U = \frac{1}{2}kx^2$ (with $x_o = 0$)

Example 5.6 A 10.0-kilogram object is moved from the second floor of a house 3.00 m above the ground to the first floor 0.30 m above the ground. What is the change in gravitational potential energy?

Solution: We choose the ground level as our reference level ($h_o = 0$).

Given: $m = 10.0$ kg, $h_1 = 3.00$ m, $h_2 = 0.30$ m. Find: ΔU.

$\Delta U = U_2 - U_1 = mgh_2 - mgh_1 = mg(h_2 - h_1) = (10.0 \text{ kg})(9.80 \text{ m/s}^2)(0.30 \text{ m} - 3.00 \text{ m}) = -2.6 \times 10^2 \text{ J}$.

As expected, ΔU is negative, since the object moves from a higher potential level to a lower potential level.

If we choose the reference level at the first floor level (height is zero at that level), then

$h_1 = 3.00 \text{ m} - 0.30 \text{ m} = 2.70$, and $h_2 = 0$.

So $\Delta U = mg(h_2 - h_1) = (10.0 \text{ kg})(9.80 \text{ m/s}^2)(0 - 2.70 \text{ m}) = -2.6 \times 10^2 \text{ J}$, independent of reference choice.

Now try to calculate the change in potential energy by choosing the second floor as the reference level.

Example 5.7 A spring with a spring constant of 15 N/m is initially compressed by 3.0 cm. How much work is required to compress the spring an additional 4.0 cm?

Solution: We choose the uncompressed position as $x_o = 0$.

Given: $k = 15$ N/m, $x_1 = 0.030$ m, $x_2 = x_1 + \Delta x = 0.030 \text{ m} + 0.040 \text{ m} = 0.070$ m.

Find: W.

The work required goes into the change in elastic potential energy. $W = \Delta K + \Delta U = \Delta U$ ($\Delta K = 0$).

$W = \Delta U = U_2 - U_1 = \frac{1}{2}kx_2^2 - \frac{1}{2}kx_1^2 = \frac{1}{2}k(x_2^2 - x_1^2) = \frac{1}{2}(15 \text{ N/m})[(0.070 \text{ m})^2 - (0.030 \text{ m})^2] = 0.030 \text{ J}.$

Note: Why $W \neq \frac{1}{2}k(x_2 - x_1)^2 = \frac{1}{2}(14 \text{ m/s})(0.070 \text{ m} - 0.030 \text{ m})^2 = 0.012 \text{ J}$?

---

5. The Conservation of Energy (Section 5.5)

A force is **conservative** if the work done by or against the force is independent of the path, but dependent on only the initial and final locations. Gravitational force is an example of a conservative force. A force is **nonconservative** if the work done by or against it depends on the path. Force of friction is an example of a nonconservative force.

The **total mechanical energy**, E, of a system is defined as the sum of the kinetic energy and potential energy, i.e, $E = K + U$. If the working forces (the forces which are doing work) in a system are conservative, the total mechanical energy of the system is conserved. This is **the conservation of total mechanical energy.**

$$K_o + U_o = K + U \quad \text{or} \quad \tfrac{1}{2}mv^2 + U = \tfrac{1}{2}mv_o^2 + U_o.$$

Note: When applying the conservation of mechanical energy, you should choose a zero reference point/level for position to determine U values. The choice is arbitrary, that is, you can choose the zero reference point/level to be anywhere it is convenient. Also clearly identify the initial and final velocities, and the initial and final positions. These are the only four physical quantities involved in mechanical energy conservation so you need to know three of them before you can solve the problem.

Example 5.8 A 70-kilogram skier starts from rest on the top of a 25-meter high slope. What is the speed of the skier on reaching the bottom of the slope? (Neglect friction.)

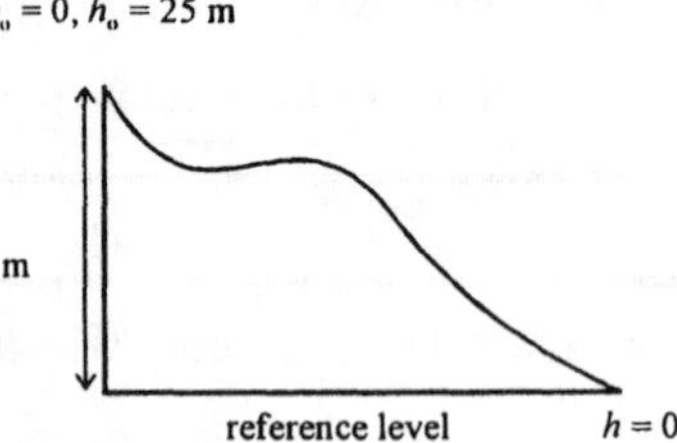

Solution: Given: $v_o = 0$, $h_o = 50$ m, $h = 0$.

Find: v.

We choose the bottom of the slope as the zero reference level ($h = 0$).

From the conservation of mechanical energy

$$K_o + U_o = K + U \quad \text{or} \quad \tfrac{1}{2}mv^2 + U = \tfrac{1}{2}mv_o^2 + U_o.$$

we have $\frac{1}{2}mv^2 + mgh = \frac{1}{2}mv_o^2 + mgh_o$.

So $\frac{1}{2}mv^2 + mg(0) = \frac{1}{2}m(0)^2 + mgh_o$,

therefore $v = \sqrt{2gh_o} = \sqrt{2(9.80 \text{ m/s}^2)(25 \text{ m})} = 22 \text{ m/s}$.

Note: The mass of the skier cancels out in the equation and we did not even use the mass of the skier!

Example 5.9 A 1500-kilogram car moving at 25 m/s hits an initially uncompressed horizontal spring with spring constant of 2.0×10^6 N/m. What is the maximum compression of the spring? (Neglect the mass of the spring.)

Solution: Given: $m = 1500$ kg, $k = 2.0 \times 10^6$ N/m, $v_o = 25$ m/s, $v = 0$, $x_o = 0$.

(Remember we need three known velocity and/or position quantities.)

Find: x.

Here we choose the uncompressed position of the spring as the reference point ($x_o = 0$). Before the car hits the spring, the car is moving with an initial speed of 25 m/s and the compression of the spring is zero. When the spring is maximally compressed, the car stops (transfer all its kinetic energy to elastic potential energy in the spring) and the spring is compressed by a distance of x. From the conservation of mechanical energy, $K_o + U_o = K + U$ or $\frac{1}{2}mv^2 + U = \frac{1}{2}mv_o^2 + U_o$,

we have $\frac{1}{2}mv^2 + \frac{1}{2}kx^2 = \frac{1}{2}mv_o^2 + \frac{1}{2}kx_o^2$.

So $\frac{1}{2}m(0) + \frac{1}{2}kx^2 = \frac{1}{2}mv_o^2 + \frac{1}{2}k(0)^2$,

therefore $x = \sqrt{\dfrac{mv_o^2}{k}} = \sqrt{\dfrac{m}{k}}\, v_o = \sqrt{\dfrac{1500 \text{ kg}}{2.0 \times 10^6 \text{ N/m}}}\,(25 \text{ m/s}) = 0.68$ m.

If there is a nonconservative force doing work in a system, the total mechanical energy of the system is *not* conserved. However, the total energy (not mechanical!) of the system is still conserved. Some of the total energy is used to overcome the work done by the nonconservative force. The difference in mechanical energy is equal to the work done by the nonconservative force, that is $W_{nc} = E_o - E = -\Delta E$.

Example 5.10 In Example 5.8, if the work done by the kinetic friction force is -6.0×10^3 J (the work done by kinetic friction force is negative because the angle between the friction force and the displacement is 180°). What is the speed of the skier at the bottom of the slope?

Solution:

Since the kinetic friction force is a nonconservative force, mechanical energy is *not* conserved. However, the difference in mechanical energy is equal to the work done by the friction force.

$W_{nc} = E - E_o = (\frac{1}{2}mv^2 + mgh) - (\frac{1}{2}m\,v_o^2 + mgh_o)$.

So $-6.0 \times 10^3 \text{ J} = \frac{1}{2}(70 \text{ kg})v^2 + mg(0) - \frac{1}{2}m\,(0)^2 - (70 \text{ kg})(9.80 \text{ m/s}^2)(25 \text{ m})$.

Solving, $v = 18$ m/s.

6. Power (Section 5.6)

Average **power** is the average rate of doing work (work done divided by time interval), $\overline{P} = \frac{W}{t}$. The SI unit of power is watt (W). A common British unit of power is horsepower (hp) and 1 hp = 746 W. If the work is done by a constant force in the direction of motion or displacement ($\theta = 0°$) and the object is moved through a distance of d, $\overline{P} = \frac{Fd}{t} = F\,\overline{v}$, where $\frac{d}{t} = \overline{v}$ is the magnitude of the average velocity.

Example 5.11 A 1500-kilogram car accelerates from 0 to 25 m/s in 7.0 s. What is the average power delivered to the car by the engine? Ignore all frictional and other losses.

Solution: Given: $m = 1500$ kg, $v_o = 0$, $v = 25$ m/s, $t = 7.0$ s. Find: $\overline{P}$.

Since power is the rate of doing work, we need to calculate the work done to the car first.

From work-energy theorem, $W = \Delta K = \frac{1}{2}mv^2 - \frac{1}{2}mv_o^2 = \frac{1}{2}(1500\text{ kg})[(25\text{ m/s})^2 - (0)^2] = 4.69 \times 10^5$ J.

So $\overline{P} = \frac{W}{t} = \frac{4.69\times10^5\text{ J}}{7.0\text{ s}} = 6.7 \times 10^4$ W (= 90 hp).

Alternate method: The average velocity of the car is $\overline{v} = \frac{v + v_o}{2} = \frac{25\text{ m/s} + 0}{2} = 12.5$ m/s.

From Newton's second law $F = ma = m\frac{v - v_o}{t} = (1500\text{ kg}) \times \frac{25\text{ m/s} - 0}{7.0\text{ s}} = 5.36 \times 10^3$ N.

So $\overline{P} = F\,\overline{v} = (5.36 \times 10^3\text{ N})(12.5\text{ m/s}) = 6.7 \times 10^4\text{ W} = 90$ hp.

IV. Mathematical Summary

Work	$W = (F\cos\theta)d$	(5.2)	Defines work.
Hooke's Law (spring force)	$F_s = -kx$	(5.3)	Relates spring force with spring constant and change in length.
Work done in a Spring	$W = \frac{1}{2}kx^2$	(5.4)	Relates work done by external force in stretching or compressing a spring.
Kinetic Energy	$K = \frac{1}{2}mv^2$	(5.5)	Defines kinetic energy in terms of mass and velocity.
Work-Energy Theorem	$W_{net} = K - K_o = \Delta K$	(5.6)	The net work done on an object is equal to the change in kinetic energy.

Elastic (spring) Potential Energy	$U = \frac{1}{2}kx^2$ (with $x_o = 0$) (5.7)	Defines elastic potential energy.
Gravitational Potential Energy	$U = mgh$ (with $h_o = 0$) 5.8	Defines gravitational potential energy.
Conservation of Mechanical Energy	$\frac{1}{2}mv^2 + U = \frac{1}{2}mv_o^2 + U_o$ (5.10)	States that the total mechanical energy of a system is conserved if only conservative forces are doing work.
Conservation of Energy (with a nonconservative force)	$W_{nc} = E - E_o = \Delta E$ (5.13)	Equates the work done by nonconservative force to the change in mechanical energy of a system.
Average Power	$\overline{P} = \frac{W}{t} = \frac{Fd}{t} = F\overline{v}$ (5.15) $\overline{P} = \frac{Fd\cos\theta}{t}$ (5.16)	Defines and calculates the average power delivered by a constant force in direction of d and v. For if the force is making an angle θ with d or v.
Efficiency (percent)	$\varepsilon = \frac{W_{out}}{W_{in}}$ (× 100%) (5.17) $= \frac{P_{out}}{P_{in}}$ (× 100%) (5.18)	Defines the mechanical efficiency of a system.

V. Solutions of Selected Exercises and Paired/Trio Exercises

6. From the definition of work $W = (F\cos\theta)d$,

we have $F = \dfrac{W}{d\cos\theta} = \dfrac{50\text{ J}}{(10\text{ m})\cos 0^\circ} = \boxed{5.0\text{ N}}$.

7. The kinetic friction force is $f_k = \mu_k N = \mu_k mg$ and the angle between the kinetic friction force and displacement is 0°.

$W = (F\cos\theta)d = \mu_k mg\cos\theta\, d = 0.20(5.0\text{ kg})(9.80\text{ m/s}^2)\cos 180^\circ\,(10\text{ m}) = \boxed{-98\text{ J}}$.

14. $\Sigma F_y = N + F\sin\theta - mg = 0$, or $N = mg - F\sin\theta$.

$\Sigma F_x = F\cos\theta - f_k = 0$, or $F\cos\theta = \mu_k N = \mu_k(mg - F\sin\theta) = 0$.

So $F = \dfrac{\mu_k mg}{\cos\theta + \mu_k\sin\theta} = \dfrac{0.20(35\text{ kg})(9.80\text{ m/s}^2)}{\cos 30^\circ + 0.20\sin 30^\circ} = 71.0\text{ N}$.

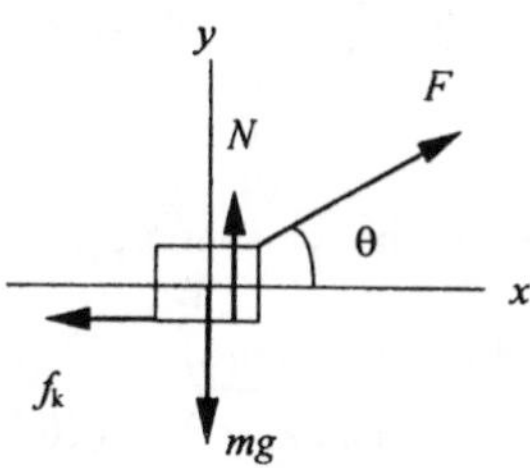

Therefore $W = (F\cos\theta)d = (71.0\text{ N})\cos 30^\circ\,(10\text{ m}) = \boxed{6.1\times 10^2\text{ J}}$.

16. (a) $\boxed{1.0 \times 10^3\ \text{J}}$. (b) $\boxed{-6.2 \times 10^2\ \text{J}}$. (c) $\boxed{3.8 \times 10^2\ \text{J}}$.

21. $\boxed{\text{No}}$, more work is required, because the force increases as the spring stretches, according to Hooke's law: $F_s = -kx$.

24. $W = \frac{1}{2}kx^2 = \frac{1}{2}(40\ \text{N/m})(0.020\ \text{m})^2 = \boxed{8.0 \times 10^{-3}\ \text{J}}$.

28. (a) $W = \frac{1}{2}kx^2 = \frac{1}{2}(2.5 \times 10^3\ \text{N/m})(0.060\ \text{m})^2 = \boxed{4.5\ \text{J}}$.

(b) $W = \frac{1}{2}k(x_2^2 - x_1^2) = \frac{1}{2}(2.5 \times 10^3\ \text{N/m})[(0.080\ \text{m})^2 - (0.060\ \text{m})^2] = \boxed{3.5\ \text{J}}$.

33. Because the heel can lift from the blade, the blade will be in contact with the ice longer. This will make the displacement a bit greater (longer stride) so that the work done is greater. Greater work translates to faster speed according to the work-energy theorem.

34. (a) $K = \frac{1}{2}mv^2 = \frac{1}{2}(4m)v^2 = 2mv^2$. (b) $K = \frac{1}{2}(3m)(2v)^2 = 6mv^2$.

(c) $K = \frac{1}{2}(2m)(3v)^2 = 9mv^2$. (d) $K = \frac{1}{2}(m)(4v)^2 = 8mv^2$.

So (a) has the smallest kinetic energy.

38. 90 km/h = 25 m/s.

(a) $K_o = \frac{1}{2}mv^2 = \frac{1}{2}(1.2 \times 10^3\ \text{kg})(25\ \text{m/s})^2 = \boxed{3.8 \times 10^5\ \text{J}}$.

(b) From the work-energy theorem,

$W_{net} = \frac{1}{2}mv^2 - \frac{1}{2}mv_o^2 = 0 - 3.8 \times 10^5\ \text{J} = \boxed{-3.8 \times 10^5\ \text{J}}$.

40. $-\boxed{1.5 \times 10^3\ \text{N}}$, opposite to direction of velocity.

43. From the work-energy theorem $W = \frac{1}{2}mv^2 - \frac{1}{2}mv_o^2 = \frac{1}{2}m(v^2 - v_o^2)$,

$$\frac{W_2}{W_1} = \frac{(30\ \text{km/h})^2 - (20\ \text{km/h})^2}{(20\ \text{km/h})^2 - (10\ \text{km/h})^2} = 1.67,$$

so $W_2 = 1.67W_1 = 1.67(5.0 \times 10^3\ \text{J}) = \boxed{8.3 \times 10^3\ \text{J}}$.

49. From the definition of gravitational potential energy $U = mgh$,

we have $\Delta U = mg\Delta h = (1.0 \text{ kg})(9.80 \text{ m/s}^2)(1.5 \text{ m} - 0.90 \text{ m}) = \boxed{5.9 \text{ J}}$.

52. (a) On the board: $U = mgh = (60 \text{ kg})(9.80 \text{ m/s}^2)(5.0 \text{ m}) = \boxed{2.9 \times 10^3 \text{ J}}$.

At the bottom of pool: $U = (60 \text{ kg})(9.80 \text{ m/s}^2)(-3.0 \text{ m}) = \boxed{-1.8 \times 10^3 \text{ J}}$.

(b) To the board: $\Delta U = mg\Delta h = (60 \text{ kg})(9.80 \text{ m/s}^2)(-8.0 \text{ m} - 0) = \boxed{-4.7 \times 10^3 \text{ J}}$.

To the surface: $\Delta U = (60 \text{ kg})(9.80 \text{ m/s}^2)(-3.0 \text{ m} - 5.0 \text{ m}) = \boxed{-4.7 \times 10^3 \text{ J}}$.

To the bottom of pool: $\Delta U = (60 \text{ kg})(9.80 \text{ m/s}^2)(0 - 8.0 \text{ m}) = \boxed{-4.7 \times 10^3 \text{ J}}$.

60. (a) $E_o = K_o + U_o = 0 + (0.250 \text{ kg})(9.80 \text{ m/s}^2)(115 \text{ m}) = \boxed{282 \text{ J}}$.

(b) $U_1 = (0.250 \text{ kg})(9.80 \text{ m/s}^2)(115 \text{ m} - 75.0 \text{ m}) = \boxed{98.0 \text{ J}}$.

Since $E = E_o$ is conserved, $K_1 = E_o - U_1 = 282 \text{ J} - 98.0 \text{ J} = \boxed{184 \text{ J}}$.

(c) $E_2 = K_2 + 0 = K_2 = \boxed{282 \text{ J}}$. $K_2 = \frac{1}{2}mv^2$,

so $v = \sqrt{\dfrac{2K_2}{m}} = \dfrac{2(282 \text{ J})}{0.250 \text{ kg}} = \boxed{47.5 \text{ m/s}}$.

(d) For (a) $E_o = 0 + 0 = \boxed{0}$.

For (b) $U_1 = (0.250 \text{ kg})(9.80 \text{ m/s}^2)(-75.0 \text{ m}) = \boxed{-184 \text{ J}}$. $K_1 = 0 - (-184 \text{ J}) = \boxed{184 \text{ J}}$.

For (c) $E_2 = K_2 + U_2 = \boxed{0}$. $K_2 = 0 - (0.250 \text{ kg})(9.80 \text{ m/s}^2)(-115 \text{ m}) = 282 \text{ J}$.

So $v = \dfrac{2(282 \text{ J})}{0.250 \text{ kg}} = \boxed{47.5 \text{ m/s}}$.

62. $\boxed{5.10 \text{ m}}$.

66. We choose the bottom of the slope (point B) as the reference for height ($h_o = 0$).

From the conservation of mechanical energy $\frac{1}{2}mv_B^{\ 2} + U_B = \frac{1}{2}mv_A^{\ 2} + U_A$,

we have $\frac{1}{2}mv_B^{\ 2} + mg(0) = \frac{1}{2}m(5.0 \text{ m/s})^2 + mg\,(10 \text{ m})$,

so $v_B = \sqrt{(5.0 \text{ m/s})^2 + 2(9.80 \text{ m/s}^2)(10 \text{ m})} = \boxed{15 \text{ m/s}}$.

67. We choose the lowest point on the course (point B) as the reference for height ($h_o = 0$).

(a) From the conservation of mechanical energy $\frac{1}{2}mv_B{}^2 + U_B = \frac{1}{2}mv_A{}^2 + U_A$,

we have $\frac{1}{2}mv_B{}^2 + mg(0) = \frac{1}{2}m(5.0 \text{ m/s})^2 + mg(5.0 \text{ m})$,

so $v_B = \sqrt{(5.0 \text{ m/s})^2 + 2(9.80 \text{ m/s}^2)(5.0 \text{ m})} = \boxed{11 \text{ m/s}}$.

(b) $E_A = E_B = \frac{1}{2}m\,(11 \text{ m/s})^2 = 60.5m$. $E_C = mg(8.0 \text{ m}) = m(9.80 \text{ m/s}^2)(8.0 \text{ m}) = 78.4m > E_A$.

So $\boxed{\text{no}}$, it will not reach point C.

(c) $\frac{1}{2}mv_A{}^2 + mg(5.0 \text{ m}) = \frac{1}{2}m(0)^2 + mg(8.0 \text{ m})$, solving, $v_A = \boxed{7.7 \text{ m/s}}$.

71. When a nonconservative force does work, the work done by the nonconservative force is equal to the change in mechanical energy. $W_{nc} = \Delta E = E_o - E = [\frac{1}{2}m(5.0 \text{ m/s})^2 + mg(10 \text{ m})] - [\frac{1}{2}mv_B{}^2 + mg(0)]$.

So $2500 \text{ J} = [\frac{1}{2}(60 \text{ kg})(5.0 \text{ m/s})^2 + (60 \text{ kg})(9.80 \text{ m/s}^2)(10 \text{ m})] - [\frac{1}{2}(60 \text{ kg})v_B{}^2 + mg(0)]$.

Solving, $v_B = \boxed{12 \text{ m/s}}$.

78. 90 km/h = 25 m/s. From work-energy theorem $W = \Delta K = \frac{1}{2}mv^2 - 0$.

$$\overline{P} = \frac{W}{t} = \frac{mv^2}{2t} = \frac{(1500 \text{ kg})(25 \text{ m/s})^2}{2(5.0 \text{ s})} = \boxed{9.4 \times 10^4 \text{ W} = 1.3 \times 10^2 \text{ hp}}.$$

80. (a) $\boxed{4.4 \times 10^2 \text{ W}}$. (b) $\boxed{0.59 \text{ hp}}$.

85. (a) $\Sigma F_x = F - f - mg \sin\theta = 0$,

so $F = f + mg \sin\theta = 950 \text{ N} + (120 \text{ kg})(9.80 \text{ m/s}^2) \sin 15° = 1254 \text{ N}$.

Also $v = 5.0 \text{ km/h} = 1.389 \text{ m/s}$.

So $P = Fv = (1254 \text{ N})(1.389 \text{ m/s}) = 1742 \text{ W} = \boxed{2.3 \text{ hp}}$.

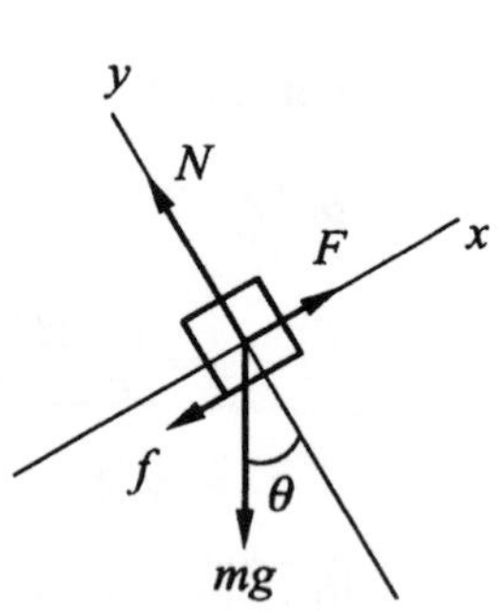

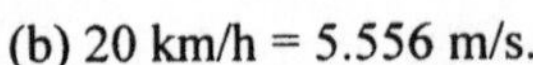
The horse is working hard (it is working as hard as 2.3 horses. In spurts a horse can be more than 1 hp).

(b) 20 km/h = 5.556 m/s.

$$a = \frac{5.556 \text{ m/s} - 1.389 \text{ m/s}}{5.0 \text{ s}} = 0.833 \text{ m/s}^2.$$

Now $\Sigma F_x = F - f - mg \sin\theta = ma$,

so $F = 1254 \text{ N} + (120 \text{ kg})(0.833 \text{ m/s}^2) = 1354 \text{ N}$.

$P = (1354 \text{ N})(5.556 \text{ m/s}) = 7522 \text{ W} = \boxed{10 \text{ hp}}$.

96. (a) We choose the stopped position as $h = 0$ and assume the ball compresses the spring by x. Then the initial height $h_o = (1.20\text{ m} + x)$ high.

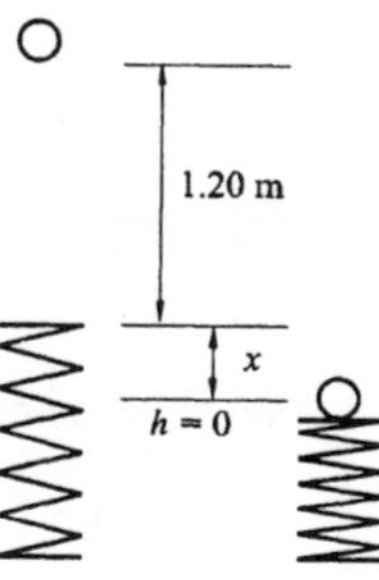

From conservation of mechanical energy: $mgh_o + 0 = 0 + \frac{1}{2}kx^2$,

so $mg(1.20\text{ m} + x) = \frac{1}{2}kx^2$, simplifying, $175x^2 - 3.53x - 4.23 = 0$.

Solving, $x = \boxed{0.166\text{ m}}$ or -0.150 m.

The negative answer has no physical meaning and is discarded.

(b) $mg(1.20\text{ m} + 0.0500\text{ m}) = \frac{1}{2}k(0.0500\text{ m})^2 + \frac{1}{2}mv^2$,

or $4.41\text{ J} = 0.438\text{ J} + \frac{1}{2}(0.360\text{ kg})v^2$, so $v = \boxed{4.70\text{ m/s}}$.

VI. Practice Quiz

1. Which one of the following is the correct unit of work expressed in SI base units?
(a) kg·m/s (b) kg·m/s^2 (c) kg·m^2/s (d) kg·m^2/s^2 (e) kg^2·m/s^2

2. A 40-newton crate is pulled 5.0 m up along a 37° inclined plane. What is the magnitude of the work done by the weight (gravitational force) of the crate? (Hint: draw a diagram.)
(a) 6.0 J (b) 12 J (c) 1.2×10^2 J (d) 2.0×10^2 J (e) 1.2×10^3 J.

3. What work is required to stretch a spring of spring constant 40 N/m from $x = 0.20$ m to 0.25 m? (The unstretched position is at $x = 0$.)
(a) 0.45 J (b) 0.80 J (c) 1.3 J (d) 0.050 J (e) 0.90 J

4. A force of 200 N, directed at 20° above the horizontal, is applied to move a 50-kilogram cart (initially at rest) across a 10 m level surface. What is the speed of the cart at the end of the 10 m distance?
(a) 5.2 m/s (b) 8.6 m/s (c) 8.9 m/s (d) 6.8×10^2 m/s (e) 2.0×10^3 m/s

5. A roller coaster makes a run down a track from a vertical distance of 25 m. If there is negligible friction and the coaster starts from rest, what is its speed at the bottom of the track?
(a) 5.0 m/s (b) 16 m/s (c) 22 m/s (d) 2.5×10^2 m/s (e) 4.9×10^2 m/s

6. A 10-newton force is needed to move an object with a constant velocity of 5.0 m/s. What power must be delivered to the object by the force?
(a) 0.50 W (b) 1.0 W (c) 2.0 W (d) 50 W (e) 100 W

7. If it takes 50 m to stop a car initially moving at 15 m/s, what distance is required to stop a car moving at 30 m/s? (Assume the same braking force.)

(a) 25 m (b) 50 m (c) 100 m (d) 150 m (e) 200 m

8. What is the minimum speed of the ball at the bottom of its swing (point B) in order for it to reach point A, which is 0.20 m above the bottom of the swing?

(a) 0.40 m/s (b) 1.4 m/s (c) 2.0 m/s (d) 3.1 m/s (e) 3.9 m/s

9. A force of 10 N is applied horizontally to a 2.0-kilogram mass on a level surface. The coefficient of kinetic friction between the mass and the surface is 0.20. If the mass is moved a distance of 10 m, what is the change in its kinetic energy?

(a) 100 J (b) 61 J (c) 46 J (d) 39 J (e) 20 J

10. A 1500-kilogram car is moving with a speed of 25 m/s. How much work is required to stop the car?

(a) 1.5×10^3 J (b) 1.9×10^4 J (c) 3.8×10^4 J (d) 4.7×10^5 J (e) 9.4×10^5 J

Answers to Practice Quiz:

1.d 2.c 3.a 4.b 5.c 6.d 7.e 8.c 9.b 10.d

CHAPTER 6

Momentum and Collisions

I. Chapter Objectives

Upon completion of this chapter, you should be able to:

1. compute linear momentum and the components of momentum.
2. relate impulse and momentum, and kinetic energy and momentum.
3. explain the condition for the conservation of linear momentum and apply it to physical situations.
4. describe the conditions on kinetic energy and momentum in elastic and inelastic collisions.
5. explain the concept of the center of mass and compute its location for simple systems, and describe how the center of mass and center of gravity are related.
6. apply the conservation of momentum in the explanation of jet propulsion and the operation of rockets.

II. Key Terms

Upon completion of this chapter, you should be able to define and/or explain the following key terms:

linear momentum
total linear momentum
impulse
impulse-momentum theorem
conservation of linear momentum
elastic collision
inelastic collision
completely inelastic collision
center of mass (CM)
center of gravity (CG)
jet propulsion

The definitions and/or explanations of the most important key terms can be found in the following section: **III. Chapter Summary and Discussion.**

III. Chapter Summary and Discussion

1. Linear Momentum (Section 6.1)

The **linear momentum** of an object is defined as the product of its mass and velocity, $\mathbf{p} = m\,\mathbf{v}$. Since velocity is a vector, so is momentum. The SI unit of momentum is kg·m/s.

Note: Momentum depends on *both* the mass and velocity, not just either mass or velocity.

The **total linear momentum** of a system is the vector sum of the momenta of the individual particles.

$$\mathbf{P} = \mathbf{p}_1 + \mathbf{p}_2 + \mathbf{p}_3 + \ldots = \sum_i \mathbf{p}_i$$

Example 6.1 Which has more linear momentum:

(a) a 1500-kilogram car moving at 25.0 m/s or

(b) a 40 000-kilogram truck moving at 1.00 m/s?

Solution: Given: mass, m, and velocity, v.

Find: magnitude of momentum, p.

(a) $p = mv = (1500 \text{ kg})(25.0 \text{ m/s}) = 3.75 \times 10^4 \text{ kg·m/s}$.

(b) $p = (40\,000 \text{ kg})(1.00 \text{ m/s}) = 4.00 \times 10^4 \text{ kg·m/s}$.

So the much slower truck has more momentum than the faster car because the truck has more mass.

Example 6.2 Two identical 1500-kilogram cars are moving perpendicular to each other. One moves with a speed of 25.0 m/s due north and the other moves at 15.0 m/s due east. What is the total linear momentum of the system?

Solution: Given: $m_1 = m_2 = 1500$ kg, $v_1 = 25.0$ m/s, $v_2 = 15.0$ m/s.

Find: **P**.

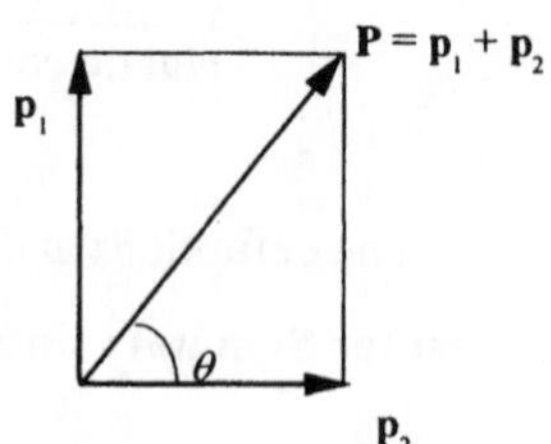

$p_1 = m_1 v_1 = (1500 \text{ kg})(25.0 \text{ m/s}) = 3.75 \times 10^4 \text{ kg·m/s}$.

$p_2 = m_2 v_2 = (1500 \text{ kg})(15.0 \text{ m/s}) = 2.25 \times 10^4 \text{ kg·m/s}$.

So $P = \sqrt{p_1^2 + p_2^2} = \sqrt{(3.75 \times 10^4 \text{ kg·m/s})^2 + (2.25 \times 10^4 \text{ kg·m/s})^2}$

$= 4.4 \times 10^4 \text{ kg·m/s}$.

$$\theta = \tan^{-1}\frac{p_1}{p_2} = \frac{3.75 \times 10^4 \text{ kg·m/s}}{2.25 \times 10^4 \text{ kg·m/s}} = 59.1° \text{ north of east.}$$

Note: Momentum is a vector quantity. You must use vector addition when adding momenta.

Newton's second law can also be expressed in terms of momentum: $\overline{\mathbf{F}} = \frac{\Delta \mathbf{p}}{\Delta t}$. It is equivalent to $\mathbf{F} = m\mathbf{a}$ if mass is a constant. (Actually, Newton used the momentum form of his second law when he first started formatting the law.) For system in which mass is not a constant, such rocket propulsion, $\overline{\mathbf{F}} = \frac{\Delta \mathbf{p}}{\Delta t}$ should be used. The impulse-momentum theorem discussed later is a variation of this form of Newton's second law.

2. **Impulse** (Section 6.2)

From Newton's second law, $\overline{\mathbf{F}} = \frac{\Delta \mathbf{p}}{\Delta t}$, we can derive the **impulse-momentum theorem**. This theorem states that *impulse is equal to the change in momentum*, or $\overline{\mathbf{F}}\,\Delta t = \Delta \mathbf{p} = \mathbf{p} - \mathbf{p}_o$, where $\overline{\mathbf{F}}\,\Delta t$ is called impulse ($\overline{\mathbf{F}}$ is the average force and Δt is the time interval the force is in action).

Impulse-momentum is very useful in explaining some everyday phenomena. For example, why do tennis players follow through? Why do football players wear pads? Why can some not-so-strong martial artists break objects like bricks with their bare fists? Try to answer some of these questions and the answers may surprise you.

Note: Again, momentum is a vector quantity and so must be treated as a vector.

Example 6.3 A 0.10-kilogram ball is dropped onto a table top. The speeds of the ball right before hitting the table top and right after hitting the table top are 5.0 m/s and 4.0 m/s, respectively. If the collision between the ball and the tabletop lasts 0.15 s, what is the average force exerted on the ball by the table top?

Solution: Given: $m = 0.10$ kg, $v_o = -5.0$ m/s (downward), $v = +4.0$ m/s (upward), $\Delta t = 0.15$ s.

Find: $\overline{\mathbf{F}}$.

The velocity of the ball before the collision is downward and the velocity of the ball after the collision is upward. Since these two velocities are opposite, we have to assign signs (+ or −) to them to find the change in velocity, Δv, properly. Conventionally, we chose the upward direction as positive so the downward direction is negative.

From impulse-momentum theorem, we have $\overline{\mathbf{F}}\,\Delta t = \Delta \mathbf{p} = \mathbf{p} - \mathbf{p}_o$.

So $\overline{\mathbf{F}} = \frac{\mathbf{p} - \mathbf{p}_o}{\Delta t} = \frac{m\,v - m\,v_o}{\Delta t} = \frac{(0.10\text{ kg})(4.0\text{ m/s}) - (0.10\text{ kg})(-5.0\text{ m/s})}{0.15\text{ s}} = +6.0\text{ N}.$

The positive sign indicates that the force on the ball by the tabletop is upward, which makes sense.

---

3. The Conservation of Linear Momentum (Section 6.3)

The total linear momentum of a system is conserved if the net external force on the system is zero.

$$\mathbf{P} = \mathbf{P}_o, \quad \text{or} \quad \mathbf{p}_1 + \mathbf{p}_2 + \ldots = \mathbf{p}_{1o} + \mathbf{p}_{2o} + \ldots.$$

Note: Momentum is a vector quantity. You must use vector addition when applying the conservation of linear momentum.

When applied to a "collision" involving two objects, a more convenient form of the conservation of momentum can be written as $m_1 v_1 + m_2 v_2 = m_1 v_{1o} + m_2 v_{2o}$, where the m's are the masses of the two objects, the v_o's are the initial velocities, and the v's are the final velocities.

Note: The terms initial and final are always relative and here they are relative to the "collision" process. A collision is generally defined in physics as a process in which forces are exerted.

Example 6.4 A 50-kilogram pitching machine (excluding the baseball) is placed on a frozen pond. The machine fires a 0.40-kilogram baseball with a speed of 35 m/s in the horizontal direction. What is the recoil velocity of the pitching machine? (Assume negligible friction.)

Solution: Given: $m_1 = 50$ kg (machine) $\quad m_2 = 0.40$ kg (ball)

$v_{1o} = 0 \quad v_{2o} = 0,$

$v_2 = 35$ m/s

Find: v_1.

Here the "collision" process is the firing of the baseball. Before the baseball is fired, neither the machine nor the baseball is moving so both have zero velocity and momentum (the total initial momentum $P_o = 0$). After the ball is fired, the ball moves in one direction and the machine must recoil in the opposite direction so that the total momentum $P = 0$.

From momentum conservation, we have $\mathbf{P} = \mathbf{P}_o$, or $\mathbf{p}_1 + \mathbf{p}_2 = \mathbf{p}_{1o} + \mathbf{p}_{2o}$.

So $m_1 v_1 + m_2 v_2 = m_1 v_{1o} + m_2 v_{2o} = 0,$

therefore $v_1 = -\dfrac{m_2 v_2}{m_1} = -\dfrac{(0.40 \text{ kg})(35 \text{ m/s})}{50 \text{ kg}} = -0.28 \text{ m/s}.$

The negative sign here indicates the machine is moving in exactly the opposite direction to the ball.

Example 6.5 A 10-gram bullet moving at 300 m/s is fired into a 1.0-kilogram block. The bullet emerges (does not stay embedded in the block) with half of its original speed. What is the velocity of the block right after the collision?

Solution: Given: $m_1 = 0.010$ kg (bullet) $m_2 = 1.0$ kg (block)

$v_{1o} = 300$ m/s $v_{2o} = 0$

$v_1 = 150$ m/s

Find: v_2.

Right before the bullet hits the block, the bullet is moving at 300 m/s and the block is at rest. Right after the bullet hits the block, it emerges with (300 m/s)/2 = 150 m/s and the block should be moving in the same direction as the bullet. (Why?)

From momentum conservation, we have $\mathbf{P} = \mathbf{P}_o$, or $\mathbf{p}_1 + \mathbf{p}_2 = \mathbf{p}_{1o} + \mathbf{p}_{2o}$,

we have $m_1 v_1 + m_2 v_2 = m_1 v_{1o} + m_2 v_{2o} = m_1 v_{1o} + 0 = m_1 v_{1o}$.

So $v_2 = \dfrac{m_1 v_{1o} - m_1 v_1}{m_2} = \dfrac{(0.010 \text{ kg})(300 \text{ m/s} - 150 \text{ m/s})}{1.0 \text{ kg}} = +1.5 \text{ m/s}.$

The result is positive because the block is moving in the same direction as the bullet.

4. Elastic and Inelastic Collision (Section 6.4)

Linear momentum is always conserved in a collision, as long as the net external force is zero on the system, which is approximately true at least during the small time interval Δt of the collision. However, in an **elastic collision**, kinetic energy is also conserved while in an **inelastic collision**, kinetic energy is not conserved. (**Note**: when kinetic energy is not conserved as is the usual case, this does not mean the total energy is not conserved. Some of the kinetic energy is converted to heat, sound, etc. during a collision. Total energy is always conserved as we shall see!). If the objects in a system stick together after collision, the collision is called **completely inelastic**. In an inelastic collision, the kinetic energy of the system before the collision is always greater than the kinetic energy of the system after the collision. Why?

Example 6.6 While standing on skates on a frozen pond, a student of mass 70.0 kg catches a 2.00-kilogram ball travelling horizontally at 15.0 m/s toward him.

(a) What is the speed of the student and the ball immediately after he catches it?

(b) How much kinetic energy is lost in the process?

Solution: Given: $m_1 = 70.0$ kg $m_2 = 2.00$ kg

$v_{1o} = 0$ $v_{2o} = 15.0$ m/s

Find: v_1 v_2.

Since the student catches the ball, they must have the same final velocity, $v_1 = v_2 = v$. Here the "collision" is the catch action.

(a) From momentum conservation, we have $\mathbf{P} = \mathbf{P}_o$, or $\mathbf{p}_1 + \mathbf{p}_2 = \mathbf{p}_{1o} + \mathbf{p}_{2o}$,

we have $m_1 v_1 + m_2 v_2 = m_1 v + m_2 v = (m_1 + m_2)v = m_1 v_{1o} + m_2 v_{2o}$.

So $v = \dfrac{m_1 v_{1o} + m_2 v_{2o}}{m_1 + m_2} = \dfrac{(70.0 \text{ kg})(0) + (2.00 \text{ kg})(15.0 \text{ m/s})}{70.0 \text{ kg} + 2.00 \text{ kg}} = 0.417 \text{ m/s}.$

(b) Initial kinetic energy $K_o = \frac{1}{2} m_1 v_{1o}^2 + \frac{1}{2} m_2 v_{2o}^2 = \frac{1}{2}(70.0 \text{ kg})(0)^2 + \frac{1}{2}(2.00 \text{ kg})(15.0 \text{ m/s})^2 = 225 \text{ J}.$

Final kinetic energy $K = \frac{1}{2} m_1 v_1^2 + \frac{1}{2} m_2 v_2^2 = \frac{1}{2}[(70.0 \text{ kg}) + (2.00 \text{ kg})](0.417 \text{ m/s})^2 = 207 \text{ J}.$

So the kinetic energy lost in the collision is $|\Delta K| = K_o - K = 225 \text{ J } 207 \text{ J} = 18 \text{ J}.$

The percentage of kinetic energy loss is $\dfrac{K - K_o}{K_o} = \dfrac{-18 \text{ J}}{225 \text{ J}} = -0.080 = -8.0\%.$

Example 6.7 A rubber ball with a speed of 5.0 m/s collides head on elastically with an identical ball at rest. Find the velocity of each object after the collision.

Solution: Given: $m_1 = m$ $m_2 = m$ (identical ball)

$v_{1o} = 5.0$ m/s $v_{2o} = 0$

Find: v_1 v_2.

We use Equations (6.15) and (6.16).

$$v_1 = \left(\frac{m_1 - m_2}{m_1 + m_2}\right) v_{1o} = \frac{m - m}{m + m}(5.0 \text{ m/s}) = 0. \quad v_2 = \left(\frac{2m_1}{m_1 + m_2}\right) v_{1o} = \frac{2\,m}{m + m}(5.0 \text{ m/s}) = 5.0 \text{ m/s}.$$

The two balls exchange velocities. This is always the case if $m_1 = m_2$ in such collisions.

---

5. Center of Mass (Section 6.5)

The **center of mass** of a system is the point at which all the mass of the system may be considered to be concentrated. If the acceleration due to gravity, *g*, is a constant, then the **center of gravity**, or the point at which all the weight of the system may be considered to be concentrated, is at the center of mass. For a system of particles, the coordinates of the center of mass are calculated by $X_{CM} = \dfrac{\sum_i m_i x_i}{M}$ and $Y_{CM} = \dfrac{\sum_i m_i y_i}{M}$, where x_i and y_i are the coordinates of the particle m_i, and $M = \sum_i m_i$ is the total mass of the system.

The motion of the center of mass also obeys Newton's second law: $\mathbf{F}_{\text{net external}} = M\,\mathbf{A}_{CM}$, where $\mathbf{F}_{\text{net external}}$ is the net external force, *M* is the total mass of the system, and $\mathbf{A}_{CM}$ is the acceleration of the center of mass.

Example 6.8 Find the location of the center of mass of the following three mass system.

mass	location
$m_1 = 1.0$ kg	(0, 0)
$m_2 = 2.0$ kg	(1.0 m, 1.0 m)
$m_3 = 3.0$ kg	(2.0 m, −2.0 m)

Solution:

$$X_{CM} = \frac{\sum_i m_i x_i}{M} = \frac{(1.0\text{ kg})(0) + (2.0\text{ kg})(1.0\text{ m}) + (3.0\text{ kg})(2.0\text{ m})}{1.0\text{ kg} + 2.0\text{ kg} + 3.0\text{ kg}} = 1.3\text{ m}.$$

$$Y_{CM} = \frac{\sum_i m_i y_i}{M} = \frac{(1.0\text{ kg})(0) + (2.0\text{ kg})(1.0\text{ m}) + (3.0\text{ kg})(-2.0\text{ m})}{1.0\text{ kg} + 2.0\text{ kg} + 3.0\text{ kg}} = -0.67\text{ m}.$$

So the location of the center of mass is at $(X_{CM}, Y_{CM}) = (1.3\text{ m}, -0.67\text{ m})$.

IV. Mathematical Summary

Linear Momentum	$\mathbf{p} = m\mathbf{v}$ (6.1)	Defines linear momentum.
Total Linear Momentum	$\mathbf{P} = \mathbf{p}_1 + \mathbf{p}_2 + \mathbf{p}_3 + \ldots = \sum_i \mathbf{p}_i$ (6.2)	Computes total linear momentum of a system.
Newton's Second Law in terms of Momentum	$\overline{\mathbf{F}} = \frac{\Delta \mathbf{p}}{\Delta t}$ (6.3)	Rewrites Newton's second law in terms of momentum.
Impulse-momentum theorem	Impulse = $\overline{\mathbf{F}}\,\Delta t = \Delta \mathbf{p} = m\mathbf{v} - m\mathbf{v}_o$ (6.5)	States that the impulse is equal to the change in momentum.
Conditions for an Elastic Collision	$\mathbf{P}_f = \mathbf{P}_i, \quad K_f = K_i$ (6.8)	Define the conditions for an elastic collision.
Conditions for an Inelastic Collision	$\mathbf{P}_f = \mathbf{P}_i, \quad K_f < K_i$ (6.9)	Define the conditions for an inelastic collision.
Final Velocities in Head-On Elastic Collision ($v_{2_o} = 0$)	$v_1 = \left(\frac{m_1 - m_2}{m_1 + m_2}\right) v_{1_o}$ (6.15) $v_2 = \left(\frac{2m_1}{m_1 + m_2}\right) v_{1_o}$ (6.16)	Express the final velocities in head-on elastic collisions.

Coordinate of center of Mass (using sign for directions)	$X_{CM} = \frac{\sum_i m_i x_i}{M}$ (6.20)	Calculates the coordinate the center of mass of a system (using signs for directions).

V. Solutions of Selected Exercises and Paired/Trio Exercises

6. (a) $p = mv = (7.1\text{ kg})(12\text{ m/s}) = \boxed{85\text{ kg·m/s}}$.

   (b) 90 km/h = 25 m/s. $p = (1200\text{ kg})(25\text{ m/s}) = \boxed{3.0 \times 10^4\text{ kg·m/s}}$.

10. Since the ball moves in the opposite direction, the initial velocity must have opposite sign as the final velocity. If $v_o = 4.50$ m/s then $v = -34.7$ m/s.

    $\Delta p = mv - mv_o = (0.150\text{ kg})(-34.7\text{ m/s}) - (0.150\text{ kg})(4.50\text{ m/s}) = -5.88\text{ kg·m/s}$

    $= \boxed{5.88\text{ kg·m/s in the direction opposite } v_o}$.

13. (a) From $v = v_o - gt$,

    $p = mv = m(v_o - gt) = (0.50\text{ kg})[0 - (9.80\text{ m/s}^2)(0.75\text{ s})] = -1.8\text{ kg·m/s} = \boxed{3.7\text{ kg·m/s down}}$.

    (b) From $v^2 = v_o^2 - 2gy = 0 - 2(9.80\text{ m/s}^2)(-10\text{ m}) = 196\text{ m}^2/\text{s}^2$, we have $v = -14$ m/s.

    So $p = (0.50\text{ kg})(-14\text{ m/s}) = -7.0\text{ kg·m/s} = \boxed{7.0\text{ kg·m/s down}}$.

18. From Newton's second law in terms of momentum,

    $$\bar{F} = \frac{\Delta p}{\Delta t} = \frac{mv - mv_o}{\Delta t} = \frac{(10\text{ kg})(4.0\text{ m/s} - 0)}{2.5\text{ s}} = \boxed{16\text{ N}}.$$

20. $\boxed{68\text{ N}}$.

26. We consider only the horizontal motion and use the impulse-momentum theorem.

    Since $\bar{F}\Delta t = mv - mv_o = mv$, $v = \frac{\bar{F}\Delta t}{m} = \frac{3.0\text{ N·s}}{0.20\text{ kg}} = \boxed{15\text{ m/s}}$.

28. $\boxed{13\text{ m/s}}$.

33. From the impulse-momentum theorem, $\bar{F}\Delta t = mv - mv_o = -mv_o$,

we have $\bar{F} = -\dfrac{mv_o}{\Delta t}$. So the magnitude is $\dfrac{mv_o}{\Delta t}$.

$$\bar{F}_1 = \frac{(0.16 \text{ kg})(25 \text{ m/s})}{3.5 \times 10^{-3} \text{ s}} = \boxed{1.1 \times 10^3 \text{ N}};$$

$$\bar{F}_2 = \frac{(0.16 \text{ kg})(25 \text{ m/s})}{8.5 \times 10^{-3} \text{ s}} = \boxed{4.7 \times 10^3 \text{ N}}.$$

37. 40 km/h = 11.1 m/s, 240 lb = 1068 N.

The force on the infant is opposite to velocity because the infant is decelerating.

From the impulse-momentum theorem, $F\Delta t = mv - mv_o$,

we have $\Delta t = \dfrac{mv - mv_o}{F} = \dfrac{(5.5 \text{ kg})(0 - 11.1 \text{ m/s})}{-1068 \text{ N}} = \boxed{0.057 \text{ s}}$.

42. According to the conservation of momentum, the astronaut moves in the opposite direction.

Given: $m_1 = 0.50$ kg, $m_2 = 60$ kg, $v_{1o} = 0$, $v_{2o} = 0$, $v_1 = 10$ m/s. find: v_2.

From momentum conservation, $\mathbf{P}_o = \mathbf{P}$,

we have $m_1 v_{1o} + m_2 v_{2o} = m_1 v_1 + m_2 v_2$.

So $v_2 = \dfrac{m_1 v_{1o} + m_2 v_{2o} - m_1 v_1}{m_2} = \dfrac{0 + 0 - (0.50 \text{ kg})(10 \text{ m/s})}{60 \text{ kg}} = \boxed{0.083 \text{ m/s}}$.

46. Apply momentum conservation $\mathbf{P}_o = \mathbf{P}$

in x axis: $(2.0 \text{ kg})(0) = (0.50 \text{ kg})(-2.8 \text{ m/s}) + (1.3 \text{ kg})(0) + (1.2 \text{ kg})v_x$, ☞ $v_x = 1.17$ m/s;

in y axis: $(3.0 \text{ kg})(0) = (0.50 \text{ kg})(0) + (1.3 \text{ kg})(-1.5 \text{ m/s}) + (1.2 \text{ kg})v_y$, ☞ $v_y = 1.63$ m/s.

Therefore $v = \sqrt{(1.17 \text{ m/s})^2 + (1.63 \text{ m/s})^2} = \boxed{2.0 \text{ m/s}}$,

and $\theta = \tan^{-1}\left(\dfrac{1.63}{1.17}\right) = \boxed{54° \text{ above } +x \text{ axis}}$.

53. We first use energy conservation to find the velocity of the bullet and the bob right after collision from the swing motion. The velocity right after the collision is the same as the velocity at the start of the swing.

$\frac{1}{2}(m + M)v^2 + (m + M)g(0) = \frac{1}{2}(m + M)(0)^2 + (m + M)g(h)$, Solving, $v = \sqrt{2gh}$.

Now apply momentum conservation $\mathbf{P}_o = \mathbf{P}$,

we have $mv_o + M(0) = (m + M)v = (m + M)\sqrt{2gh}$, so $v_o = \dfrac{m + M}{m}\sqrt{2gh}$.

58. From Equations (6.15) and (6.16),

$$v_1 = \frac{m_1 - m_2}{m_1 + m_2} v_{1o} = \frac{4.0 \text{ kg} - 2.0 \text{ kg}}{4.0 \text{ kg} + 2.0 \text{ kg}} (4.0 \text{ m/s}) = \boxed{+1.3 \text{ m/s}}.$$

$$v_2 = \frac{2m_1}{m_1 + m_2} v_{1o} = \frac{2(4.0 \text{ kg})}{4.0 \text{ kg} + 2.0 \text{ kg}} (4.0 \text{ m/s}) = \boxed{+5.3 \text{ m/s}}.$$

62. We first find the velocity of the 6.0-kilogram ball right after collision from momentum conservation.

Given: $m_1 = 2.0$ kg, $m_2 = 6.0$ kg, $v_{1o} = 12$ m/s, $v_{2o} = -4.0$ m/s ("toward each other"),

$v_1 = -8.0$ m/s ("recoil").

(2.0 kg)(12 m/s) + (6.0 kg)(−4.0 m/s) = (2.0 kg)(−8.0 m/s) + (6.0 kg)v_2, so $v_2 = 2.67$ m/s.

The initial kinetic energy $K_o = \frac{1}{2}(2.0 \text{ kg})(12 \text{ m/s})^2 + \frac{1}{2}(6.0 \text{ kg})(4.0 \text{ m/s})^2 = 192$ J.

The final kinetic energy $K = \frac{1}{2}(2.0 \text{ kg})(8.0 \text{ m/s})^2 + \frac{1}{2}(6.0 \text{ kg})(2.67 \text{ m/s})^2 = 84.5$ J.

So the kinetic energy lost is $K_o - K = \boxed{1.1 \times 10^2 \text{ J}}$.

64. (a) Apply momentum conservation $\mathbf{P}_o = \mathbf{P}$

in x: $mv + M(0) = (m + M)v'_x$, so $v'_x = \frac{mv}{m + M} = \frac{(2.0 \text{ kg})(3.0 \text{ m/s})}{(2.0 \text{ kg}) + 4.0 \text{ kg}} = \boxed{1.0 \text{ m/s}}$;

in y: $m(0) + M(V) = (m + M)v'_y$, so $v'_y = \frac{MV}{m + M} = \frac{(4.0 \text{ kg})(5.0 \text{ m/s})}{(2.0 \text{ kg}) + 4.0 \text{ kg}} = \boxed{3.3 \text{ m/s}}$.

(b) $\theta = \tan^{-1}\left(\frac{3.3}{1.0}\right) = \boxed{73°}$.

66. $\boxed{15°}$; $\boxed{0.57 \text{ m/s}}$.

71. (a) From momentum conservation, $\mathbf{P}_o = \mathbf{P}$,

we have $mv_o + M(0) = (m + M)v$, so $v = \frac{m\,v_o}{m + M} = \frac{0.010 \text{ kg}}{0.010 \text{ kg} + 0.890 \text{ kg}} v_o = \boxed{\frac{v_o}{90}}$.

(b) From energy conservation: $v = \sqrt{2gh} = \sqrt{2(9.80 \text{ m/s}^2)(0.40 \text{ m})} = 2.8$ m/s.

So $v_o = 90v = \boxed{2.5 \times 10^2 \text{ m/s}}$.

(c) The fraction of kinetic energy lost is

$$\frac{|\Delta K|}{K_o} = \frac{K_o - K}{K_o} = 1 - \frac{K}{K_o} = 1 - \frac{\frac{1}{2}\frac{(m\,v_o)^2}{m + M}}{\frac{1}{2}m\,v_o^2} = 1 - \frac{m}{m + M} = \frac{M}{m + M}.$$

$$= \frac{0.890 \text{ kg}}{0.010 \text{ kg} + 0.890 \text{ kg}} = \boxed{99\%}.$$

75. This pole will $\boxed{\text{lower the center of mass}}$ of the walker-pole system. The pole will also increase the moment of inertia of the system, and with a torque that rotates around the rope, the angular acceleration is smaller, giving the walker more time to recover.

80. We choose the less massive mass as the origin ($x = 0$).

$$X_{CM} = \frac{\Sigma_i m_i x_i}{M} = \frac{(4.0\text{ kg})(0) + (7.5\text{ kg})(1.5\text{ m})}{4.0\text{ kg} + 7.5\text{ kg}} = \boxed{0.98\text{ m}} \text{ from the less massive sphere.}$$

88. Due to the lack of external force, the CM is stationary and is at where they meet.

$$X_{CM} = \frac{\Sigma_i m_i x_i}{M} = \frac{(3000\text{ kg})(0) + (100\text{ kg})(5.0\text{ m})}{3000\text{ kg} + 100\text{ kg}}$$

$$= \boxed{0.16\text{ m from capsule's original position}}.$$

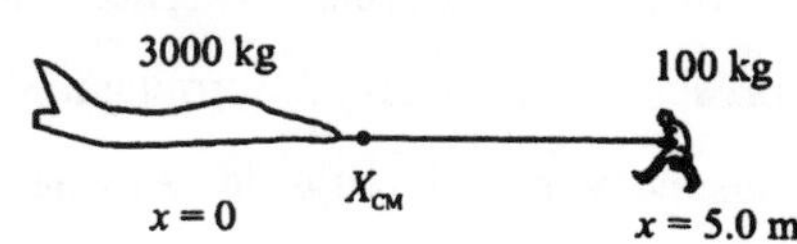

95. (a) $p_x = p_y = (0.50\text{ kg})(3.3\text{ m/s}) = 1.65\text{ kg·m/s}$. So

$$p = \sqrt{(1.65\text{ kg·m/s})^2 + (1.65\text{ kg·m/s})^2} = \boxed{2.3\text{ kg·m/s}},$$

$$\theta = \tan^{-1}\left(\frac{1.65}{1.65}\right) = \boxed{45° \text{ below the } -x \text{ axis}}.$$

(b) $\boxed{\text{Not necessarily}}$, a collision does not have to occur; momentum would be the same.

99. (a) The stunt man has zero horizontal velocity before he jumps onto the sled.
Apply momentum conservation $P_o = P$ in the horizontal direction.

$(75\text{ kg})(0) + (50\text{ kg})(10\text{ m/s}) = (75\text{ kg} + 50\text{ kg})v = (125\text{ kg})v$, so $v = \boxed{4.0\text{ m/s}}$.

(b) The stunt man's momentum is still conserved, so he continues to move with a speed of $\boxed{4.0\text{ m/s}}$.

105. If the triangle is suspended at one corner, the CM will be on a line perpendicular to the base and through the corner. If the triangle is suspended at a second corner, the CM will be where the two lines cross (see diagram). From symmetry, $Y_{CM} = 15$ cm, and $X_{CM} = (15\text{ cm})\tan 30° = 8.7$ cm.

Thus the CM is at $\boxed{(8.7\text{ cm}, 15\text{ cm})}$.

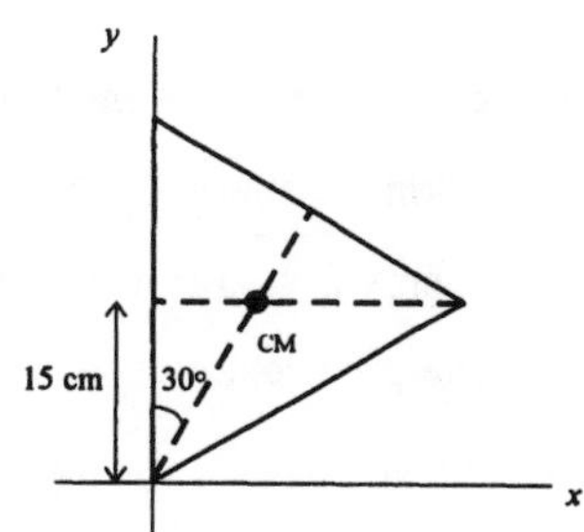

VI. Practice Quiz

1. The SI unit of impulse is which one of the following?

   (a) N·m (b) N/s (c) N·s (d) N/m (e) kg·m/s^2

2. A force of 10 N acts on a 5.0-kilogram object, initially at rest, for 2.5 s. What is the final speed of the object?

   (a) 1.0 m/s (b) 2.0 m/s (c) 3.0 m/s (d) 4.0 m/s (e) 5.0 m/s

3. A 70-kilogram astronaut is space walking outside the space capsule and is stationary when the tether line breaks. As a means of returning to the capsule he throws his 2.0-kilogram space wrench at a speed of 14 m/s away from the capsule. At what speed does the astronaut move toward the capsule?

   (a) 0.40 m/s (b) 1.5 m/s (c) 3.5 m/s (d) 5.0 m/s (e) 7.0 m/s

4. A 1500-kilogram, is allowed to coast along a level track at a speed of 8.0 m/s. It collides and couples with a 2000-kilogram truck, initially at rest and with brakes released. What is the speed of the two vehicles after they collide?

   (a) 0.75 m/s (b) 3.4 m/s (c) 4.6 m/s (d) 6.0 m/s (e) 11 m/s

5. A 0.060-kilogram tennis ball, initially moving at a speed of 12 m/s, is struck by a racket causing it to rebound in the opposite direction at a speed of 18 m/s. What is the change in momentum of the ball?

   (a) 0.18 kg·m/s (b) 0.36 kg·m/s (c) 0.72 kg·m/s (d) 1.1 kg·m/s (e) 1.8 kg·m/s.

6. The center of mass of a two-particle system is at the origin. One particle is located at (3.0 m, 0 m) and has a mass of 2.0 kg. What is the location of the second mass of 4.0 kg?

   (a) (−3.0 m, 0 m) (b) (−2.0 m, 0 m) (c) (−1.5 m, 0 m) (d) (−0.75 m, 0 m) (e) (−0.50 m, 0 m)

7. In an elastic collision, if the momentum of the system is conserved, then which of the following statements is true about kinetic energy?

   (a) kinetic energy is also conserved. (b) kinetic energy is gained.

   (c) kinetic energy is lost. (d) kinetic energy is halved.

   (e) none of the above.

8. A 0.10-kilogram object with a velocity of 0.20 m/s in the $+x$ direction makes a head-on elastic collision with a 0.15-kilogram object initially at rest. What is the velocity of the 0.10-kilogram object after collision?

   (a) −0.16 m/s (b) +0.16 m/s (c) 0 (d) −0.040 m/s (e) +0.040 m/s

9. If the momentum of an object is halved, by what factor will its kinetic energy change?

(a) 2 (b) 4 (c) 0 (d) 1/2 (e) 1/4

10. A model rocket sits on the launch pad and its fuel is ignited, blasting the rocket upward. What happens to the center of mass of the rocket-fuel system?

(a) it goes up (b) it is stationary (c) it follows the path of the rocket

(d) it follows the path of the fuel (e) not enough information given

Answers to Practice Quiz:

1. c 2. e 3. a 4. b 5. e 6. c 7. a 8. d 9. e 10. b

CHAPTER 7

Circular Motion and Gravitation

I. Chapter Objectives

Upon completion of this chapter, you should be able to:

1. define units of angular measure and show how angular measure is related to circular arc length.
2. describe and compute angular speed and velocity and explain their relationship to tangential speed.
3. explain why there is a centripetal acceleration in constant or uniform circular motion and compute centripetal acceleration.
4. define angular acceleration and analyze rotational kinematics.
5. describe Newton's law of gravitation and how it relates to the acceleration due to gravity, and apply the general formulation of gravitational potential energy.
6. state and explain Kepler's laws of planetary motion and describe the orbits and motions of satellites.

II. Key Terms

Upon completion of this chapter, you should be able to define and/or explain the following key terms:

angular displacement
radian (rad)
average angular speed
angular velocity
 average
 instantaneous
tangential speed
period (*T*)
frequency (*f*)
hertz (Hz)
uniform circular motion
centripetal acceleration
centripetal force
average angular acceleration
tangential acceleration
universal law of gravitation
universal gravitational constant, *G*
gravitational potential energy
Kepler's first law (the law of orbits)
Kepler's second law (the law of area)
Kepler's third law (the law of periods)
escape speed

The definitions and/or explanations of the most important key terms can be found in the following section: **III. Chapter Summary and Discussion.**

III. Chapter Summary and Discussion

1. Angular Measure (Section 7.1)

Circular motion is conveniently described using the polar coordinates (r, θ) because r is a constant and only θ varies. The relationships between rectangular coordinates and polar coordinates are as follows:

$$x = r \cos \theta \quad \text{and} \quad y = r \sin \theta, \text{ where } \theta \text{ is measured ccw from the } +x \text{ axis}$$

Angular distance ($\Delta\theta = \theta - \theta_o = \theta$ if $\theta_o = 0$) is measured in degrees or radians. A **radian** (rad) is defined as the angle that subtends an arc length that is equal to the radius: 1 rad = 57.3° or 2π rad = 360°. Similarly, $s = r\,\theta$, where s is the arc length, r is the radius, and θ is the angle in radians.

Example 7.1 When you are watching the NASCAR Daytona 500, the 5.5-meter long race car subtends an angle of 0.31°. What is the distance from the race car to you?

Solution: Given: $\theta = 0.31° = (0.31°) \times \dfrac{\pi \text{ rad}}{180°} = 5.41 \times 10^{-3}$ rad, $s = 5.5$ m.

Find: r.

From $s = r\,\theta$, we have $r = \dfrac{s}{\theta} = \dfrac{5.5 \text{ m}}{5.41 \times 10^{-3} \text{ rad}} = 1.0 \times 10^{4}$3m = 1.0 km.

Note: The angle θ must be in radians.

---

2. Angular Speed and Velocity (Section 7.2)

Angular speed and **angular velocity** are defined analogously to their linear motion counterparts. The direction of angular velocity is determined by the right-hand rule: when the fingers of the right hand are curled in the direction of the rotation, the extended thumb points in the direction of the velocity vector. Therefore, there are only two possible directions for angular velocity, perpendicularly in or out of a plane, for a given observer. For convenience, they may be expressed with plus (ccw) and minus (cw) signs. They both have the units rad/s. Like their linear conterparts, angular speed and angular velocity could both be average and instantaneous. Instantaneous angular speed is the magnitude of the instantaneous angular velocity. Often, the word instantaneous is omitted.

Average angular speed is defined by $\bar{\omega} = \dfrac{\Delta\theta}{\Delta t} = \dfrac{\theta - \theta_o}{t - t_o}$.

Sometimes angular speed and velocity are given in units of rpm (revolutions per minute). You should first convert them to rad/s before trying to solve the problems. For example:

$$(33 \text{ rmp}) = \frac{33 \text{ rev}}{\text{min}} \times \frac{2\pi \text{ rad}}{1 \text{ rev}} \times \frac{1 \text{ min}}{60 \text{ s}} = 3.5 \text{ rad/s}.$$

Tangential (linear) speed and angular speed are related to each other through $v = r\,\omega$, where r is the radius. (Generally, linear quantity = radius × angular quantity, e.g., $s = r\theta$.)

In circular motion, the time it takes for an object to go through one revolution is called the **period** (T) and the number of revolutions in one second is called **frequency** (f). They are related through $f = \frac{1}{T}$. The SI unit of frequency is 1/s or hertz (Hz).

Example 7.2 A bicycle wheel rotates uniformly through 2.0 revolutions in 4.0 s.

(a) What is the average angular speed of the wheel?

(b) What is the tangential speed of a point 0.10 m from the center of the wheel?

(c) What is the period?

(d) What is the frequency?

Solution: Given: $\theta = 2.0 \text{ rev} = (2.0 \text{ rev}) \times \frac{2\pi \text{ rad}}{1 \text{ rev}} = 4\pi \text{ rad}$, $t = 4.0$ s, $r = 0.10$ m.

Find: (a) $\bar{\omega}$ (b) v (c) T (d) f.

(a) $\bar{\omega} = \frac{\Delta\theta}{\Delta t} = \frac{4\pi \text{ rad}}{4.0 \text{ s}} = \pi \text{ rad/s} = 3.1 \text{ rad/s}.$

(b) Since the rotation is uniform, $\omega = \bar{\omega}$. So $v = r\omega = (0.10 \text{ m})(3.1 \text{ rad/s}) = 0.31 \text{ m/s}.$

(c) Period is the time for one revolution. So $T = \frac{4.0 \text{ s}}{2.0} = 2.0 \text{ s}.$

(d) $f = \frac{1}{T} = \frac{1}{2.0 \text{ s}} = 0.50 \text{ Hz}.$

---

3. Uniform Circular Motion and Centripetal Acceleration (Section 7.3)

For **uniform circular motion**, the speed (tangential and angular) is a constant, but there is an acceleration. The linear tangential velocity vector changes direction as the object moves along the circle. Since velocity has both magnitude and direction, a change in direction results in a change in velocity, therefore, an acceleration (see the discussion in Chapter 2). This acceleration is called **centripetal acceleration** (center-seeking) because it is always directed toward the center of the circle. The magnitude of centripetal acceleration is given by $a_c = \frac{v^2}{r} = r\omega^2$.

From Newton's second law, net force = mass × acceleration, we conclude that there must be a net force associated with centripetal acceleration. In the case of uniform circular motion, this force is called **centripetal force** and always directed toward the center of the circle since we know the net force on an object is in the same direction as acceleration. Its magnitude is $F_c = ma_c = \dfrac{m\,v^2}{r} = mr\omega^2$.

When analyzing circular motions, always think about centripetal acceleration and centripetal force. (**Note**: centripetal force is not a separate or extra force. It is a net force toward the center of the circle.) A centripetal force is always required for objects to stay in circular path. Without the necessary centripetal force, an object will not stay in a circular orbit and instead fly out along a tangent line due to its inertia. Can you identify the centripetal force when a car makes a turn on a flat road and when clothes move around in a dryer? Or how about an Earth satellite orbiting the Earth?

Example 7.3 A car of mass 1500 kg is negotiating a flat circular curve of radius 50 m with a speed of 20 m/s.

(a) What is the source of centripetal force on the car?

(b) What is the magnitude of the centripetal acceleration of the car?

(b) What is the magnitude of the centripetal force on the car?

Solution: Given: m = 1500 kg, r = 50 m, v = 20 m/s.

Find: (b) a_c (b) F_c.

(a) Since the car is on a flat curve, the only forces acting on it are the vertically downward weight, the vertically upward normal force by the surface, and a static friction force. Also because the center of the circle is a horizontal distance 50 m away from the car, so the centripetal force cannot be provided by the vertical forces. Therefore we conclude that the static friction force is the source of this centripetal force. this conclusion is also supported vy your everyday experience. For example, why new tires "grip" better and icy road makes driving dangerous when you negotiate a curve?

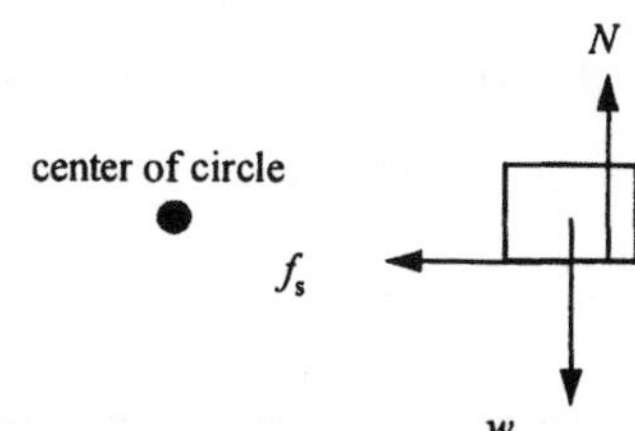

(b) $a_c = \dfrac{v^2}{r} = \dfrac{(20 \text{ m/s})^2}{50 \text{ m}} = 8.0 \text{ m/s}^2$.

(c) $F_c = ma_c$ = (15=00 kg)(8.0 m/s^2) = 1.2×10^4 N.

---

4. Angular Acceleration (Section 7.4)

Average **angular acceleration** is defined analogously as its linear counterpart.

$$\bar{\alpha} = \frac{\Delta\omega}{\Delta t} = \frac{\omega - \omega_0}{t - t_0}.$$ The unit of angular acceleration is rad/s^2.

An object having angular acceleration has also tangential acceleration, that is, its tangential speed changes. They are related by $a_t = r\alpha$ (again, linear quantity = radius × angular quantity, as in $s = r\theta$ and $v = r\omega$). If an object is in nonuniform circular motion, it will have both centripetal acceleration (due to circular motion) and tangential acceleration (due to the change in tangential speed). the total acceleration is given by $\mathbf{a} = a_t\,\hat{\mathbf{t}} + a_c\,\hat{\mathbf{r}}$, where $\hat{\mathbf{t}}$ is the unit vector in the tangential direction and $\hat{\mathbf{r}}$ is the unit vector pointing toward the center of the circle.

Note: There is *always* centripetal acceleration no matter whether the circular motion is uniform or nonuniform. It is the tangential acceleration that is zero in uniform circular motion.

As you can see, circular motion and linear motion are analogous (at least mathematically). As a matter of fact, we can arrive at all the equations for angular motion from the kinematic equations in Chapter 2 if we just use the following substitutions: $\theta \to x$, $\omega \to v$, and $\alpha \to a$ (or add the word angular to every linear quantity except time). The angular kinematic equations are (their linear counterparts are in parentheses):

$\theta = \bar{\omega}\, t$ ($x = \bar{v}\, t$),

$\bar{\omega} = \dfrac{\omega + \omega_0}{2}$ ($\bar{v} = \dfrac{v + v_0}{2}$),

$\omega = \omega_0 + \alpha t$ ($v = v_0 + a t$),

$\theta = \omega_0 t + \frac{1}{2}\alpha t^2$ ($x = v_0 t + \frac{1}{2} a t^2$),

$\omega^2 = \omega_0^2 + 2\alpha\theta$ ($v^2 = v_0^2 + 2 a x$).

Example 7.4 A wheel is rotating with a constant angular acceleration of 3.5 rad/s^2. If the initial angular velocity is 2.0 rad/s and is speeding up, find

(a) the angle the wheel rotates through in 2.0 s,

(b) the angular speed at $t = 2.0$ s.

Solution: Given: $\alpha = 3.5$ rad/s^2, $\omega_0 = 0$, $t = 2.0$ s.

Find: (a) θ (b) ω.

(a) $\theta = \omega_0 t + \frac{1}{2}at^2 = (2.0 \text{ rad/s})(2.0 \text{ s}) + \frac{1}{2}(3.5 \text{ rad/s}^2)(2.0 \text{ s})^2 = 11$ rad.

(b) $\omega = \omega_0 + \alpha t = 2.0 \text{ rad/s} + (3.5 \text{ rad/s})(2.0 \text{ s}) = 9.0$ rad/s.

Example 7.5 The power on a medical centrifuge rotating at 12 000 rpm is cut off. If the magnitude of the maximum deceleration of the centrifuge is 50 rad/s^2, how many revolutions does it rotate before coming to rest?

Solution: Given: $\omega_o = 12\,000 \text{ rpm} = \dfrac{12\,000 \text{ rev}}{\text{min}} \times \dfrac{2\pi \text{ rad}}{1 \text{ rev}} \times \dfrac{1 \text{ min}}{60 \text{ s}} = 1.26 \times 10^3 \text{ rad/s}$,

$\omega = 0$ (coming to rest), $\alpha = -50 \text{ rad/s}^2$ (deceleration).

Find: θ (in terms of revolutions).

The unknown (how many turns) is related to the angle, θ, since 2π rad is one revolution or turn.

From $\omega^2 = \omega_o^2 + 2\alpha\theta$, we have

$$\theta = \frac{\omega^2 - \omega_o^2}{2\,\alpha} = \frac{0 - (1.26 \times 10^3 \text{ rad/s})^2}{2(-50 \text{ rad/s}^2)} = (1.59 \times 10^4 \text{ rad}) \times \frac{1 \text{ rev}}{2\pi \text{ rad}} = 2.5 \times 10^3 \text{ rev (turns)}.$$

5. Newton's Law of Gravitation (Section 7.5)

Newton's **universal law of gravitation** states that the mutual gravitational attraction between any two point masses is directly proportional to the product of their masses and inversely proportional to the square of the distance between them. The magnitude is given by $F = \dfrac{Gm_1 m_2}{r^2}$, where $G = 6.67 \times 10^{-11}$ N·m^2/kg^2, is the **universal gravitational constant.**

Note: The magnitude of the force depends on $\dfrac{1}{r^2}$ (inverse square). For example, if the distance between the masses is doubled, the force between them would decrease to $\dfrac{1}{2^2} = \dfrac{1}{4}$ (not $\dfrac{1}{2}$).

According to Newton's second law, $F = ma$, the acceleration due to gravity by a mass M acting on another object m is then equal to $a_g = \dfrac{F}{m} = \dfrac{GM}{r^2}$. At the Earth's surface: $a_g = g = \dfrac{GM_E}{R_E^2}$, where M_E and R_E are the mass of radius of the Earth. At an altitude h above the Earth: $a_g = \dfrac{GM_E}{(R_E + h)^2}$.

The **gravitational potential energy** between two masses is given by $U = -\dfrac{Gm_1 m_2}{r}$, **note:** it is just r (not r^2) in the denominator. The minus sign arises from the choice of zero reference point (point where $U = 0$), which is $r = \infty$.

Example 7.6 The hydrogen atom consists of a proton of mass 1.67×10^{-27} kg and an orbiting electron of mass 9.11×10^{-31} kg. In one of its orbits, the electron is 5.3×10^{-11} m from the proton and in another orbit, it is 10.6×10^{-11} m from the proton.

(a) What are the mutual attractive forces when the electron is in these orbits, respectively?

(b) If the electron jumps from the large orbit to the small one, what is the change in potential energy?

Solution: Given: $m_1 = 1.67 \times 10^{-27}$ kg, $m_2 = 9.11 \times 10^{-31}$ kg, $r_1 = 5.3 \times 10^{-11}$ m, $r_2 = 10.6 \times 10^{-11}$ m.

Find: (a) F_1 and F_2 (b) ΔU.

(a) From Newton's law of gravitation,

$$F_1 = \frac{Gm_1 m_2}{r_1^2} = \frac{(6.67 \times 10^{-11}\ \text{N}\cdot\text{m}^2/\text{kg}^2)(1.67 \times 10^{-27}\ \text{kg})(9.11 \times 10^{-31}\ \text{kg})}{(5.3 \times 10^{-11}\ \text{m})^2} = 3.6 \times 10^{-47}\ \text{N}.$$

Since $r_2 = 2r_1$ and $F \propto \frac{1}{r^2}$, $\frac{F_2}{F_1} = \frac{r_1^2}{r_2^2} = \frac{1}{2^2} = \frac{1}{4}$.

So $F_2 = \frac{1}{4} F_1 = \frac{1}{4}(3.6 \times 10^{-47}\ \text{N}) = 9.0 \times 10^{-48}\ \text{N}.$

(c) $\Delta U = U_1 - U_2 = -\frac{Gm_1 m_2}{r_1} - (-\frac{Gm_1 m_2}{r_2}) = Gm_1 m_2 \left(\frac{1}{r_2} - \frac{1}{r_1}\right)$

$$= (6.67 \times 10^{-11}\ \text{N}\cdot\text{m}^2/\text{kg}^2)(1.67 \times 10^{-27}\ \text{kg})(9.11 \times 10^{-31}\ \text{kg}) \left(\frac{1}{10.6 \times 10^{-11}\ \text{m}} - \frac{1}{5.3 \times 10^{-11}\ \text{m}}\right)$$

$$= -9.6 \times 10^{-58}\ \text{J}.$$

So the atom loses potential energy. You will learn in Chapter 27 that a loss of energy is accompanied by the emission of light.

Example 7.7 Calculate the acceleration due to gravity at the surface of the Moon.

Solution: Given: $R_M = 1750$ km $= 1.75 \times 10^6$ m, $M_M = 7.4 \times 10^{22}$ kg (from back inside cover).

Find: a_g.

$$a_g = \frac{GM}{r^2} = \frac{GM_M}{R_M^2} = \frac{(6.67 \times 10^{-11}\ \text{N}\cdot\text{m}^2/\text{kg}^2)(7.4 \times 10^{22}\ \text{kg})}{(1.75 \times 10^6\ \text{m})^2} = 1.6\ \text{m/s}^2.$$

This is about $\frac{1}{6}$ of the value at the surface of the Earth, $g = 9.80\ \text{m/s}^2$.

6. Kepler's Laws and Earth Satellites (Section 7.6)

(1) The law of orbits: Planets move in elliptical orbits with the Sun at one of the focal points.

(2) The law of areas: A line from the Sun to a planet sweeps out equal area in equal time interval.

(3) The law of periods: The square of the period of a planet is directly proportional to the cube of the average distance of the planet from the Sun, that is, $T^2 \propto r^3$. Or $T^2 = K r^3$, where $K = 2.97 \times 10^{-19}$ s²/m³ for the Sun.

The **escape speed** is the initial speed needed to escape from the surface of a planet or moon. For Earth satellites, this speed is $v_{esc} = \sqrt{\dfrac{2GM_E}{R_E}} = \sqrt{2gR_E}$, since $g = \dfrac{GM_E}{R_E}$.

Example 7.8 The planet Saturn is 1.43×10^{12} m from the Sun. How long does it take for Jupiter to orbit once about the Sun?

Solution: Given: $r = 1.43 \times 10^{12}$ m.

Find: T.

From Kepler's law of periods, $T^2 = (2.97 \times 10^{-19} \text{ s}^2/\text{m}^3)r^3$, we have

$$T = \sqrt{(2.97 \times 10^{-19} \text{ s}^2/\text{m}^3)r^3} = \sqrt{(2.97 \times 10^{-19} \text{ s}^2/\text{m}^3)(1.43 \times 10^{12} \text{ m})^3} = 9.32 \times 10^8 \text{ s} \approx 30 \text{ years.}$$

Example 7.9 If a satellite were launched from the surface of the Moon, at what initial speed would it need to begin in order for it to escape the gravitational attraction of the Moon?

Solution: With the known data:

$$v_{esc} = \sqrt{\frac{2GM_M}{R_M}} = \sqrt{\frac{2(6.67 \times 10^{-11} \text{ N·m}^2/\text{kg}^2)(7.4 \times 10^{22} \text{ kg})}{1.75 \times 10^6 \text{ m}}} = 2.4 \times 10^3 \text{ m/s.}$$

IV. Mathematical Summary

Arc Length	$s = r\theta$ (7.3)	Relates arc length to radius and angle (in radians).
Angular Kinematic Equation 1	$\theta = \bar{\omega} t$ (7.5)	Relates angular displacement with average angular velocity and time.
Angular Kinematic Equation 2	$\bar{\omega} = \dfrac{\omega + \omega_o}{2}$ (2, Table 7.2)	Defines average angular velocity for circular motion with constant angular acceleration.

Angular Kinematic Equation 3	$\omega = \omega_0 + \alpha t$ (7.12)	Relates final angular velocity with initial angular velocity, angular acceleration, and time (constant angular acceleration only).
Angular Kinematic Equation 4	$\theta = \omega_0 t + \frac{1}{2}\alpha t^2$ (4, Table 7.2)	Relates angular displacement with initial angular velocity, angular acceleration, and time (constant angular acceleration only).
Angular Kinematic Equation 5	$\omega^2 = \omega_0^2 + 2\alpha\theta$ (5, Table 7.2)	Relates final angular velocity with initial angular velocity, angular acceleration, and angular displacement (constant angular acceleration only).
Tangential and Angular Speeds	$v = r\omega$ (7.6)	Relates tangential speed with radius and angular speed.
Angular Speed	$\omega = \frac{2\pi}{T} = 2\pi f$ (7.8)	Defines angular speed for uniform circular motion.
Frequency and Period	$f = \frac{1}{T}$ (7.7)	Relates frequency with period.
Centripetal Acceleration	$a_c = \frac{v^2}{r} = r\omega^2$ (7.10)	Defines centripetal acceleration.
Tangential and Angular Accelerations	$a_t = r\alpha$ (7.13)	Relates tangential acceleration with radius and angular acceleration.
Centripetal Force and Acceleration	$F_c = m\,a_c = \frac{mv^2}{r}$ (7.11)	Defines centripetal force.
Newton's Law of Gravitation	$F = \frac{Gm_1 m_2}{r^2}$ (7.15) $G = 6.67 \times 10^{-11}$ N·m²/kg²	Calculates the mutual attractive forces between two masses.
Acceleration due to Gravity at an Altitude h	$a_g = \frac{GM_E}{(R_E + h)^2}$ (7.18)	Calculates the acceleration due to gravity at an altitude of h above the Earth's surface.
Gravitational Potential Energy	$U = -\frac{Gm_1 m_2}{r}$ (7.19)	Defines gravitational potential energy for a two mass system ($U_\infty = 0$).
Kepler's Law of Periods	$T^2 = Kr^3$ (7.23) $K = 2.97 \times 10^{-19}$ s²/m³ for Sun	Relates period with radius for objects orbiting the Sun.
Escape Speed	$v_{esc} = \sqrt{\frac{2GM_E}{R_E}} = \sqrt{2gR_E}$ (7.24)	Gives the escape speed of the Earth.
Energy of Orbiting Satellites Orbiting the Earth	$E = -\frac{GmM_E}{2r}$ (7.28) $K = \lvert E \rvert$ (7.29)	Calculates the total energy and kinetic energy of objects orbiting the Earth.

V. Solutions of Selected Exercises and Paired/Trio Exercises

8. From $s = r\theta$, we have $r = \dfrac{s}{\theta} = \dfrac{5.0 \text{ m}}{2.0°(\pi \text{ rad}/180°)} = \boxed{1.4 \times 10^2 \text{ m}}$.

10. In 3 months, the Earth travels $\dfrac{3}{12} = \dfrac{1}{4}$ of a circle or $\dfrac{1}{4} \times (2\pi \text{ rad}) = \dfrac{\pi}{2}$ rad.

So $s = r\theta = (1.5 \times 10^8 \text{ km}) \times \dfrac{\pi \text{ rad}}{2} = \boxed{2.4 \times 10^8 \text{ km}}$.

12. In 30 min, the hour hand travels $\pi/12 =$ rad, the minute hand π rad, and the second hand $30(2\pi) = 60\pi$ rad.

Hour hand: $s = r\theta = (0.25 \text{ m})(\pi/12 \text{ rad}) = \boxed{0.065 \text{ m}}$.

Minute hand: $s = (0.30 \text{ m})(\pi \text{ rad}) = \boxed{0.94 \text{ m}}$.

Second hand: $s = (0.35 \text{ m})(60\pi \text{ rad}) = \boxed{66 \text{ m}}$.

15. (a) $\theta = \dfrac{s}{r} = \dfrac{3500 \text{ km}}{3.8 \times 10^5 \text{ km}} = \boxed{9.2 \times 10^{-3} \text{ rad} = 0.53°}$.

(b) $\theta = \dfrac{2(6.4 \times 10^3 \text{ km})}{3.8 \times 10^5 \text{ km}} = \boxed{3.4 \times 10^{-2} \text{ rad} = 1.9°}$.

23. The $\boxed{\text{point farthest from the center}}$ has the greatest tangential speed and $\boxed{\text{the point closest to the center}}$ has the smallest tangential speed, because the tangential speed is directly proportional to the radius.

26. $\omega = \dfrac{\Delta\theta}{\Delta t} = \dfrac{2.5(2\pi \text{ rad})}{(3.0 \text{ min})(60 \text{ s/min})} = \boxed{0.087 \text{ rad/s}}$.

30. $\omega = \dfrac{v_t}{r} = \dfrac{3.0 \text{ m/s}}{0.20 \text{ m}} = 15$ rad/s.

From $\omega = \dfrac{\Delta\theta}{\Delta t}$, we have $\Delta t = \dfrac{\Delta\theta}{\omega} = \dfrac{2\pi \text{ rad}}{15 \text{ rad/s}} = \boxed{0.42 \text{ s}}$.

32. (a) $\boxed{3.5 \times 10^{-2} \text{ rad/s}}$. (b) $\boxed{17 \text{ m/s}}$.

39. There is insufficient centripetal force (provided by friction and adhesive forces) on the water drops so the water drops fly out along a tangent and the clothes get dry.

44. 120 km/h = 33.33 m/s. $a_c = \dfrac{v^2}{r} = \dfrac{(33.33 \text{ m/s})^2}{(1.00 \times 10^3 \text{ m})} = \boxed{1.11 \text{ m/s}^2}$.

48. (a) $v = \dfrac{d}{t} = \dfrac{2\pi r}{t} = \dfrac{2\pi(1.50 \text{ m})}{1.20 \text{ s}} = \boxed{7.85 \text{ m/s}}$.

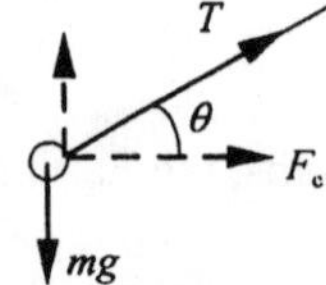

(b) $F_c = ma_c = m\dfrac{v^2}{r} = \dfrac{(0.250 \text{ kg})(7.85 \text{ m/s})^2}{1.50 \text{ m}} = \boxed{10.3 \text{ N}}$.

(c) $\boxed{\text{No}}$, the string cannot be exactly horizontal. There must be something upward (a component of the tension) to balance the downward gravitational force.

51. Static friction force provides centripetal force. $f_s = \mu_s N = \mu_s mg = F_c = m\dfrac{v^2}{r}$,

so $v = \sqrt{\mu_s g r} = \sqrt{0.50(9.80 \text{ m/s}^2)(20 \text{ m})} = \boxed{9.9 \text{ m/s}}$.

52. (a) 700 km/h = 194 m/s. At the bottom, the centripetal force is provided by

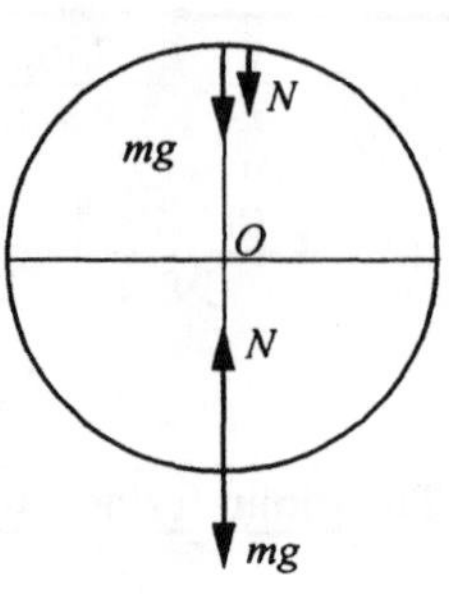

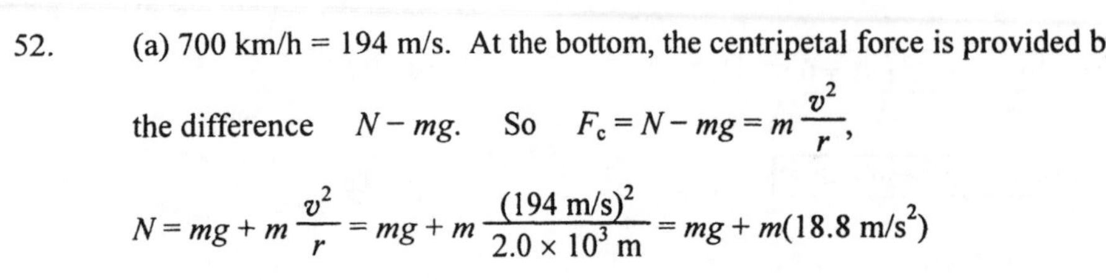

the difference $N - mg$. So $F_c = N - mg = m\dfrac{v^2}{r}$,

$$N = mg + m\frac{v^2}{r} = mg + m\frac{(194 \text{ m/s})^2}{2.0 \times 10^3 \text{ m}} = mg + m(18.8 \text{ m/s}^2)$$

$= mg + 1.9mg = \boxed{2.9mg}$.

(b) At the top, the centripetal force is provided by $N + mg$.

$$N = m\frac{v^2}{r} - mg = m\frac{(194 \text{ m/s})^2}{2.0 \times 10^3 \text{ m}} - mg = m(18.8 \text{ m/s}^2) - mg = 1.93mg - mg = \boxed{0.93mg}.$$

59. $\boxed{\text{No}}$, this is not possible. Any car in circular motion always has centripetal acceleration.

60. 700 rpm = 73.3 rad/s, 3000 rpm = 314 rad/s.

$$\alpha = \frac{\Delta\omega}{\Delta t} = \frac{314 \text{ rad/s} - 73.3 \text{ rad/s}}{3.0 \text{ s}} = \boxed{80 \text{ rad/s}^2}.$$

62. (a) $\boxed{4.28 \text{ rad}}$. (b) $\boxed{2.14 \text{ ft}}$.

64. (a) Given: $\omega_0 = 0$, $\omega = \frac{v}{r} = \frac{2.20 \text{ m/s}}{17.5 \text{ m}} = 0.126$ rad/s, $t = 15.0$ s. Find: α.

$$\alpha = \frac{\omega - \omega_0}{t} = \frac{0.126 \text{ rad/s} - 0}{15.0 \text{ s}} = \boxed{8.40 \times 10^{-3} \text{ rad/s}^2}.$$

(b) After reaching the constant operating speed, $\alpha = 0$ and so $a_t = r\alpha = \boxed{0}$.

67. (a) Given: $\omega_0 = 0$, $\alpha = 4.5 \times 10^{-3}$ rad/s^2, $\theta = 1$ rev $= 2\pi$ rad. Find: t.

from $\theta = \omega_0 t + \frac{1}{2}\alpha t^2 = 0 + \frac{1}{2}\alpha t^2$,

we have $t = \sqrt{\frac{2\theta}{\alpha}} = \sqrt{\frac{2(2\pi \text{ rad})}{4.5 \times 10^{-3} \text{ rad/s}^2}} = \boxed{53 \text{ s}}$.

(b) After half a lap, $\omega^2 = \omega_o^2 + 2\alpha\theta = 0 + 2(4.5 \times 10^{-3} \text{ rad/s}^2)(\pi \text{ rad}) = 0.0283 \text{ rad}^2/\text{s}^2$,

so $\omega = 0.168$ rad/s.

The centripetal acceleration is $a_c = r\omega^2 = (0.30 \times 10^3 \text{ m})(0.168 \text{ rad/s})^2 = 8.5 \text{ m/s}^2$,

the tangential acceleration is $a_t = r\alpha = (0.30 \times 10^3 \text{ m})(4.5 \times 10^{-3} \text{ rad/s}^2) = 1.4 \text{ m/s}^2$.

So the total acceleration is $\mathbf{a} = \boxed{(8.5 \text{ m/s}^2)\,\hat{\mathbf{r}} + (1.4 \text{ m/s}^2)\,\hat{\mathbf{t}}}$.

73. $\boxed{\text{Yes}}$, if we also know the radius of the Earth. The acceleration due to gravity near the surface of the Earth can be written as $a_g = \frac{GM_E}{R_E^2}$. By simply measuring a_g, you can determine $M_E = \frac{a_g R_E^2}{G}$.

76. $F = \frac{GM_E M_M}{r_{E\text{-}M}^2} = \frac{(6.67 \times 10^{-11} \text{ N·m}^2/\text{kg}^2)(5.98 \times 10^{24} \text{ kg})(7.4 \times 10^{22} \text{ kg})}{(3.8 \times 10^8 \text{ m})^2} = \boxed{2.0 \times 10^{20} \text{ N}}$.

79. $F_1 = F_3 = \frac{Gm^2}{d^2} = \frac{(6.67 \times 10^{-11} \text{ N·m}^2/\text{kg}^2)(2.5 \text{ kg})^2}{(1.0 \text{ m})^2} = 4.17 \times 10^{-10}$ N,

The diagonal distance is $\sqrt{(1.0 \text{ m})^2 + (1.0 \text{ m})^2} = \sqrt{2}$ m,

so $F_3 = \frac{(6.67 \times 10^{-11} \text{ N·m}^2/\text{kg}^2)(2.5 \text{ kg})^2}{(\sqrt{2} \text{ m})^2} = 2.08 \times 10^{-10}$ N.

From symmetry the net force is

$F = \sqrt{(4.17 \times 10^{-10} \text{ N})^2 + (4.17 \times 10^{-10} \text{ m})^2} + 2.08 \times 10^{-10} \text{ N} = \boxed{8.0 \times 10^{-10} \text{ N, toward opposite corner}}$.

80. $a_g = \frac{GM_E}{(R_E + h)^2} = \frac{(6.67 \times 10^{-11} \text{ N·m}^2/\text{kg}^2)(5.98 \times 10^{24} \text{ kg})}{(6.38 \times 10^6 \text{ m} + 8.80 \times 10^3 \text{ m})^2} = \boxed{9.77 \text{ m/s}^2}$.

82. When the Earth's gravitational force equals the lunar gravitational force,

$$F_E = \frac{GM_E m}{x^2} = F_M = \frac{GM_M m}{(3.8 \times 10^8 \text{ m} - x)^2}.$$

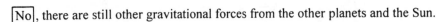

Taking the square root on both sides gives

$$\frac{\sqrt{M_E}}{x} = \frac{\sqrt{M_M}}{3.8 \times 10^8 \text{ m} - x},$$

or $\sqrt{7.4 \times 10^{22} \text{ kg}}\; x = \sqrt{5.98 \times 10^{24} \text{ kg}}\; (3.8 \times 10^8 \text{ m} - x)$.

Solving, $x = \boxed{3.4 \times 10^8 \text{ m from Earth}}$.

$\boxed{\text{No}}$, there are still other gravitational forces from the other planets and the Sun.

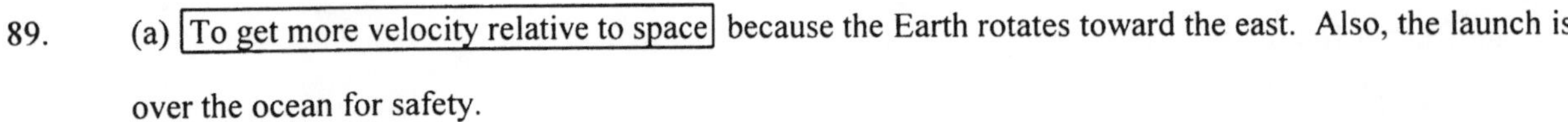

89. (a) $\boxed{\text{To get more velocity relative to space}}$ because the Earth rotates toward the east. Also, the launch is over the ocean for safety.

(b) The $\boxed{\text{tangential speed of the Earth is higher in Florida}}$ because Florida is closer to the equator than California. Also, California launches are polar (not eastward) for safety.

92. For the Earth orbiting the Sun, $K = \frac{4\pi^2}{GM_S}$.

Replace the mass of the Sun with the mass of the Earth for satellites orbiting the Earth.

$$K = \frac{4\pi^2}{GM_E} = \frac{4\pi^2}{(6.67 \times 10^{-11} \text{ N·m}^2/\text{kg}^2)(5.98 \times 10^{24} \text{ kg})} = 9.90 \times 10^{-14} \text{ s}^2/\text{m}.$$

$T = 1\text{day} = 24(3600 \text{ s}) = 86\,400 \text{ s}$ (synchronous satellite).

From $T^2 = Kr^3 = K(R_E + h)^3$, we have

$$h = \sqrt[3]{\frac{T^2}{K}} - R_E = \sqrt[3]{\frac{(86\,400 \text{ s})^2}{9.90 \times 10^{-14} \text{ s}^2/\text{m}}} - 6.38 \times 10^6 \text{ m} = \boxed{3.6 \times 10^7 \text{ m}}.$$

96. The Moon's gravitational attraction on the near side is greater on the water than on the Earth and produces one bulge for one tide; the attraction is greater on the Earth than on the water on the far side and so the Earth moves toward the Moon and leaves the water behind for another bulge.

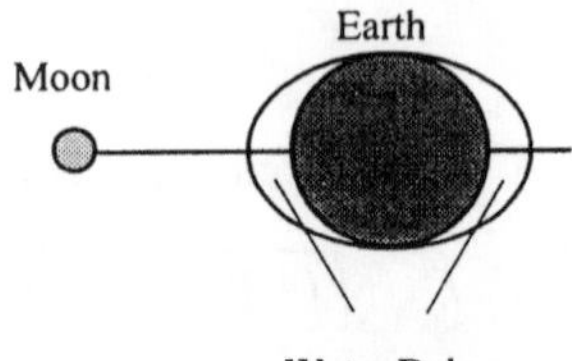

97. The centripetal force is provided by the combination of

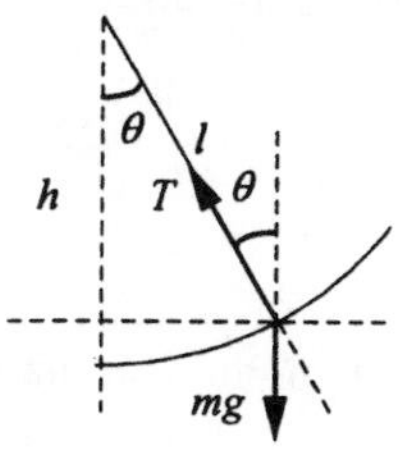

$T - mg\cos\theta = m\frac{v^2}{r}$, where $\cos\theta = \frac{h}{l}$ and v could be found from energy conservation. When the girl is h below the original position,

we have $\frac{1}{2}m(0)^2 + mgh = \frac{1}{2}mv^2 + mg(0)$, so $v^2 = 2gh$.

Therefore $T = mg\cos\theta + m\frac{v^2}{r} = \frac{mgh}{l} + \frac{m(2gh)}{l} = \frac{3mgh}{l}$.

(a) $h = 0$, so $T = \boxed{0}$.

(b) $h = 12\ m - 5.0\ \text{m} = 7.0\ \text{m}$, so $T = \frac{3(60\ \text{kg})(9.80\ \text{m/s}^2)(7.0\ \text{m})}{10\ \text{m}} = \boxed{1.2 \times 10^3\ \text{N}}$.

(c) $h = 12\ \text{m} - 2.0\ \text{m} = 10\ \text{m}$, so $T = \frac{3(60\ \text{kg})(9.80\ \text{m/s}^2)(10\ \text{m})}{10\ \text{m}} = \boxed{1.8 \times 10^3\ \text{N}}$.

103. For the Earth, $T = 1$ year and $r = 1$ AU.

From Kepler's third law, $T^2 = Kr^3$., we have $(1\ \text{y})^2 = K(1\ \text{AU})^3$.

So $K = \boxed{1\ \text{y}^2/\text{AU}^3}$.

VI. Practice Quiz

1. Convert 5.0 rad/s to revolutions per minute.

(a) 0.53 rpm (b) 16 rpm (c) 31 rpm (d) 48 rpm (e) 150 rpm

2. The cutting cord on a gas-powered weed cutter is 0.16 m in length. If the motor rotates at the rate of 20 rev/s, what is the approximate tangential velocity of the end of the cord?

(a) 20 m/s (b) 25 m/s (c) 35 m/s (d) 65 m/s (e) 630 m/s

3. A 0.300-kg mass, attached to the end of a 0.75-meter string, is whirled around in a smooth level table. If the maximum tension that the string can withstand is 250 N, then what maximum tangential speed can the mass have if the string is not to break?

(a) 22.4 m/s (b) 25 m/s (c) 19.4 m/s (d) 32.7 m/s (e) 275 m/s

4. How many revolutions does a 0.100-meter radius wheel rotate after starting from rest and accelerating at a constant angular acceleration of 2.00 rad/s^2 over a 5.00 s interval?

(a) 157 rev (b) 50.0 rev (c) 3.98 rev (d) 12.5 rev (e) 25.0 rev

5. The gravitation attractive force between two masses is F. If the masses are moved to twice of their initial distance, what is the gravitational attractive force?

(a) $F/4$ (b) $F/2$ (c) F (d) $2F$ (e) $4F$

6. A hypothetical planet has a mass of half that of the Earth and a radius of twice that of the Earth. What is the acceleration due to gravity on the planet in terms of g?

(a) g (b) $g/2$ (c) $g/4$ (d) $g/8$ (e) $g/16$

7. A centrifuge, rotating at 1.2×10^3 rad/s, slows to a stop while turning through 2.0×10^3 revolutions. What is the magnitude of the angular acceleration of the centrifuge?

(a) 0.30 rad/s^2 (b) 1.7 rad/s^2 (c) 57 rad/s^2 (d) 1.1×10^2 rad/s^2 (e) 3.6×10^2 rad/s^2

8. An object moves with a constant speed of 20 m/s on a circular track of radius 100 m. What is the magnitude of the centripetal acceleration of the object?

(a) zero (b) 0.20 rad/s^2 (c) 0.40 m/s^2 (d) 2.0 m/s^2 (e) 4.0 rad/s^2

9. The minute hand in a clock has a length of 0.30 m. What distance does the tip of the minute hand sweep through in 15 minutes?

(a) 0.12 m (b) 0.47 m (c) 0.36 m (d) 0.24 m (e) 27 m

10. At what angular speed must a circular, rotating spacestation (r = 1000 m) rotate to produce an artificial gravity of 9.80 m/s^2?

(a) 9.8×10^{-3} rad/s (b) 9.9×10^{-2} rad/s (c) 0.98 rad/s (d) 10 rad/s (e) 1.0×10^2 rad/s

Answers to Practice Quiz:

1. d 2. a 3. b 4. c 5. a 6. d 7. c 8. c 9. b 10. b

CHAPTER 8

Rotational Motion and Equilibrium

I. Chapter Objectives

Upon completion of this chapter, you should be able to:

1. distinguish between pure translational and pure rotational motions of a rigid body, and state the condition(s) for rolling without slipping.
2. define torque, apply the conditions for mechanical equilibrium, and describe the relationship between the location of the center of gravity and stability.
3. describe the moment of inertia of a rigid body and apply the rotational form of Newton's second law to physical situations.
4. discuss, explain, and use the rotational forms of work, kinetic energy, and power.
5. define angular momentum and apply the conservation of angular momentum to physical situations.

II. Key Terms

Upon completion of this chapter, you should be able to define and/or explain the following key terms:

rigid body
translational motion
rotational motion
instantaneous axis of rotation
moment (lever arm)
torque
translational equilibrium
concurrent forces
rotational equilibrium
mechanical equilibrium
static equilibrium
center of gravity
stable equilibrium
unstable equilibrium
moment of inertia
parallel axis theorem
rotational work
rotational power
rotational kinetic energy
angular momentum
conservation of angular momentum

The definitions and/or explanations of the most important key terms can be found in the following section: **III. Chapter Summary and Discussion.**

III. Chapter Summary and Discussion

1. Rigid Bodies, Translation, and Rotation (Section 8.1)

A **rigid body** is an object or system of particles in which the interparticle distances (distances between particles) are fixed and remain constant. In pure **translational motion**, every particle of an object or system of particles has the same instantaneous velocity, which means there is no rotation. In pure **rotational motion**, all particles of an object or system of particles have the same instantaneous angular velocity.

Generally, rigid body motion is a combination of translational and rotational motions. If an object is rolling without slipping, the following conditions must be satisfied:

$s = r\theta$, or $v_{CM} = r\omega$, or $a_{CM} = r\alpha$, where the subscripts CM stand for center of mass.

Note: When $v_{CM} = r\omega$, the object is rolling without slipping. If $v_{CM} > r\omega$, the object is sliding. The object rolls with slipping when $v_{CM} < r\omega$.

2. Torque, Equilibrium, and Stability (Section 8.2)

The magnitude of the **torque** (τ) produced by a force about an axis of rotation is given by $\tau = r_{\perp} F$. The distance $r_{\perp} = r \sin\theta$ is called the **moment arm** or **lever arm**, which is the *perpendicular* distance from the axis of rotation to the line of the action of the force. The SI unit of torque is m·N (the same as for work N·m or J, but which we write in reverse for distinction). By convention, counterclockwise torque is positive and clockwise torque is negative.

Note: The moment arm is the *perpendicular* distance from the axis of rotation to the *line of the action* of the force, which is usually not the same as simply the distance from the axis to the force.

An object is in **translational equilibrium** if the net force on it is zero, and an object is in **rotational equilibrium** if the net torque is zero. If an object is in both translational equilibrium and rotational equilibrium, it is said to be in **mechanical equilibrium**. So the conditions for an object in mechanical equilibrium are $\Sigma \mathbf{F}_i = 0$ and $\Sigma \tau_i = 0$. A special case of mechanical equilibrium is **static equilibrium** in which objects are and remain at rest.

Note: When applying $\Sigma \tau_i = 0$ to rotational or static equilibrium situations, you can choose anywhere on the object as the axis of rotation because the object is not rotating about any point. However, some choices of axes of rotation can greatly simplify the solutions of such problems. Generally, the axis of rotation should be chosen through a point through which some unknown force(s) act so to make the moment of arm(s) of the force(s) zero, therefore the torque(s) zero.

Example 8.1 The bolts on a car wheel require tightening to a torque of 90 m·N. If a 20-centimeter long wrench is used, what is the magnitude of the force required

(a) when the force is perpendicular to the wrench,

(b) when the force is $\theta = 35°$ to the wrench as shown.

Solution: Given: $r = 0.20$ m, $\tau = 90$ m·N, (a) $\theta = 90°$, (b) $\theta = 35°$.

Find: F in (a) and (b).

(a) When the force is applied at a 90° angle as shown, the lever arm is simply equal to the length of the wrench.

$r_\perp = r \sin\theta = (0.20 \text{ m}) \sin 90° = 0.20 \text{ m}.$

From $\tau = r_\perp F$, we have $F = \dfrac{\tau}{r_\perp} = \dfrac{90 \text{ m·N}}{0.20 \text{ m}} = 4.5 \times 10^2 \text{ N}.$

(b) When the force is applied at a non-90° angle, the lever arm *is not* equal to the length of the wrench. The perpendicular distance from the axis to the line of the action of the force is

$r_\perp = (0.20 \text{ m}) \sin 35° = 0.115 \text{ m}.$ $F = \dfrac{90 \text{ m·N}}{0.115 \text{ m}} = 7.8 \times 10^2 \text{ N}.$

Why does it need more force in (b) than in (a)?

Example 8.2 A uniform board of weight 40 N supports two children weighing 500 N and 350 N, respectively. If the support is at the center of the board and the 500-newton child is 1.5 m from the center, what is the position of the 350-newton child?

Solution:

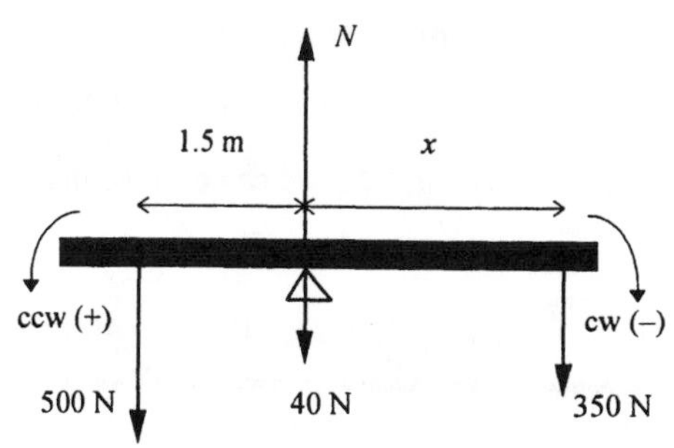

Since the board is uniform, its center of mass and center of gravity are at the center of the board. We choose the support as the axis of rotation since there is an unknown normal force N by the support on the board (although we can find it easily with $\Sigma \mathbf{F}_i = 0$ but this way we can save a step). Once an axis of rotation is chosen, we can clearly see, from the free-body diagram of the board, that the weight of the 500-newton child produces a ccw (counterclockwise) torque, the weight of the 350-newton child causes a cw (clockwise) torque, and the weight of the board and the normal force have no contribution to the total torque because their moment arms are zero (force through the axis).

Note: Whether a torque is ccw or cw depends on the location of the axis of rotation. For example, if the axis is to the left of the 500-newton force it generates a cw torque. So make sure you chose an axis before you apply the condition for rotational equilibrium.

From the condition for rotational equilibrium $\Sigma\tau_i = 0$,

we have $\Sigma\tau_i = (500\text{ N})(1.5\text{ m}) - (350\text{ N})\,x + N\,(0) = 0$. Solving, $x = 2.1$ m.

Example 8.3 A 10-meter long uniform beam of weight 100 N is supported by two ropes at the ends as shown. If a 400-newton person sits at 2.0 m from one end of the beam, what are the tensions in the ropes?

Solution:

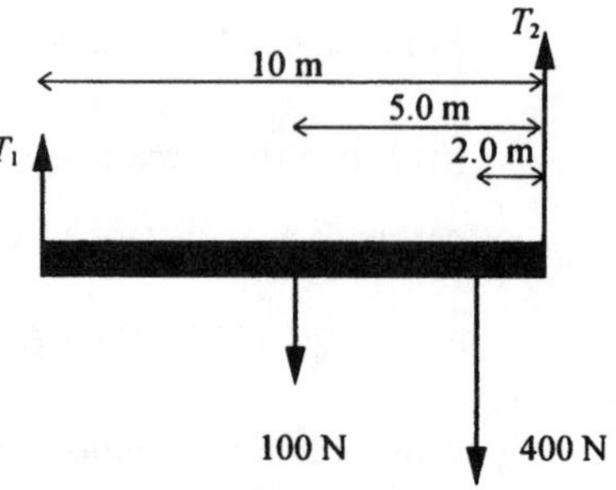

Since the beam is uniform, its center of mass and center of gravity are at its geometrical center, which is 5.0 m from one end. We first draw the free-body diagram of the beam. Where should we choose the axis of rotation? What if we chose the center of the beam as the axis? If we do so, we will have two unknowns (T_1 and T_2) in our $\Sigma\tau_i = 0$ equation. We cannot solve for two unknowns within just one equation. (Although we can get another equation from $\Sigma\mathbf{F}_i = 0$. Then we have to solve simultaneous equations.) We can simplify the solution of this problem by choosing our axis at either end (either at T_1 or T_2). Let's try T_2 first, i.e., we chose the axis of rotation at the right end of the beam.

About the right end, T_1 has a cw torque, the 100-newton and 400-newton forces have ccw torques, and T_2 has zero torque since its lever arm is zero.

From the condition for rotational equilibrium, $\Sigma\tau_i = 0$, we have

$\Sigma\tau_i = -T_1\,(10\text{ m}) + (100\text{ N})(5.0\text{ m}) + (400\text{ N})(2.0\text{ m}) + T_2\,(0) = 0$. Solving, $T_1 = 130$ N.

To find T_2, we can choose the left end as the axis of rotation and repeat our calculation. Or we can use the condition for translational equilibrium, $\Sigma\mathbf{F}_i = 0$.

$\Sigma\mathbf{F}_i = T_1 + T_2 - 100\text{ N} - 400\text{ N} = 0$. So $T_2 = 500\text{ N} - T_1 = 500\text{ N} - 130\text{ N} = 370$ N.

If an object is in **stable equilibrium**, any small displacement results in a restoring force or torque, which tends to return the object to its original equilibrium. For an object in **unstable equilibrium**, any small displacement from equilibrium results in a force or torque that tends to take the object farther away from its equilibrium position. An object will be in stable equilibrium as long as its center of gravity lies above and inside its original base of support., i.e., line of action of the weight force of the center of gravity intersects the original base of support.

3. Rotational Dynamics (Section 8.3)

The torque on a particle due to a constant force is $\tau = mr^2\alpha$. Similarly for a rotating body about a fixed axis, $\tau = \Sigma\,(m_i r_i^2)\alpha = I\alpha$, where $I = \Sigma\, m_i r_i^2$ is called the **moment of inertia** (rotational analog of mass). For a single particle, the moments of inertia is simply equal to $I = mr^2$, where r is the distance from the mass to the axis. However, for many continuous objects (objects treated as an infinite number of particles, each with a very small mass) the moments of inertia have to be determined with calculus. The results are listed in Figure 8.16 on page 269 in the textbook.

The moment of inertia about an axis parallel to an axis through its center of mass is given by the **parallel axis theorem**: $I = I_{CM} + Md^2$, where I_{CM} is the moment of inertia about an axis through the center of mass, M is the mass of the object, and d is the distance between the parallel axes.

In Chapter 7, we discussed the fact that the kinematic equations for angular motion are identical to those for linear motion if the linear quantities are replaced by their respective angular counterparts (x by θ, v by ω, and a by α). In dynamics, the rotational counterparts of force and mass are torque and moment of inertia. Therefore we can write the **rotational form of Newton's second law** as $\tau = I\alpha$ (for linear motion, it is $\mathbf{F} = m\mathbf{a}$).

Example 8.4 The moment of inertia of a solid disk rotating about an axis through its center is $\frac{1}{2}MR^2$, where M is the mass of the disk and R is the radius of the disk. What is the moment of inertia of the disk about an axis through the contact point when the disk is rolling on a horizontal surface?

Solution:

When the disk is rolling, the axis of rotation is though the point where the disk makes contact with the horizontal surface. The distance from this axis to an axis through the center of the disk is R, the radius of the disk. From the parallel axis theorem, we have $I = I_{CM} + Md^2 = \frac{1}{2}MR^2 + MR^2 = \frac{3}{2}MR^2$.

Example 8.5 A solid cylinder of mass 10 kg is pivoted about a frictionless axis through its center O. A rope wrapped around the outer radius R_1 = 1.0 m, exerts a force of F_1 = 5.0 N to the right. A second rope wrapped around another section of radius R_2 = 0.50 m exerts a force of F_2 = 6.0 N downward.

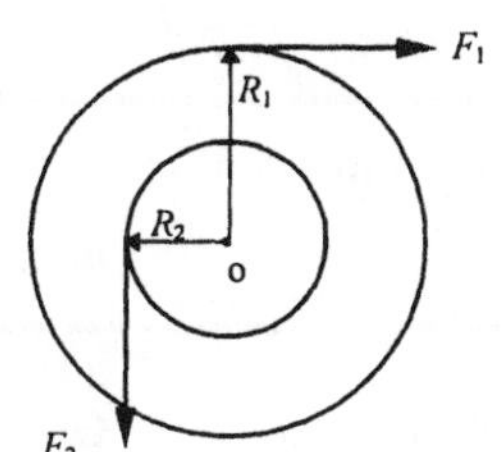

(a) What is the angular acceleration of the disk?

(b) If the disk starts from rest, how many radians does it rotate through in the first 5.0 s?

Solution: Given: $M = 10$ kg, $F_1 = 5.0$ N, $R_1 = 1.0$ m, $F_2 = 6.0$ N, $R_2 = 0.50$ m, $t = 5.0$ s.

Find: (a) α (b) θ.

(a) About an axis through O, the torque by F_1 is cw and the torque by F_2 is ccw. From Figure 8.16 in the textbook, the moment of inertia of a disk is given by $I = \frac{1}{2}MR_2^2 = \frac{1}{2}(10 \text{ kg})(1.0 \text{ m})^2 = 5.0 \text{ kg·m}^2$.

The net torque on the disk is $\tau_{net} = -F_1 R_1 + F_2 R_2 = -(5.0 \text{ N})(1.0 \text{ m}) + (6.0 \text{ N})(0.50 \text{ m}) = -2.0 \text{ m·N}$.

From Newton's second law, $\tau_{net} = I\alpha$, we have $\alpha = \frac{\tau_{net}}{I} = \frac{-2.0 \text{ m·N}}{5.0 \text{ kg·m}^2} = -0.40 \text{ rad/s}^2$. The negative sign indicates that the disk will accelerate clockwise.

(b) From rotational kinematics, $\theta = \omega_o t + \frac{1}{2}\alpha t^2 = 0 + \frac{1}{2}(-0.40 \text{ rad/s}^2)(5.0 \text{ s})^2 = -5.0 \text{ rad}$.

Again, the negative sign indicates that the angular displacement is counterclockwise.

---

4. Rotational Work and Kinetic Energy (Section 8.4)

As was discussed earlier, the rotational counterparts of the linear quantities x, v, a, F, and m are θ, ω, α, τ, and I. The equations for work and energy in linear motion are still valid if we replace the linear quantities by their respective rotational counterparts. The following are the equations for rotational work and energy with the original linear equations being given in parentheses (a detailed comparison can be found in Table 8.1 on page 275 in the textbook).

Work:	$W = \tau\theta$	$(W = Fd = Fx)$
Kinetic Energy:	$K = \frac{1}{2}I\omega^2$	$(K = \frac{1}{2}mv^2)$
Power:	$P = \tau\omega$	$(P = Fv)$
Work-Energy Theorem:	$W = \Delta K = \frac{1}{2}I\omega^2 - \frac{1}{2}I\omega_o^2$	$(W = \Delta K = \frac{1}{2}mv^2 - \frac{1}{2}mv_o^2)$

The kinetic energy of a **rolling body** (without slipping) relative to an axis through the contact point is the sum of the rotational kinetic energy about an axis through the center of mass and the translational kinetic energy of the center of mass and, i.e., $K = \frac{1}{2}I_{CM}\,\omega^2 + \frac{1}{2}Mv_{CM}^2$.

Example 8.6 A solid sphere of mass 1.0 kg and radius 0.010 m rolls with a speed of 10 m/s. How high up an inclined plane can it roll before coming to rest?

Solution: Given: $M = 1.0$ kg, $R = 0.010$ m, $v_{CM} = 10$ m/s.

Find: h.

We use the conservation of mechanical energy to solve this problem. First we need to choose the bottom of the inclined plane as the reference level for zero gravitational potential energy ($U_o = 0$ at $h_o = 0$). The mechanical energy at the bottom should be equal to the mechanical energy at the top. When the sphere is at the bottom of the plane, its potential energy is zero, and it has both translational and rotational kinetic energies. When the sphere reaches the maximum height, both its linear and angular speeds are zero so it has only potential energy. We also need to use $v_{CM} = R\omega$ and $I_{CM} = \frac{2}{5}MR^2$ in our solution.

At the bottom the mechanical energy is $\frac{1}{2}I_{CM}\,\omega^2 + \frac{1}{2}Mv_{CM}^2 = \frac{1}{2}\left(\frac{2}{5}MR^2\right)\frac{v_{CM}^2}{R^2} + \frac{1}{2}Mv_{CM}^2 = \frac{7}{10}Mv_{CM}^2$.

At the highest point on the incline, the mechanical energy is Mgh.

From the conservation of mechanical energy, we have $\frac{7}{10}Mv_{CM}^2 = Mgh$.

Solving, $h = \dfrac{7v_{CM}^2}{10\,g} = \dfrac{7(10\text{ m/s})^2}{10(9.80\text{ m/s}^2)} = 7.1$ m.

Example 8.7 A cylindrical hoop of mass 10 kg and radius 0.20 m is accelerated by a motor from rest to an angular speed of 20 rad/s during a 0.40 s interval.

(a) How much work is required?

(b) What is the power output of the motor?

Solution: Given: $M = 10$ kg, $R = 0.20$ m, $\omega_0 = 0$, $\omega = 20$ rad/s, $t = 0.40$ s.

Find: (a) W (b) P.

(a) From Fig. 8.16 in the textbook, the moment of inertia of a cylindrical hoop is given by $I = MR^2 = (10\text{ kg})(0.20\text{ m})^2 = 0.40\text{ kg·m}^2$. From the work-energy theorem, we have $W = \Delta K = \frac{1}{2}I\omega^2 - \frac{1}{2}I\omega_0^2 = \frac{1}{2}I\omega^2 = \frac{1}{2}(0.40\text{ kg·m}^2)(20\text{ rad/s})^2 = 80$ J.

(b) $P = \dfrac{W}{t} = \dfrac{80\text{ J}}{0.40\text{ s}} = 200$ W.

---

5. Angular Momentum (Section 8.5)

The definition of angular momentum is analogous to linear momentum. It is defined as the product of moment of inertia and angular velocity. $\mathbf{L} = I\omega$ (it is $p = mv$ for linear momentum). The SI unit of angular momentum is kg·m^2/s. The vector direction of angular momentum is determined by the right hand rule as applied to angular velocity in Chapter 7. The rotational form of Newton's second law can also be written in terms of angular momentum: $\tau = \dfrac{\Delta \mathbf{L}}{\Delta t}$.

In the absence of an external, unbalanced torque, the total angular momentum of a system is conserved (remains constant). Mathematically, this can be written as $\mathbf{L} = \mathbf{L}_o$ or $I\omega = I_o\,\omega_0$.

Angular momentum has many practical applications in our everyday lives such as the gyroscope used in navigation, the twin-rotor helicopters, and even the tight spiral of a football.

Example 8.8 A figure skater rotating at 4.00 rad/s with arms extended has a moment of inertia of 2.25 kg·m². If she pulls her arms in so the moment of inertia decreases to 1.80 kg·m², what is the magnitude of her final angular speed?

Solution: Given: $I_o = 2.25\ \text{kg·m}^2$ $\quad I = 1.80\ \text{kg·m}^2$

$\omega_o = 4.00$ rad/s

Find: ω.

From the conservation of angular momentum, $I\omega = I_o\,\omega_o$, we have

$$\omega = \frac{I_o\,\omega_o}{I} = \frac{(2.25\ \text{kg·m}^2)(4.00\ \text{rad/s})}{1.80\ \text{kg·m}^2} = 5.00\ \text{rad/s}.$$

The figure skater rotates faster after pulling the arms in.

Why does the moment of inertia decrease when the arms are pulled in?

IV. Mathematical Summary

Condition for Rolling without Slipping	$v_{CM} = r\omega$ (or $s = r\theta$ or $a_{CM} = r\alpha$) (8.1)	Defines the condition for rolling without slipping.
Torque (magnitude)	$\tau = r_\perp F = rF\sin\theta$ (8.2)	Defines the magnitude of torque.
Conditions for Equilibrium	$\Sigma \mathbf{F}_i = 0$ and $\Sigma \tau_i = 0$ (8.3)	Define the conditions for translational, rotational, and mechanical equilibria.
Torque on a particle (magnitude)	$\tau = mr^2\alpha$ (8.4)	Calculates the magnitude of torque on a particle.
Moment of Inertia	$I = \Sigma m_i r_i^2$ (8.6)	Defines the moment of inertia.
Newton's Second Law (magnitude)	$\tau = I\alpha$ (8.7)	Gives the rotational form of Newton's second law.
Parallel Axis Theorem	$I = I_{CM} + Md^2$ (8.8)	Calculates the moment of inertia about an axis parallel to one through the center of mass.
Rotational Work	$W = \tau\theta$ (8.9)	Defines rotational work.
Rotational Power	$P = \tau\omega$ (8.10)	Defines rotational power.
Work-Energy Theorem	$W = \Delta K = \frac{1}{2}I\omega^2 - \frac{1}{2}I\omega_o^2$ (8.11)	Relates rotational work with change in rotational kinetic energy.

Rotational Kinetic Energy	$K = \frac{1}{2}I\omega^2$ (8.12)	Defines rotational kinetic energy.
Kinetic Energy of a Rolling Object	$K = \frac{1}{2}I_{CM}\,\omega^2 + \frac{1}{2}Mv_{CM}^2$ (8.13)	Calculates the total kinetic energy of a rolling object.
Angular Momentum of a Particle (magnitude)	$L = mr_\perp^2\,\omega$ (8.14)	Defines the angular momentum of a particle in circular motion.
Angular Momentum of a Rigid Body	$\mathbf{L} = I\omega$ (8.16)	Defines the angular momentum of a rigid body.
Torque in Terms of Angular Momentum	$\tau = \dfrac{\Delta \mathbf{L}}{\Delta t}$ (8.17)	Expresses Newton's second law in terms of angular momentum.
Conservation of Angular Momentum	$I\omega = I_o\,\omega_o$ (8.18)	Gives the law of the conservation of angular momentum when the net external torque is zero.

V. Solutions of Selected Exercises and Paired/Trio Exercises

6. $s = r\theta = (0.065 \text{ m})(4 \text{ rev})(2\pi \text{ rad/rev}) = \boxed{1.6 \text{ m}}$.

10. From $v_{CM} = r\omega$, we have $\omega = \dfrac{v_{CM}}{r} = \dfrac{0.25 \text{ m/s}}{0.15 \text{ m}} = \boxed{1.7 \text{ rad/s}}$.

13. $\alpha = \dfrac{a_t}{r} = \dfrac{0.018 \text{ m/s}^2}{0.10 \text{ m}} = 0.18 \text{ rad/s}^2$. From $\omega^2 = \omega_o^2 + 2\alpha\theta$,

we have $\theta = \dfrac{\omega^2 - \omega_o^2}{2\alpha} = \dfrac{(1.25 \text{ rad/s})^2 - (0.50 \text{ rad/s})^2}{2(0.18 \text{ rad/s}^2)} = 36.5 \text{ rad} = \boxed{0.58 \text{ rotations}}$.

18. When the force is applied perpendicular to the length of the wrench, minimum force is required and the lever arm equals the length of the wrench. At $\theta = 90°$, $r_\perp = 0.15$ m.

From $\tau = Fr_\perp$, we have $F = \dfrac{\tau}{r_\perp} = \dfrac{25 \text{ m·N}}{0.15 \text{ m}} = \boxed{1.7 \times 10^2 \text{ N}}$.

19. In this case, the lever arm is *not* equal to the length of the wrench.

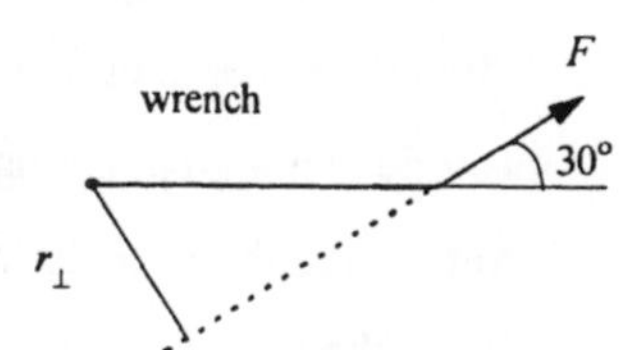

$r_\perp = (0.15 \text{ m}) \sin 30°$.

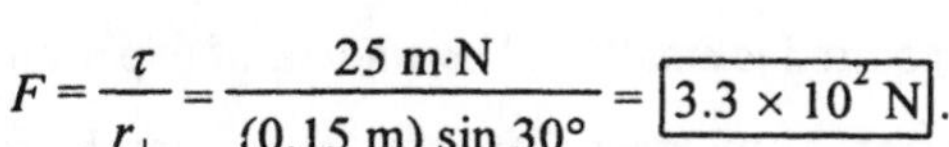

$F = \dfrac{\tau}{r_\perp} = \dfrac{25 \text{ m·N}}{(0.15 \text{ m}) \sin 30°} = \boxed{3.3 \times 10^2 \text{ N}}$.

20. $\boxed{5.6 \times 10^2 \text{ N}}$.

24. (a) Apply $\Sigma\tau = 0$, we have $(0.100 \text{ kg})g(0.500 \text{ m} - 0.250 \text{ m}) - (0.0750 \text{ kg})g(x - 0.500 \text{ m}) = 0$.

Solving, $x = 0.833 \text{ m} = \boxed{83.3 \text{ cm}}$.

(b) $(0.100 \text{ kg})g(0.500 \text{ m} - 0.250 \text{ m}) - m(0.900 \text{ m} - 0.500 \text{ m}) = 0$,

so $0.0625 \text{ kg} = \boxed{62.5 \text{ g}}$.

29. Apply $\Sigma\tau = 0$, we have

$-(5.0 \text{ N})(0.50 \text{ m}) - (0.15 \text{ kg})(9.80 \text{ m/s}^2)(0.75 \text{ m}) + F(1.0 \text{ m}) = 0$.

Solving, $F = \boxed{3.6 \text{ N}}$.

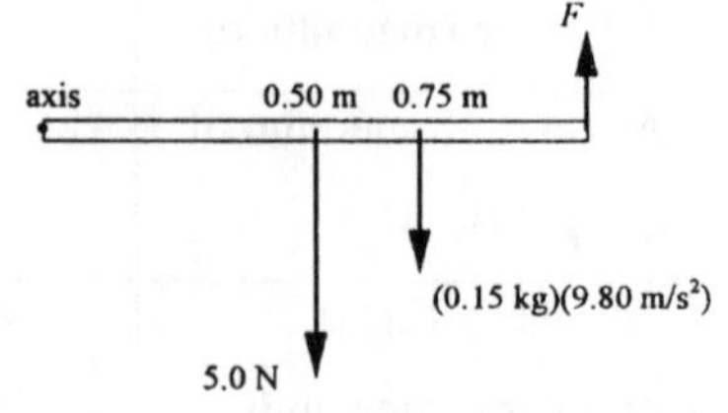

32. (a) The center of gravity (CG) of the first book is at the center. So for the last book not to fall, its CG can not displace more than 12.5 cm relative to the CG of the first book (within the base). The CG of each successive book on the top is moved 1.5 cm relative to that of the one below. Therefore the number of books which can be on top of the first one is $\dfrac{12.5 \text{ cm}}{1.5 \text{ cm}} = 8.33$.

Thus we can stack a total of $1 + 8 = \boxed{9}$ books, including the first one.

(b) The total height is $9(5.0) \text{ cm} = 45 \text{ cm}$. So the CM is at $\dfrac{45 \text{ cm}}{2} = \boxed{22.5 \text{ cm}}$.

37. (a) Assume the distance from the center of gravity (CG) to the point where the wheel touches the ground is d. We choose the axis of rotation through the CG. Apply $\Sigma\tau = 0$, we have

$f_s d \cos\theta - Nd \sin\theta = 0$, or $f_s d \cos\theta = Nd \sin\theta$, so $\tan\theta = f_s/N$.

(b) $f_s = \mu_s N = N \tan\theta$, or $\mu_s = \tan\theta = \tan 11° = \boxed{0.19}$.

(c) $\Sigma F_y = N - mg = 0$, or $N = mg$.

So $f_s = \mu_s N = \mu_s mg = F_c = m\dfrac{v^2}{r}$, and $v = \sqrt{\mu_s g r} = \sqrt{0.19(9.80 \text{ m/s}^2)(6.5 \text{ m})} = \boxed{3.5 \text{ m/s}}$.

43. This is the rotational analog of "pulling the table cloth" in Exercise 4.9. It takes a certain amount of torque to accelerate the paper tower and the paper can only exert certain amount of force, and therefore torque. When the paper is pulled quickly (a great force is required to accelerate the roll), the force the paper can provide is not great enough to accelerate the paper roll. However, if the paper is pulled slowly, the paper is strong enough to accelerate the roll because the force required is smaller. The amount of paper on the roll affects the results. The more paper the roll has, the greater the moment of inertia, the greater the force required to accelerate the roll, and therefore the easier to tear.

46. From Fig. 8.16 on page 269 in the textbook, $I = \frac{1}{2}mr^2 = \frac{1}{2}(0.15 \text{ kg})(0.075 \text{ m})^2 = 4.219 \times 10^{-4} \text{ kg·m}^2$.

From Newton's second law $\tau = I\alpha$, we have $\alpha = \frac{\tau}{I} = \frac{6.4 \text{ m·N}}{4.219 \times 10^{-4} \text{ kg·m}^2} = \boxed{3.4 \times 10^4 \text{ rad/s}^2}$.

50. We first calculate the angular acceleration from kinematics.

$$\alpha = \frac{\Delta\omega}{\Delta t} = \frac{2.0 \text{ rad/s} - 0}{12 \text{ s}} = 0.167 \text{ rad/s}^2.$$

Then $\tau = I\alpha = \frac{1}{2}mr^2\alpha = \frac{1}{2}(2000 \text{ kg})(30 \text{ m})^2 (0.167 \text{ rad/s}^2) = \boxed{1.5 \times 10^5 \text{ m·N}}$.

52. $\boxed{0.45 \text{ m·N}}$.

55. Apply Newton's second law and note $a = r\alpha$.

m_2: $m_2 g - T_2 = m_2 a$, Eq. (1)

pulley: $T_2 R - T_1 R - \tau_f = I\alpha = \frac{1}{2}MR^2\alpha = \frac{1}{2}MRa$,

or $T_2 - T_1 - \frac{\tau_f}{R} = \frac{1}{2}Ma$, Eq. (2)

m_1: $T_1 - m_1 g = m_1 a$. Eq. (3)

Eq. (1) + Eq. (2) + Eq. (3) gives $(m_2 - m_1)g - \frac{\tau_f}{R} = (m_1 + m_2 + 0.5M)a$,

so $a = \dfrac{(m_2 - m_1)g - \frac{\tau_f}{R}}{m_1 + m_2 + 0.5M} = \dfrac{(0.80 \text{ kg} - 0.40 \text{ kg})(9.80 \text{ m/s}^2) - \frac{0.35 \text{ m·N}}{0.15 \text{ m}}}{0.40 \text{ kg} + 0.80 \text{ kg} + 0.5(0.20 \text{ kg})} = \boxed{1.2 \text{ m/s}^2}$.

59. (a) From Fig. 8.16 on page 269 in the textbook, the moment of inertia of a meterstick about its end is $I = \frac{1}{3}ML^2$. The torque is generated by the weight of the stick through its center of mass.

So $\tau = RF = \frac{1}{2}LMg = I\alpha = \frac{1}{3}ML^2\alpha$, or $\alpha = \frac{3g}{2L}$.

Therefore $a = r\alpha = L\frac{3g}{2L} = \boxed{1.5g}$.

(b) $a = g = r\frac{3g}{2L}$, or $r = \frac{2L}{3} = 0.67 \text{ m} = \boxed{67 \text{ cm position}}$.

62. The hoop rotates about an instantaneous axis of rotation through the point of contact (point O). From the parallel-axis theorem, the moment of inertia about this axis is

$I = I_{CM} + Md^2 = MR^2 + MR^2 = 2MR^2$.

The torque by gravity is $\tau = MgR\sin\theta$.

So $a = R\alpha = R\dfrac{\tau}{I} = R\dfrac{MgR\sin\theta}{2MR^2} = \dfrac{g\sin\theta}{2}$

$= \dfrac{(9.80\text{ m/s}^2)\sin 15°}{2} = \boxed{1.3\text{ m/s}^2}$.

68. From the work energy theorem:

$W = \tau\theta = \frac{1}{2}I\omega^2 - \frac{1}{2}I\omega_0^2 = \frac{1}{2}I\omega^2 - \frac{1}{2}I(0)^2 = \frac{1}{2}I\omega^2 = \frac{1}{2}\frac{1}{2}MR^2\omega^2 = \frac{1}{4}MR^2\omega^2$.

So $\omega = \sqrt{\dfrac{4\tau\theta}{MR^2}} = \sqrt{\dfrac{4(10\text{ m·N})(2.0)(2\pi\text{ rad})}{(10\text{ kg})(0.20\text{ m})^2}} = \boxed{35\text{ rad/s}}$.

72. The center of mass (CM) lowers by an amount of $h = 0.50$ m.

From energy conservation: $\frac{1}{2}I(0)^2 + mgh = \frac{1}{2}I\omega^2 + mg(0)$,

so $\omega = \sqrt{\dfrac{2mgh}{I}} = \sqrt{\dfrac{2mgh}{\frac{1}{3}mL^2}} = \sqrt{\dfrac{6gh}{L^2}} = \dfrac{6(9.80\text{ m/s}^2)(0.50\text{ m})}{(1.0\text{ m})^2} = \boxed{5.4\text{ rad/s}}$.

74. $\boxed{3.4\text{ m/s}}$.

76. $K = \frac{1}{2}mv^2 + \frac{1}{2}I\omega^2 = \frac{1}{2}mv^2 + \frac{1}{2}I\dfrac{v^2}{R^2}$. So $K_h = \frac{1}{2}mv_h^2 + \frac{1}{2}mR^2\dfrac{v_h^2}{R^2} = mv_h^2$,

$K_c = \frac{1}{2}mv_c^2 + \frac{1}{2}(\frac{1}{2}mR^2)\dfrac{v_c^2}{R^2} = \frac{3}{4}mv_c^2$, and $K_s = \frac{1}{2}mv_s^2 + \frac{1}{2}(\frac{2}{5}mR^2)\dfrac{v_s^2}{R^2} = \frac{7}{10}mv_s^2$.

Since they are all released from the same height, the K's are the same. That means the v is the greatest for the sphere and smallest for the hoop. Therefore the sphere gets to the bottom first and the hoop last.

$v_s = \sqrt{\dfrac{10K}{7m}}$, $v_c = \sqrt{\dfrac{4K}{3m}}$, and $v_h = \sqrt{\dfrac{K}{m}}$.

79. (a) The centripetal force is provided solely by gravity at the minimum speed. In this case the centripetal force at the top of the track is just equal to the weight of the ball. $Mg = F_c = M\dfrac{v^2}{R}$, so $v = \boxed{\sqrt{gR}}$.

(b) From energy conservation:

$\frac{1}{2}M(0)^2 + \frac{1}{2}I(0)^2 + Mgh = \frac{1}{2}Mv^2 + \frac{1}{2}I\omega^2 + Mg(2R) = \frac{1}{2}Mv^2 + \frac{1}{2}\frac{2}{5}MR^2\dfrac{v^2}{R^2} + Mg(2R)$

$= \frac{7}{10}MgR + 2MgR = \frac{27}{10}MgR$, so $h = \boxed{2.7R}$.

(c) Since all the gravity is "used up" as centripetal force, the rider feels $\boxed{\text{weightless}}$.

83. The arms and legs are put onto these positions to decrease the moment of inertia. This decrease in moment of inertia increases the rotational speed.

88. Orbital: The Earth can be considered as a particle to the sun.

$\omega_o = \dfrac{2\pi \text{ rad}}{(365)(24)(3600 \text{ s})} = 1.99 \times 10^{-7}$ rad/s, and $I_o = MR^2$,

so $L_o = I_o\,\omega_o = (6.0 \times 10^{24} \text{ kg})(1.5 \times 10^{11} \text{ m})^2(1.99 \times 10^{-7} \text{ rad/s}) = 2.69 \times 10^{40} \text{ kg·m}^2\text{/s}$.

Spin: The Earth has to be considered as a sphere.

$\omega_s = \dfrac{2\pi \text{ rad}}{(24)(3600 \text{ s})} = 7.27 \times 10^{-5}$ rad/s, and $I_s = \frac{2}{5}Mr^2$,

so $L_s = \frac{2}{5}(6.0 \times 10^{24} \text{ kg})(6.4 \times 10^6 \text{ m})^2\,(7.27 \times 10^{-5} \text{ rad/s}) = 7.15 \times 10^{33} \text{ kg·m}^2\text{/s}$.

Therefore $\dfrac{L_o}{L_s} = \dfrac{2.69 \times 10^{40}}{7.15 \times 10^{33}} = \boxed{3.8 \times 10^6}$.

They are not in the same direction because the Earth's axis is tilted.

92. From angular momentum conservation: $I\omega = I_o\,\omega_o$, we have

$\omega = \dfrac{I_o\,\omega_o}{I} = \dfrac{(100 \text{ kg·m}^2)(2.0 \text{ rps})}{75 \text{ kg·m}^2} = \boxed{2.7 \text{ rps}}$.

96. We chose the axis of rotation at the support on the right. Apply $\Sigma\tau = 0$, we have $Mg(5.0 \text{ m}) + mg(7.0 \text{ m}) - F_L(10 \text{ m}) = 0$, so

$(10\,000 \text{ kg})(9.80 \text{ m/s}^2)(5.0 \text{ m}) + (2000 \text{ kg})(9.80 \text{ m/s}^2)(7.0 \text{ m}) = F_L(10 \text{ m})$

Solving, $F_L = 6.27 \times 10^4 \text{ N} = \boxed{6.3 \times 10^4 \text{ N}}$.

Apply $\Sigma F_y = F_L + F_R - mg - Mg = 0$, we have

$F_R = (m + M)g - F_L = (10\,000 \text{ kg} + 2000 \text{ kg})(9.80 \text{ m/s}^2) - 6.27 \times 10^4 \text{ N}$

$= \boxed{5.5 \times 10^4 \text{ N}}$.

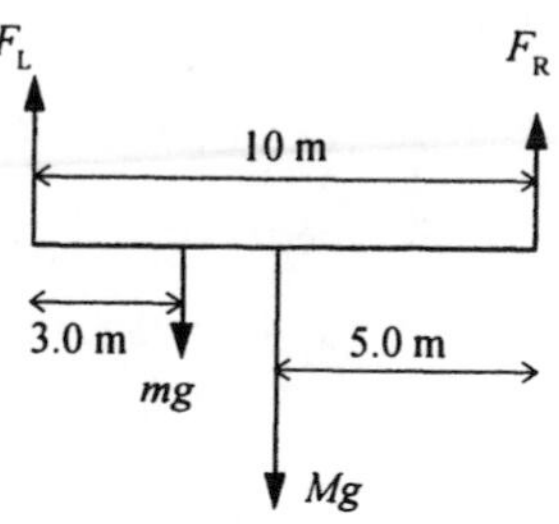

99. (a) For the mass: $\Sigma F = mg - T = ma$ Eq. (1)

For the pulley: $\Sigma\tau = rT = I\alpha = \frac{1}{2}Mr^2\dfrac{a}{r} = \frac{1}{2}Mra$, or $T = \frac{1}{2}Ma$ Eq. (2)

Solving for $a = \dfrac{mg}{m + \frac{1}{2}M} = \dfrac{(5.0 \text{ kg})(9.80 \text{ m/s}^2)}{5.0 \text{ kg} + \frac{1}{2}(10 \text{ kg})} = \boxed{4.9 \text{ m/s}^2}$.

(b) $\alpha = \dfrac{a}{r} = \dfrac{4.9 \text{ m/s}^2}{0.50 \text{ m}} = \boxed{9.8 \text{ rad/s}^2}$.

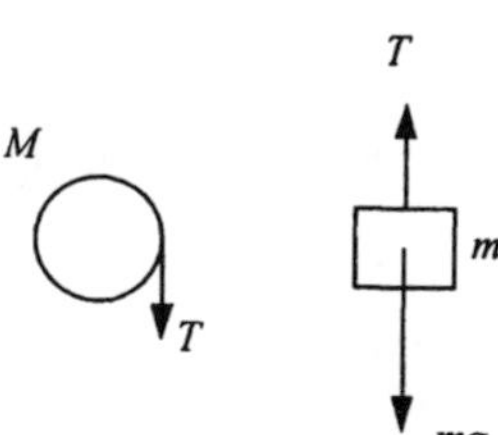

103. (a) The first brick is not displaced.

So for each brick, the maximum displacement is $\dfrac{20\text{ cm}}{8} = \boxed{2.5\text{ cm}}$.

(b) The height of the center of mass is $\dfrac{9(8.0\text{ cm})}{2} = \boxed{36\text{ cm}}$.

108. On the verge of the unstable equilibrium, the weight goes through the lower corner of the trailer. So $\tan\theta = \dfrac{L/2}{h} = \dfrac{3.66\text{ m}}{2(3.58\text{ m})} = 0.511$,

therefore $\theta = \boxed{27°}$.

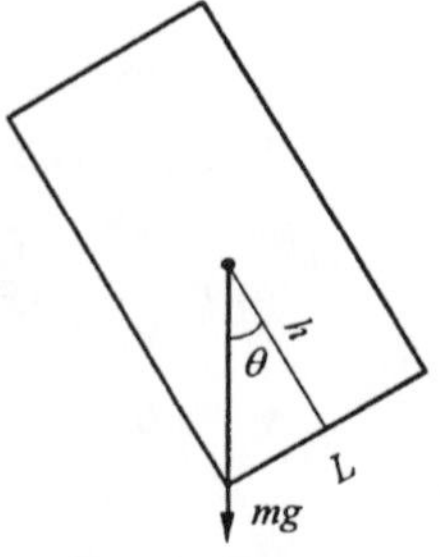

VI. Practice Quiz

1. A meter stick is supported by a knife edge at the 50 cm mark and has masses of 0.40 kg and 0.60 kg hanging at the 20 cm and 80 cm marks, respectively. Where (at what mark) should a third mass of 0.30 kg be hung to keep the stick balanced?

(a) 20 cm (b) 25 cm (c) 30 cm (d) 50 cm (e) 70 cm

2. A constant torque of 20 m·N is applied to a flywheel. If the wheel starts from rest and has moment of inertia of 12 kg·m^2, what is its angular speed after it rotated through 5.0 revolutions?

(a) 4.1 rad/s (b) 7.2 rad/s (c) 10 rad/s (d) 14 rad/s (e) 17 rad/s

3. The Earth moves about the Sun in an elliptical orbit. As the Earth moves farther from the Sun, then which of the following best describes the orbiting speed of the Earth about the Sun?

(a) increases (b) decreases (c) conserves (d) remains constant (e) none of the above

4. A wheel with moment of inertia of 2.00 kg·m^2 accelerates with an angular acceleration of 5.0 rad/s^2. What is the net torque on the wheel?

(a) 0.40 m·N (b) 2.5 m·N (c) 3.0 m·N (d) 7.0 m·N (e) 10 m·N

5. A wheel of radius 0.20 m rolls without slipping. If the wheel rotates through 3.0 revolutions, how far does it roll?

(a) 0.60 m (b) 1.2 m (c) 1.9 m (d) 3.8 m (e) 7.6 m

6. The rotational analog of mass in linear motion is

(a) moment of inertia. (b) kinetic energy. (c) moment arm. (d) work. (e) torque.

7. A sphere of mass 10 kg and radius 0.010 m is released from the top of a 1.0-meter high inclined plane. What is the speed of the sphere when it reaches the bottom of the inclined plane?

(a) 3.7 m/s (b) 4.4 m/s (c) 5.6 m/s (d) 6.3 m/s (e) 7.2 m/s

8. If the net torque on a rigid object is zero, that object will

(a) rotate with a constant angular velocity.
(b) rotate with a constant angular acceleration.
(c) not rotate.
(d) either (a) or (b).
(e) either (a) or (c).

9. A 4.00-meter long rod is hinged at one end. The rod is initially held in the horizontal position, and then released as the free end is allowed to fall. What is the angular acceleration as it is released? (The moment of inertia of a rod about one end is $ML^2/3$.)

(a) 2.45 rad/s^2 (b) 3.68 rad/s^2 (c) 4.90 rad/s^2 (d) 6.75 rad/s^2 (e) 7.35 rad/s^2

10. A 500-newton person stands on a uniform board of weight 100 N and length 8.0 m. The board is supported at each end. If the support force at the right end is three times that at the left end, how far from the right end is the person?

(a) 4.0 m (b) 2.0 m (c) 1.6 m (d) 1.2 m (e) 6.4 m

Answers to Practice Quiz:

1. c 2. c 3. b 4. e 5. d 6. a 7. a 8. e 9. b 10. c

CHAPTER 9

Solids and Fluids

I. Chapter Objectives

Upon completion of this chapter, you should be able to:

1. distinguish between stress and strain, and use elastic moduli to compute dimensional changes.
2. explain the pressure-depth relationship and state Pascal's principle and describe how it is used in practical applications.
3. relate the buoyant force and Archimedes' principle and tell whether an object will float in a fluid based on relative densities.
4. identify the simplifications used in describing ideal fluid flow and use the continuity equation and Bernoulli's equation to explain common effects.

*5. describe the source of surface tension and its effect and discuss fluid viscosity.

II. Key Terms

Upon completion of this chapter, you should be able to define and/or explain the following key terms:

fluid
stress
strain
elastic modulus
elastic limit
Young's modulus
shear modulus
bulk modulus
compressibility
pressure
pascal (Pa)
atmosphere (atm)
Pascal's principle
absolute pressure
gauge pressure
buoyant force
Archimedes' principle
specific gravity
ideal fluid
streamlines
equations of continuity
flow rate equation
Bernoulli's equation
***surface tension**
***viscosity**
***Poiseuille's law**

The definitions and/or explanations of the most important key terms can be found in the following section: **III. Chapter Summary and Discussion**.

III. Chapter Summary and Discussion

1. Solids and Elastic Moduli (Section 9.1)

All materials are elastic to some degree and can be deformed. **Stress** is the quantity that describes the force causing the deformation and **strain** is a relative measure of how much deformation a given stress produces. Quantitatively, stress is the applied force per unit cross-sectional area, and strain is the ratio of the change in dimensions to the original dimensions.

$$\text{Stress} = \frac{F}{A}, \quad \text{tensile strain (in length)} = \frac{\Delta L}{L_o}, \quad \text{shear strain (in area)} = \frac{x}{h}, \quad \text{volume strain} = \frac{\Delta V}{V_o}.$$

In general, stress is proportional to strain up to the elastic limit. The constant of proportionality, which depends on the nature of the material, is called the **elastic modulus** and is defined as the ratio of stress to strain,

$$\text{elastic modulus} = \frac{\text{stress}}{\text{strain}}.$$

There are three types of elastic moduli, the Young's modulus Y, the shear modulus S, and the bulk modulus B. $Y = \dfrac{F/A}{\Delta L/L_o}$, $S = \dfrac{F/A}{x/h} \approx \dfrac{F/A}{\phi}$, $B = \dfrac{F/A}{-\Delta V/V_o} = -\dfrac{\Delta p}{\Delta V/V_o}$. The SI units of moduli are N/m^2 or pascal (Pa). The compressibility is the inverse of the bulk modulus, $k = \dfrac{1}{B}$.

Example 9.1 A steel wire 2.0 m in length and 2.0 mm in diameter supports a 10-kilogram mass.
(a) What is the stress in the wire?
(b) What is the elongation of the wire?

Solution: Given: $F = w = mg = (10 \text{ kg})(9.80 \text{ m/s}^2) = 98 \text{ N}$, $L_o = 2.0 \text{ m}$,
$r = d/2 = 1.0 \text{ mm} = 1.0 \times 10^{-3} \text{ m}$, $Y = 20 \times 10^{10} \text{ N/m}^2$ (from Table 9.1)

Find: (a) stress = F/A (b) ΔL.

(a) $\text{stress} = \dfrac{F}{A} = \dfrac{F}{\pi r^2} = \dfrac{98 \text{ N}}{\pi(1.0\times10^{-3} \text{ m})^2} = 3.1 \times 10^7 \text{ N/m}^2.$

(b) From the definition of Young's modulus, $Y = \dfrac{F/A}{\Delta L/L_o} = \dfrac{L_o F/A}{\Delta L}$,

we have $\Delta L = \dfrac{L_o F/A}{Y} = \dfrac{(2.0 \text{ m})(3.1 \times 10^7 \text{ N/m}^2)}{(20 \times 10^{10} \text{ N/m}^2)} = 3.1 \times 10^{-4} \text{ m} = 0.31 \text{ mm}.$

Example 9.2 A shear force of 2.0×10^3 N is applied to one face of an aluminum cube with sides of 15 cm. What is the resulting relative displacement?

Solution: Given: $F = 2.0 \times 10^3$ N, $h = 0.15$ m, $S = 2.5 \times 10^{10}$ N/m² (from Table 9.1)

Find: x.

The area of a side is $A = h^2$. From $S = \dfrac{F/A}{x/h}$,

We have $x = \dfrac{F/A}{S/h} = \dfrac{Fh}{AS} = \dfrac{Fh}{h^2 S} = \dfrac{F}{hS} = \dfrac{2.0 \times 10^3 \text{ N}}{(0.15 \text{ m})(2.5 \times 10^{10} \text{ N/m}^2)} = 5.3 \times 10^{-7}$ m.

2. Fluids: Pressure and Pascal's Principle (Section 9.2)

A **fluid** is a substance that flows and cannot support a shear. Both liquids and gases are fluids. **Pressure** is defined as the force per unit area, $P = \dfrac{F}{A}$, and has units of N/m² or pascal (Pa).

Absolute pressure on an object submerged at a depth h below the surface of a fluid is given by the **pressure-depth equation,** $p = p_o + \rho g h$, where p_o is the pressure on the fluid surface and ρ is the density of the fluid. When this equation is applied to fluid on the surface of the Earth, $p_o = p_a = 1.01 \times 10^5$ Pa, where p_a is called the atmospheric pressure and is measured with a barometer. **Gauge pressure** (static pressure) is the difference between the absolute pressure and the atmospheric pressure, i.e., $p_{gauge} = p - p_a = \rho g h$. When a gauge is used to measure pressure, it measures the gauge pressure.

Pascal's principle states that any external pressure applied to an *enclosed* fluid is transmitted undiminished to every point in the fluid and to the walls of its container.

Hydraulic press and lift are good practical applications of this principle. In a press or lift, there are usually two pistons, one with a larger area than the other. If a small force, F_1, is applied to the smaller piston of cross sectional area A_1, the external pressure is then $p_1 = \dfrac{F_1}{A_1}$. According to Pascal's principle, this pressure will be transmitted to the larger piston of cross sectional area A_2, and $p_2 = p_1$ or $\dfrac{F_2}{A_2} = \dfrac{F_1}{A_1}$. Since $A_2 > A_1$, $F_2 > F_1$.

Example 9.3 (a) What is the absolute pressure at a location 5.00 m below the surface of a lake?

(b) What is the gauge pressure there?

Solution: Given: $p_o = p_a = 1.01 \times 10^5$ Pa, $h = 5.00$ m, $\rho = 1.00 \times 10^3$ kg/m^3 (water from Table 9.2)

Find: (a) p (b) $p - p_a$.

(a) $p = p_o + \rho g h = 1.01 \times 10^5 \text{ Pa} + (1.00 \times 10^3 \text{ kg/m}^3)(9.80 \text{ m/s}^2)(5.00 \text{ m}) = 1.50 \times 10^5 \text{ Pa}$.

(b) $p_{gauge} = p - p_a = 1.50 \times 10^5 \text{ Pa} - 1.01 \times 10^5 \text{ Pa} = 4.9 \times 10^4 \text{ Pa}$.

Example 9.4 In a hydraulic garage lift, the small piston has a radius of 5.0 cm and the large piston has a radius of 15 cm. What force must be applied on the small piston in order to lift a car weighing 20 000 N on the large piston?

Solution: Given: $r_1 = 0.050$ m, $r_2 = 0.15$ m, $F_2 = 20\,000$ N

Find: F_1.

According to Pascal's principle, the external pressure exerted at the small piston is transmitted undiminished to the large piston. Therefore $p_1 = \frac{F_1}{A_1} = p_2 = \frac{F_2}{A_2}$.

So $F_1 = \left(\frac{A_1}{A_2}\right) F_2 = \left(\frac{\pi r_1^2}{\pi r_2^2}\right) F_2 = \left(\frac{r_1}{r_2}\right)^2 F_2 = \left(\frac{0.050}{0.15}\right)^2 (20\,000 \text{ N}) \approx 2200 \text{ N}$.

Note: What a wonderful device! The radius of the large piston is only three times the radius of the small piston, (0.15 m)/(0.050 m) = 3. However, the force required on the small piston is only 1/9 of the force on the large piston, (20 000 N)/(2200 N) = 1/9. Why?

---

3. Buoyancy and Archimedes' Principle (Section 9.3)

An object that is either partially or completely submerged in a fluid will experience an upward buoyant force exerted by the fluid. **Archimedes' principle** states that the buoyant force is equal to the weight of the fluid displaced., i.e., if an object displaces 3.0 N of fluid, it will receive a 3.0 N buoyant force. Mathematically, the principle is expressed as $F_b = w_f = m_f g = (\rho_f V_f)g = \rho_f V_f g$, where ρ_f is the density of the fluid, V_f is the volume of fluid displaced (which is the same as the volume fraction of the object submerged *in* the fluid).

Archimedes' principle is very useful in determining the volume of an object and therefore its density. That was what Archimedes allegedly used to determine that the crown of his king was not made of pure gold.

From Archimedes' principle, we can draw some simple conclusions about density and floating:

(1) An object will float in a fluid if the average density of the object is less than the density of the fluid.

(2) An object will sink in a fluid if the average density of the object is greater than the density of the fluid.

(3) An object will be in equilibrium at any submerged depth in a fluid if the average densities of the object and fluid are equal.

The **specific gravity** (sp. gr.) of a substance is the ratio of the density of the substance to the density of water, and so is a pure number (dimensionless). For example, aluminum has a density of 2700 kg/m^3 and water has a density of 1000 kg/m^3. So the sp. gr. of aluminum is simply (2700 kg/m^3)/(1000 kg/m^3) = 2.7.

Example 9.5 A boat approximating a rectangular box measures 5.0 m long, 1.0 wide and 0.50 m high. Is it safe to transport a 3000-kilogram machine part with this boat across a lake? (Neglect the mass of the boat itself.)

Solution: Given: $L = 5.0$ m, $W = 1.0$ m, $H = 0.50$ m, $\rho_{water} = 1.0 \times 10^3$ kg/m^3, $m = 3000$ kg.

Find: Will the boat float or sink.

The average density of the boat (with the machine part) is

$$\rho = \frac{m}{V} = \frac{3000\ \text{kg}}{(5.0\ \text{m})(1.0\ \text{m})(0.50\ \text{m})} = 1.2 \times 10^4\ \text{kg/m}^3 > \rho_{water} = 1.0 \times 10^4\ \text{kg/m}^3.$$

Since the average density of the boats is greater than that of water, the boat would sink. So it is not safe to transport the machine part with this boat.

Example 9.6 A bargain hunter bought a pure (24-karat) "gold" crown at a flea market. After getting it home, she suspends the crown on a scale and finds its weight to be 7.84 N. She then weighs the crown while it is immersed in water and finds that the scale reads 6.86 N. Is the crown made of pure gold? (Similar to Archimedes' problem!)

Solution: Given: $w = 7.84$ N, w (in water) = 6.86 N, $\rho_{water} = 1.0 \times 10^3$ kg/m^3.

Find: ρ.

There are many different physical quantities we can use to identify matter based on the unique physical quantities of different elements. For example, pure gold and aluminum each have their own unique density. So if we can determine the density of the crown, we can determine whether it is made of pure gold. When the crown is completely submerged in water, the volume of water displaced is equal to the volume of the crown. The "apparent" weight of the crown decreases because the buoyant force is canceling out part of the crown's weight. The difference between the true weight and the apparent weight of the crown is therefore the buoyant force, $F_B = 7.84\ \text{N} - 6.86\ \text{N} = 0.98$ N.

We first find the volume of the crown with Archimedes' principle.

From $F_b = \rho_f V_f g$, we have $V_f = \dfrac{F_b}{\rho_f g} = \dfrac{0.98\ \text{N}}{(1.0 \times 10^3\ \text{kg/m}^3)(9.80\ \text{m/s}^2)} = 1.00 \times 10^{-4}\ \text{m}^3.$

Now we can find the density of the crown.

$$\rho = \frac{m}{V} = \frac{w/g}{V} = \frac{w}{gV} = \frac{7.84 \text{ N}}{(9.80 \text{ m/s}^2)(1.00 \times 10^{-4} \text{ m}^3)} = 8.0 \times 10^3 \text{ kg/m}^3.$$

From Table 9.2, this crown is not made of pure gold because the density of gold is 19.3×10^3 kg/m^3.

---

4. Fluid Dynamics and Bernoulli's Equation (Section 9.4)

Ideal fluid flow is a steady, irrotational, nonviscous, and incompressible flow. From the conservation of mass, the **equation of continuity** for fluid flow can be derived: ρAv = constant, where ρ is the density of the fluid, A is the cross-sectional area, and v is the speed. If the fluid is incompressible (ρ = constant), then Av = constant, or $A_1 v_1 = A_2 v_2$, which is called the **flow rate equation**, since the quantity, Av, measures flow rate (volume per unit time).

Bernoulli's equation is the direct result of the application of conservation of energy to fluid. It is written as $p + \frac{1}{2}\rho v^2 + \rho g y$ = constant. If the flow is at a constant height, y = constant, then $p + \frac{1}{2}\rho v^2$ = constant. In verbal statement, this is "the higher the speed, the lower the pressure, or vice versa." Since speed is related to kinetic energy and pressure is associated with fluid height and so potential energy, Bernoulli's equation simply restates that kinetic energy plus potential energy is a constant. This equation is very successful in explaining physical phenomena such as the curve ball in a baseball game.

Example 9.7 An ideal fluid flows at 4.0 m/s in a horizontal circular pipe. If the pipe narrows to half of its original radius, what is the flow speed in narrow section?

Solution: Given: v_1 = 12 m/s, $r_2 = r_1/2$

Find: v_2.

From the flow rate equation, $A_1 v_1 = A_2 v_2$, we have

$$v_2 = \frac{A_1 v_1}{A_2} = \frac{\pi r_1^2 v_1}{\pi r_2^2} = \frac{r_1^2 v_1}{(r_1/2)^2} = \frac{v_1}{1/4} = 4\,v_1 = 4(4.0 \text{ m/s}) = 16 \text{ m/s}.$$

Note: The pipe narrows to half of its original radius and the speed increases by a factor of 4. Why?

Example 9.8 In Example 9.7, if the fluid is water and the pressure at the narrow section is 1.8×10^5 Pa, what is the pressure at the wide section?

Solution: Given: $\rho = 1.0 \times 10^3$ kg/m^3, $p_2 = 1.8 \times 10^5$ Pa, $v_1 = 4.0$ m/s, $v_2 = 16$ m/s (Example 9.7).

Find: p_1.

Since the fluid is flowing horizontally, y is constant, so Bernoulli's equation can be written as

$p_1 + \frac{1}{2}\rho v_1^2 = p_2 + \frac{1}{2}\rho v_2^2$.

So $p_1 = p_2 + \frac{1}{2}\rho(v_2^2 - v_1^2) = 1.8 \times 10^5 \text{ Pa} + \frac{1}{2}(1.0 \times 10^3 \text{ kg/m}^3)[(16 \text{ m/s})^2 - (4.0 \text{ m/s})^2] = 3.0 \times 10^5$ Pa.

Note: the speed is lower but the pressure is higher in the wide section.

---

*5. Surface Tension; Viscosity and Poiseuille's Law (Section 9.5)

The **surface tension** of a liquid is caused by the inward pull on the surface molecules which causes the surface of the liquid to contract and be stretched. **Coefficient of viscosity** (or **viscosity**), η, is a measure of the fluid's internal resistance to flow.

The average **flow rate**, $Q = Av$ (volume/time, m^3/s), depends on the characteristics of the fluid and the pipe as well as on the pressure difference between the ends of the pipe. **Poiseuille's law** gives a relationship for the flow rate: $Q = \dfrac{\pi r^4 \Delta p}{8\eta L}$, where r is the radius of the pipe, L its length, Δp the pressure difference between the ends of the pipe, and η the viscosity of the fluid. An interesting result is that the flow rate is proportional to r^4, that is, doubling the radius of a pipe can increase the flow rate by 2^4 =- 16 times.

IV. Mathematical Summary

Stress	$\text{stress} = \dfrac{F}{A}$ (9.1)	Defines stress.
Strain (tensile)	$\text{strain} = \dfrac{\Delta L}{L_o} = \dfrac{L - L_o}{L_o}$ (9.2)	Defines tensile strain.
Young's Modulus	$Y = \dfrac{F/A}{\Delta L/L_o}$ (9.4)	Relates Young's modulus with stress and strain.
Shear Modulus	$S = \dfrac{F/A}{x/h} \approx \dfrac{F/A}{\phi}$ (9.5)	Relates shear modulus with stress and shear strain.
Bulk Modulus	$B = \dfrac{F/A}{-\Delta V/V_o} = -\dfrac{\Delta p}{\Delta V/V_o}$ (9.6)	Relates bulk modulus with stress and volume strain.
Compressibility	$k = \dfrac{1}{B}$ (9.7)	Defines compressibility.

Pressure	$p = \frac{F}{A}$ (9.8a)	Defines pressure in terms of force and area.
Pressure-Depth Equation	$p = p_o + \rho g h$ (9.10)	Expresses pressure as a function of depth in fluid.
Archimedes' Principle	$F_b = m_f g = \rho_f g V_f$ (9.14)	Calculates buoyant force.
Equation of Continuity	$\rho_1 A_1 v_1 = \rho_2 A_2 v_2$ or $\rho A v = \text{constant}$ (9.16)	Relates flow characteristics for ideal fluid.
Flow Rate Equation	$A_1 v_1 = A_2 v_2$ or $Av = \text{constant}$ (9.17)	Rewrites equation of continuity for an incompressible fluid.
Bernoulli's Equation	$p_1 + \frac{1}{2}\rho v_1^2 + \rho g y_1 = p_2 + \frac{1}{2}\rho v_2^2 + \rho g y_2$ (9.18)	Applies the conservation of energy to a fluid.
*Poiseuille's Law	$Q = \frac{\pi r^4 \Delta p}{8\eta L}$ (9.19)	Relates the flow rate to fluid characteristics.

V. Solutions of Selected Exercises and Paired/Trio Exercises

9. $\text{Stress} = \frac{F}{A} = \frac{mg}{\pi r^2} = \frac{(6.0\text{ kg})(9.80\text{ m/s}^2)}{\pi(0.50 \times 10^{-3}\text{ m})^2} = 7.49 \times 10^7\text{ N/m}^2,$

$\text{strain} = \frac{\Delta L}{L_o} = \frac{1.4 \times 10^{-3}\text{ m}}{2.0\text{ m}} = 7.0 \times 10^{-4}.$

So the Young's modulus is $Y = \frac{\text{stress}}{\text{strain}} = \frac{7.49 \times 10^7\text{ N/m}^2}{7.0 \times 10^{-4}} = \boxed{1.1 \times 10^{11}\text{ N/m}^2}$.

10. From $Y = \frac{F/A}{\Delta L/L_o} = \frac{FL_o}{A\Delta L}$, we have

$\Delta L = \frac{FL_o}{YA} = \frac{(5.0\text{ kg})(9.80\text{ m/s}^2)(2.0\text{ m})}{(7.0 \times 10^{10}\text{ N/m}^2)(\pi)(1.0 \times 10^{-3}\text{ m})^2} = 4.5 \times 10^{-4}\text{ m} = \boxed{0.45\text{ mm}}$.

15. The shear strain is given by

$\phi = \frac{\text{shear stress}}{S} = \frac{F/A}{S} = \frac{F}{SA} = \frac{500\text{ N}}{(2.5 \times 10^{10}\text{ N/m}^2)(0.10\text{ m})^2} = 2.0 \times 10^{-6}$

Also $\phi = \frac{x}{h}$, so $x = (2.0 \times 10^{-6})(0.10\text{ m}) = \boxed{2.0 \times 10^{-7}\text{ m}}$.

19. (a) Since the bulk modulus is $B = -\dfrac{\Delta p}{\Delta V/V_o}$, the smaller the B, the greater the compressibility.

So $\boxed{\text{ethyl alcohol}}$ has the greatest compressibility.

(b) $\dfrac{\Delta p_w}{\Delta p_e} = \dfrac{B_w}{B_e} = \dfrac{2.2 \times 10^9 \text{ N/m}^2}{1.0 \times 10^9 \text{ N/m}^2} = \boxed{2.2 \text{ times}}$.

21. We first need to find the tensions on the cables. The system is symmetrical.

In the vertical direction: $2T \sin 15° = mg$, so $T = \dfrac{(45 \text{ kg})(9.80 \text{ m/s}^2)}{2 \sin 15°} = 852$ N.

$$\frac{\Delta L}{L_o} = \frac{\text{stress}}{Y} = \frac{T/A}{Y} = \frac{T}{YA} = \frac{852 \text{ N}}{(20 \times 10^{10} \text{ N/m}^2)(\pi)(0.50 \times 10^{-2} \text{ m})^2} = \boxed{5.4 \times 10^{-5}}.$$

27. Bicycle tires have a much smaller contact area with the ground so they need a higher pressure to balance the weight of the bicycle and the rider.

30. (a) The pressure due to water is $p_w = \rho gh = (1000 \text{ kg/m}^3)(9.80 \text{ m/s}^2)(15 \text{ m}) = \boxed{1.5 \times 10^5 \text{ Pa}}$.

(b) The total pressure is $p = p_o + p_w = 1.01 \times 10^5 \text{ Pa} + 1.5 \times 10^5 \text{ Pa} = \boxed{2.5 \times 10^5 \text{ Pa}}$.

36. The pressure difference due to the 35 m high air is

$\Delta p = \rho gh = (1.29 \text{ kg/m}^3)(9.80 \text{ m/s}^2)(35 \text{ m}) = 442$ Pa.

So the fractional decrease is $\dfrac{\Delta p}{p_a} = \dfrac{442 \text{ Pa}}{1.013 \times 10^5 \text{ Pa}} = 4.37 \times 10^{-3} = \boxed{0.44\%}$.

42. (a) From Pascal's principle, $p_{\text{input}} = p_{\text{output}} = \dfrac{F_{\text{output}}}{A_{\text{output}}} = \dfrac{1.5 \times 10^6 \text{ N}}{0.20 \text{ m}^2} = \boxed{7.5 \times 10^6 \text{ Pa}}$.

(b) $F_{\text{input}} = P_{\text{input}} A_{\text{input}} = (7.5 \times 10^6 \text{ Pa})(\pi)(0.025 \text{ m})^2 = \boxed{1.5 \times 10^4 \text{ N}}$.

44. $\boxed{1.2 \times 10^6 \text{ Pa}}$.

49. There is no change. As the ice melts, the volume of the newly converted water decreases; however, the ice which was initially above the water surface is now under the water. This compensated for the decrease in volume. It does not matter whether the ice is hollow or not. Both can be proved mathematically.

52. The buoyant force is $F_b = \rho Vg = (1000 \text{ kg/m}^3)(0.085 \text{ m})^3(9.80 \text{ m/s}^2) = 6.02$ N.

The weight is $W = mg = (0.65 \text{ kg})(9.80 \text{ m/s}^2) = 6.37$ N.

Since $W > F_b$, $\boxed{\text{no}}$, the object sinks.

56. We first need to find the volume of the crown with Archimedes' principle.

$F_b = 8.0\text{ N} - 4.0\text{ N} = 4.0\text{ N} = \rho_f gV$,

so $V = \dfrac{F_b}{\rho_f g} = \dfrac{4.0\text{ N}}{(1000\text{ kg/m}^3)(9.80\text{ m/s}^2)} = 4.08 \times 10^{-4}\text{ m}^3$.

The density $\rho = \dfrac{m}{V} = \dfrac{w/g}{V} = \dfrac{8.0\text{ N}}{(9.80\text{ m/s}^2)(4.08 \times 10^{-4}\text{ m}^3)} = \boxed{2.0 \times 10^3\text{ kg/m}^3}$.

58. $\boxed{1.50 \times 10^{-5}\text{ m}^3}$ and $\boxed{6.00 \times 10^3\text{ kg/m}^3}$.

60. For the open cube to float, $w = mg = F_b = \rho_f gV_f = \rho_f gL^3$, where V_f is the volume of the open cube.

So $L = \sqrt[3]{\dfrac{m}{\rho_f}} = \sqrt[3]{\dfrac{\rho V}{\rho_f}} = \sqrt[3]{\dfrac{(7.8\times10^3\text{ kg/m}^3)(1.0\text{ m})^3}{1000\text{ kg/m}^3}} = \boxed{2.0\text{ m}}$,

where V is the volume of the solid cube.

63. We first need to find the volume from Archimedes' principle.

The buoyant force is equal to $F_b = 9.8\text{ N} - 9.1\text{ N} = 0.7\text{ N}$.

From $F_b = \rho_f gV$, we have $V = \dfrac{F_b}{\rho_f g} = \dfrac{0.7\text{ N}}{(1000\text{ kg/m}^3)(9.80\text{ m/s}^2)} = 7.0 \times 10^{-5}\text{ m}^3$.

The density $\rho = \dfrac{m}{V} = \dfrac{w/g}{V} = \dfrac{9.8\text{ N}}{(7.0 \times 10^{-5}\text{ m}^3)(9.80\text{ m/s}^2)} = 14.3 \times 10^3\text{ kg/m}^3 < \rho_g = 19.3 \times 10^3\text{ kg/m}^3$.

$\boxed{\text{No}}$, the bar is not gold.

69. The aspirator has suction because the water flowing by decreases the pressure at the end of the tube away from the flask. This creates a pressure difference, and suction is created in the tube. The egg is kept aloft by the pressure of the air coming out of the end of the tube. As the egg moves to one side, there is a change in the flow speed around the egg that creates an inward pressure that makes the egg move back to midstream.

70. From the equation of continuity, $A_1 v_1 = A_2 v_2$, we have

$v_2 = \dfrac{A_1}{A_2} v_1 = \dfrac{\pi(0.20\text{ m})^2}{\pi(0.35\text{ m})^2} \times (3.0\text{ m/s}) = \boxed{0.98\text{ m/s}}$.

75. (a) We use Bernoulli's principle, $p_1 + \frac{1}{2}\rho v_1^2 + \rho g y_1 = p_2 + \frac{1}{2}\rho v_2^2 + \rho g y_2$.

Here $p_1 = p_2 = p_a$, and $v_1 \approx 0$ (at the top of the water surface),

so $v_2 = \sqrt{2g\Delta y}$.

For the 40-cm high (upper) hole, $v_u = \sqrt{2(9.80 \text{ m/s}^2)(0.05 \text{ m})} = \boxed{0.99 \text{ m/s}}$;

for the 30-cm high (middle) hole, $v_m = \sqrt{2(9.80 \text{ m/s}^2)(0.15 \text{ m})} = \boxed{1.7 \text{ m/s}}$;

for the 20-cm high (bottom) hole, $v_b = \sqrt{2(9.80 \text{ m/s}^2)(0.25 \text{ m})} = \boxed{2.2 \text{ m/s}}$;

for the 10-cm high (bottom) hole, $v_b = \sqrt{2(9.80 \text{ m/s}^2)(0.35 \text{ m})} = \boxed{2.6 \text{ m/s}}$.

(b) They are all horizontal projectile motions. First find the time of flight from the vertical motion.

$y = \frac{1}{2}gt^2$, so $t = \sqrt{\frac{2y}{g}}$. Therefore the range is $x = v_x t = v_x \sqrt{\frac{2y}{g}}$.

$$x_1 = (0.99 \text{ m/s})\sqrt{\frac{2(0.40 \text{ m})}{9.80 \text{ m/s}^2}} = 0.28 \text{ m};$$

$$x_2 = (1.7 \text{ m/s})\sqrt{\frac{2(0.30 \text{ m})}{9.80 \text{ m/s}^2}} = 0.42 \text{ m};$$

$$x_3 = (2.2 \text{ m/s})\sqrt{\frac{2(0.20 \text{ m})}{9.80 \text{ m/s}^2}} = 0.44 \text{ m};$$

$$x_4 = (2.6 \text{ m/s})\sqrt{\frac{2(0.10 \text{ m})}{9.80 \text{ m/s}^2}} = 0.37 \text{ m}.$$

Hence the $\boxed{\text{20-centimeter hole}}$ has the greatest range.

83. From Poiseuille's law, $Q = \frac{\pi r^4 \Delta p}{8\eta L}$, we have

$$\Delta p = \frac{8\eta L Q}{\pi r^4} = \frac{8(1.00 \times 10^{-3} \text{ Pl})(6.0 \text{ m})(40 \text{ L/min})(10^{-3} \text{ m}^3\text{/L})(1 \text{ min/60 s})}{\pi\,(0.015 \text{ m})^4} = \boxed{2.0 \times 10^2 \text{ Pa}}.$$

87. (a) The weight of the wood must be equal to the buoyant force.

$w = mg = F_b = \rho_f V g$, so $V = \frac{m}{\rho_f} = \frac{\rho V}{\rho_f} = \frac{(700 \text{ kg/m}^3)(0.30 \text{ m})^3}{1000 \text{ kg/m}^3} = 0.0189 \text{ m}^3$.

Therefore the distance from the top of the wood to the water surface is

$$0.30 \text{ m} - \frac{0.0189 \text{ m}^3}{(0.30 \text{ m})(0.30 \text{ m})} = \boxed{0.09 \text{ m}}.$$

(b) The 0.09 m above the water surface can support the mass on top of the wood.

The mass is $\frac{(1000 \text{ kg/m}^3)(0.30 \text{ m})^2(0.09 \text{ m})g}{g} = \boxed{8.1 \text{ kg}}$.

91. The pressure by the oil is equal to the pressure by mercury.

$p_o = \rho_o g h_o = \rho_m g h_m$, so $\rho_o = \frac{\rho_m h_m}{h_o} = \frac{(13.6 \times 10^3 \text{ kg/m}^3)(5.0 \text{ cm})}{80 \text{ cm}} = \boxed{8.5 \times 10^2 \text{ kg/m}^3}$.

99. (a) When it is in the water, the force applied is

$$F = mg - F_b = \rho V g - \rho_f g V$$

$$= (\rho - \rho_f)gV = (7.8 \times 10^3 \text{ kg/m}^3 - 1.0 \times 10^3 \text{ kg/m}^3)(9.80 \text{ m/s}^2)(0.25 \text{ m})(0.20 \text{ m})(10 \text{ m})$$

$$= \boxed{3.3 \times 10^4 \text{ N}}.$$

(b) When it is out of water, the force applied is

$$F = mg = \rho V g = (7.8 \times 10^3 \text{ kg/m}^3)(9.80 \text{ m/s}^2)(0.25 \text{ m})(0.20 \text{ m})(10 \text{ m}) = \boxed{3.8 \times 10^4 \text{ N}}.$$

VI. Practice Quiz

1. What is the gauge pressure at the bottom of a 5.0-meter deep swimming pool?

(a) 4.9×10^4 Pa (b) 7.2×10^4 Pa (c) 1.01×10^5 Pa (d) 1.5×10^5 Pa (e) 2.51×10^5 Pa

2. A 4.00-kilogram cylinder made of solid iron is supported by a string while submerged in water. What is the tension in the string? (The density of iron is 7.86×10^3 kg/m^3.)

(a) 0 N (b) 2.50 N (c) 19.6 N (d) 23.7 N (e) 34.2 N

3. When you turn on a shower head quickly, you notice that the shower curtain moves inward. This is because

(a) the air inside the curtain moves faster and the pressure is higher.

(b) the air inside the curtain moves faster and the pressure is lower.

(c) the air inside the curtain moves slower and the pressure is lower.

(d) the air inside the curtain moves slower and the pressure is higher.

(e) none of the above applies.

4. An ideal fluid flows through a pipe made of two sections with diameters of 2.0 and 6.0 cm, respectively. What is the speed ratio of the flow through the 2.0 cm section to that through the 6.0 cm section?

(a) 1/9 (b) 1/3 (c) 1 (d) 3 (e) 9

5. A 25 000-newton truck on a hydraulic lift rests on a cylinder with a piston of diameter 0.40 m. What is the pressure applied to the liquid in order to lift the car?

(a) 2.0×10^4 N/m^2 (b) 4.0×10^4 N/m^2 (c) 5.0×10^4 N/m^2 (d) 1.6×10^5 N/m^2 (e) 2.0×10^5 N/m^2

6. Which of the following is associated with the law of conservation of energy for fluids?

(a) Archimedes' principle (b) Bernoulli's principle (c) Pascal's principle

(d) Poiseuille's law (e) equation of continuity

7. The same object is hung from identical wires made of aluminum, brass, copper, and steel. Which wire will stretch the least?

(a) aluminum (b) brass (c) copper (d) steel (e) all the same.

8. Water flows with a speed of 8.0 m/s in a horizontal pipe 2.0 cm in diameter. The water then enters a horizontal pipe 4.0 cm in diameter. What is the difference in pressure between the two segments?

(a) 1.0×10^4 N/m^2 (b) 2.0×10^4 N/m^2 (c) 3.0×10^4 N/m^2 (d) 4.0×10^4 N/m^2 (e) 5.0×10^4 N/m^2

9. In a gasoline spill, a gasoline layer of 0.50 cm thick was found above a surface. Estimate the gauge pressure of the gasoline.

(a) 0.33 N/m^2 (b) 3.3 N/m^2 (c) 33 N/m^2 (d) 3.3×10^2 N/m^2 (e) 3.3×10^3 N/m^2

10. If the density of gold is 19.3×10^3 kg/m^3, what buoyant force does a 0.60-kilogram gold crown experience when it is immersed in water?

(a) 3.0×10^{-5} N (b) 3.0×10^{-4} N (c) 3.0×10^{-2} N (d) 0.30 N (e) 3.0 N

Answers to Practice Quiz:

1. a 2. e 3. b 4. e 5. e 6. b 7. d 8. c 9. c 10. d

CHAPTER 10

Temperature

I. Chapter Objectives

Upon completion of this chapter, you should be able to:

1. distinguish between temperature and heat.
2. explain how a temperature scale is constructed and convert temperatures from one scale to another.
3. describe the ideal gas law and explain how it is used to determine absolute zero.
4. calculate the thermal expansions of solids and liquids.
5. relate kinetic theory and temperature and explain the process of diffusion.

*6. understand the difference between monatomic and diatomic gases, the meaning of the equipartition theorem, and the expression for the internal energy of a diatomic gas.

II. Key Terms

Upon completion of this chapter, you should be able to define and/or explain the following key terms:

temperature
heat
internal energy
thermometer
thermal expansion
Fahrenheit temperature scale
Celsius temperature scale
ideal (perfect) gas law
mole
Avogadro's number
absolute zero
Kelvin temperature scale
kelvin
triple point of water
thermal coefficient of linear expansion
thermal coefficient of area expansion
thermal coefficient of volume expansion
kinetic theory of gases
diffusion
osmosis
***degree of freedom**
***equipartition theorem**

The definitions and/or explanations of the most important key terms can be found in the following section: **III. Chapter Summary and Discussion**.

III. Chapter Summary and Discussion

1. Temperature and Heat (Section 10.1)

Temperature is a relative measure, or indication, of hotness and coldness. The result of the kinetic theory of gases states that temperature is a measure of the average kinetic energy of the molecules.

Heat is the net energy transferred from one object to another because of a temperature difference. The total energy (kinetic plus potential) of all molecules of a body or system is the **internal energy**. When heat is transferred out of or into a system while there is no other physical process present, the internal energy of the system will change.

When heat is transferred between two objects, whether or not they are physically touching, they are said to be in **thermal contact**. When there is no longer a net heat transfer between objects in thermal contact, they are at the same temperature and are said to be in **thermal equilibrium**.

2. The Celsius and Fahrenheit Temperature Scales (Section 10.2)

The two most common temperature scales are the **Celsius temperature scale** and the **Fahrenheit temperature scale**. On the Celsius scale, water freezes at 0°C and boils at 100°C; while on the Fahrenheit scale, water freezes at 32°F and boils at 212°F. The conversions between the two scales are

$T_F = \frac{9}{5} T_C + 32$, or $T_C = \frac{5}{9}(T_F - 32)$.

Note: To convert T_C to T_F, you need to multiply by $\frac{9}{5}$ and then add 32. However, to convert T_F to T_C, you need to subtract 32 and then multiply by $\frac{5}{9}$.

Example 10.1 What is the temperature 50.0°F on the Celsius scale?

Solution: Given: $T_F = 50.0$°F. Find: T_C.

$T_C = \frac{5}{9}(T_F - 32) = \frac{5}{9}(50 - 32) = 10$°C.

Example 10.2 The temperature changes from 35°F during the night to 75°F during the day. What is the temperature change on the Celsius scale?

Solution: Given: $\Delta T_F = 75°F - 35°F = 40$ F°. [Note: the unit for Fahrenheit temperature change is F° (Fahrenheit degree), not °F (degrees Fahrenheit).]

Find: ΔT_C.

Although we can convert both 35°F and 75°F to their Celsius temperatures and then calculate the change, we can take advantage of the conversion equations to calculate the temperature change ΔT.

From $T_C = \frac{5}{9}(T_F - 32)$, we can see that for every Fahrenheit degree increase, the Celsius temperature increases by $\frac{5}{9}$ of a degree, or $\Delta T_C = \frac{5}{9}\Delta T_F$.

So $\Delta T_C = \frac{5}{9}\Delta T_F = \frac{5}{9}(40) = 22$ C°. (Note: the unit for Celsius temperature change is C°, not °C.)

---

3. Gas Law and Absolute Temperature (Section 10.3)

An ideal gas is a low density and low pressure gas. The **ideal** (or perfect) **gas law** relates the pressure, volume and the temperature of the gas, $pV = Nk_B T$, where N is the number of molecules and k_B is the Boltzmann's constant which has a value of 1.38×10^{-23} J/K. It describes real, low-density gases fairly well. Two other forms of the ideal gas law are $pV = nRT$ (macroscopic form) and $\frac{p_1 V_1}{T_1} = \frac{p_2 V_2}{T_2}$, where n is the number of moles of molecules and R is the universal gas constant which has values of 8.31 J/(mol·K). One mole of substance is defined as containing $N_A = 6.02 \times 10^{23}$ molecules (Avogadro's number).

A gas can be used to measure temperature as a function of time at a constant volume. Extrapolation to zero pressure defines absolute zero temperature. **Absolute zero** is the foundation for the **Kelvin temperature scale**, which uses absolute zero and the **triple point of water** as fixed points. The conversion between Kelvin and Celsius temperatures is $T_K = T_C + 273.15$, or more commonly to three significant figures, $T_K = T_C + 273$.

Note: The temperature in the ideal gas law *must* be the Kelvin temperature.

Example 10.3 What is −40°F on the Kelvin scale?

Solution: Given: $T_F = -40°C$. Find: T_K.

Since there is no direct conversion given between Fahrenheit and Kelvin temperatures, we first convert Fahrenheit to Celsius.

$T_C = \frac{5}{9}(T_F - 32) = \frac{5}{9}(-40 - 32) = \frac{5}{9}(-72) = -40°C$.

(Wow! The Celsius and Fahrenheit have the same nominal reading at this temperature.)

Next, $T_K = T_C + 273 = -40 + 273 = 233$ K.

Example 10.4 A gas has a volume of 0.20 m^3, a temperature of 30°C, and a pressure of 1.0 atm (one atmosphere of pressure). It is heated to 60°C and compressed to a volume of 0.15 m^3. Find the new pressure in atmospheres.

Solution: Given: $T_1 = 30°C$, $T_2 = 60°C$,

$V_1 = 0.20 \text{ m}^3$, $V_2 = 0.15 \text{ m}^2$,

$p_1 = 1.0$ atm.

Find: p_2 (in atm).

The temperatures are given on the Celsius scale, so we first convert them to Kelvin temperatures.

$T_1 = 30°C = 30 + 273 = 303$ K and $T_2 = 60°C = 60 + 273 = 333$ K.

From $\frac{p_1 V_1}{T_1} = \frac{p_2 V_2}{T_2}$, we have $p_2 = \frac{V_1}{V_2} \times \frac{T_2}{T_1} \times p_1 = \frac{0.20 \text{ m}^3}{0.15 \text{ m}^2} \times \frac{333 \text{ K}}{303 \text{ K}} \times (1.0 \text{ atm}) = 1.5$ atm.

Note: Leaving the pressure in units of atm gives the new pressure in atm because of the ratio form of the ideal gas law. Also, the temperatures used in the ideal gas law *must* be the Kelvin temperatures. What would happen if you used a temperature of $T_1 = 0°C$ in the example?

Example 10.5 An ideal gas in a container of volume of 1000 cm^3 (one liter) at 20.0°C has a pressure of 1.00×10^4 N/m^2. Determine the number of gas molecules and the number of moles of gas in the container.

Solution: Given: $V = 1000 \text{ cm}^3$, $T = 20.0°C$, $p = 1.00 \times 10^4 \text{ N/m}^2$.

Find: N and n.

The volume is not given in m^3 (the standard SI unit), so we first need to convert the volume to m^3 and temperature to Kelvin. Although 1 m = 100 cm, 1 m^3 ≠ 100 cm^3.

Actually $1 \text{ m}^3 = (1 \text{ m})^3 = (100 \text{ cm})^3 = 10^6 \text{ cm}^3$.

$V = (1000 \text{ cm}^3) \times \frac{1 \text{ m}^3}{10^6 \text{ cm}^3} = 1.00 \times 10^{-3} \text{ m}^3$.

$T = T_C + 273 = 20.0 + 273 = 293$ K.

From $pV = Nk_B T$, $N = \frac{pV}{k_B T} = \frac{(1.00 \times 10^4 \text{ N/m}^2)(1.00 \times 10^{-3} \text{ m}^3)}{(1.38 \times 10^{-23} \text{ J/K})(293 \text{ K})} = 2.47 \times 10^{21}$ molecules.

$n = \frac{N}{N_A} = \frac{2.47 \times 10^{21} \text{ molecules}}{6.02 \times 10^{23} \text{ molecues/mol}} = 4.10 \times 10^{-3}$ mol.

4. Thermal Expansion (Section 10.4)

The **thermal expansion** of a material is characterized by its coefficient of expansion. For solids, the **thermal coefficient of linear expansion,** α, applies to one-dimensional length changes; the **thermal coefficient of area expansion** (approximately equal to 2α) applies to two-dimensional area changes; and the **thermal coefficient of volume expansion** (approximately equal to 3α) applies to three-dimensional volume changes. For fluids with no definite shape, only volume expansion is applicable and a special thermal coefficient of volume expansion β is used. The equations we use to calculate the thermal expansions are:

Linear: $\dfrac{\Delta L}{L_o} = \alpha\Delta T.$ Area: $\dfrac{\Delta A}{A_o} = 2\alpha\Delta T.$

Volume: $\dfrac{\Delta V}{V_o} = 3\alpha\Delta T$ (for solids) Volume: $\dfrac{\Delta V}{V_o} = \beta\Delta T$ (for fluids).

Example 10.6 You are installing some outdoor copper electric wire to a backyard fish pond on a hot 40°C summer day. The temperature could be as low as –20°C in your area during a cold winter night. How much extra wire (minimum) do you have to include to allow for thermal expansion if the distance from the electric service to the pond is 100 m?

Solution: Given: $L_o = 100$ m, $T_i = 40°C$, $T_F = -20°C$, $\alpha = 17 \times 10^{-6}$ /C° (from Table 10.1).

Find: ΔL.

If you cut the wire exactly 100 m in the summer, then it shrinks to a length smaller than 100 m in the winter and the wire will snap. So we want to make sure that the wire is at least 100 m long during the winter and calculate the corresponding length in the summer.

$\Delta T = T_f - T_i = -20°C - (40°C) = -60$ C°.

From $\dfrac{\Delta L}{L_o} = \alpha\Delta T$, we have $\Delta L = \alpha\Delta T L_o = (17\times 10^{-6}\ /C°)(-60\ C°)(100\ m) = -0.10$ m.

Here the negative sign simply means that is a compression (negative expansion).

Example 10.7 A 500-milliliter glass beaker of water is filled to the rim at a temperature of 0°C. How much water will overflow if the water is heated to a temperature of 95°C? (Ignore the expansion of the beaker, why?)

Solution: Given: $V_o = 500$ mL, $T_i = 0°C$, $T_f = 95°C$, $\beta = 2.1 \times 10^{-4}$ /C° (from Table 10.1).

Find: ΔV.

$\Delta T = T_f - T_i = 95°C - 0°C = 95$ C°.

The amount of water that overflows is simply equal to the change in volume of the water.

From $\frac{\Delta V}{V_o} = \beta \Delta T$, we have $\Delta V = \beta \Delta T V_o = (2.1 \times 10^{-4}\ /\text{C°})(95\ \text{C°})(500\ \text{mL}) = 10\ \text{mL}$.

Note: In this Example, we can ignore the expansion of the beaker because glass has a much smaller coefficient of volume expansion (approximately 10×10^{-6} /C°).

---

5. The Kinetic Theory of Gases (Section 10.5)

The **kinetic theory of gases** uses statistical methods to derive the ideal gas law from mechanical principles. Some of the important conclusions of this theory are:

(1) Temperature is a measure of the average kinetic energy of the molecules, $\frac{1}{2} m v_{rms}^2 = \frac{3}{2} k_B T$, where v_{rms} is the root-mean-square speed of the molecules and m is the mass of the molecule.

(2) The ideal gas law can be expressed in terms of the root-mean-square speed of the molecules, $pV = \frac{1}{3} N m v_{rms}^2$.

(3) The total internal energy of an ideal monatomic gas is given by $U = \frac{3}{2} N k_B T = \frac{3}{2} nRT$.

Diffusion is a process of random molecular mixing in which particular molecules move from a region of higher concentration to one of lower concentration. **Osmosis** is the diffusion of a liquid across a permeable membrane because of a concentration gradient (difference).

Example 10.8 Calculate the rms (root–mean–square) speed of a hydrogen molecule and an oxygen molecule at a temperature of 300 K. (The masses of hydrogen and oxygen molecules are 3.3×10^{-27} kg and 5.3×10^{-26} kg, respectively.)

Solution: Given: $T = 300$ K, $m_H = 3.3 \times 10^{-27}$ kg, $m_O = 5.3 \times 10^{-26}$ kg.

Find: v_{rms} for H_2 and O_2.

From $\frac{1}{2} m v_{rms}^2 = \frac{3}{2} k_B T$, we have $v_{rms} = \sqrt{\frac{3 k_B T}{m}}$.

For H_2: $v_{rms} = \sqrt{\frac{3(1.38 \times 10^{-23}\ \text{J/K})(300\ \text{K})}{3.3 \times 10^{-27}\ \text{kg}}} = 1.9 \times 10^3$ m/s (about 4000 mi/h).

For O_2: $v_{rms} = \sqrt{\frac{3(1.38 \times 10^{-23}\ \text{J/K})(300\ \text{K})}{5.3 \times 10^{-26}\ \text{kg}}} = 4.8 \times 10^2$ m/s.

Why does more massive molecule gas gave smaller v_{rms}?

Example 10.9 If the temperature of a gas increases from 20°C to 40°C, by what factor does the rms (root–mean–square) speed increases?

Solution: Given: $T_1 = 20°\text{C} = 20 + 273 = 293 \text{ K}$, $T_2 = 40°\text{C} = 40 + 273 = 313 \text{ K}$.
(The temperatures *must* be in Kelvins!)

Find: $\dfrac{(v_{\text{rms}})_2}{(v_{\text{rms}})_1}$.

From $\frac{1}{2} m v_{\text{rms}}^2 = \frac{3}{2} k_B T$, we have $v_{\text{rms}} = \sqrt{\dfrac{3k_B T}{m}}$.

So $\dfrac{(v_{\text{rms}})_2}{(v_{\text{rms}})_1} = \sqrt{\dfrac{T_2}{T_1}} = \sqrt{\dfrac{313 \text{ K}}{293 \text{ K}}} = 1.03$, or it increases by only 3%.

Note: Since k_B and m are constant, they are divided out in the ratio $\dfrac{(v_{\text{rms}})_2}{(v_{\text{rms}})_1}$. The Celsius temperature doubles in this Example, but the rms speed does not double (it increases by only 3%), nor does the Kelvin temperature.

*6. Kinetic Theory, Diatomic Gases, and the Equipartition Theorem

(Section 10.6)

For monatomic gases, the total internal energy, U, consists solely of translational kinetic energy because a monatomic molecule cannot rotate. However, diatomic molecules can rotate so the kinetic energy associated with these motions should also be included. The average translational kinetic energy of any molecule is always equal to $\frac{1}{2} m v_{\text{rms}}^2 = \frac{3}{2} k_B T$.

For a monatomic molecule, there are three independent ways of possessing kinetic energy: with x, y, or z linear motion. For a diatomic molecule, there are three independent ways of possessing translational kinetic energy and two independent ways of possessing rotational kinetic energy. Each independent way a molecule has for possessing energy is called a **degree of freedom**.

The **equipartition theorem** states: On average, the total internal energy (U) of an ideal gas is divided equally among each degree of freedom its molecules possess. Furthermore, each degree of freedom contributes $\frac{1}{2} N k_B T$ (or $\frac{1}{2} nRT$) to the total internal energy.

According to this theorem, a monatomic gas possesses $3(\frac{1}{2}Nk_B T) = \frac{3}{2}Nk_B T$ (or $\frac{3}{2}nRT$) of internal energy because it has three degrees of freedom, and a diatomic gas possesses $5(\frac{1}{2}Nk_B T) = \frac{5}{2}Nk_B T$ (or $\frac{5}{2}nRT$) of internal energy because it has five degrees of freedom. Among the $\frac{5}{2}Nk_B T$ for a diatomic gas, $\frac{3}{2}Nk_B T$ are from translational motion and $\frac{2}{2}Nk_B T$ are from rotational motion. (A diatomic molecule has a vibrational degree of freedom as well. However, the contribution from vibration at room temperature is negligible to total internal energy.)

IV. Mathematical Summary

Celsius—Fahrenheit Conversion	$T_F = \frac{9}{5}T_C + 32$ (10.1) $T_C = \frac{5}{9}(T_F - 32)$ (10.2)	Converts between Celsius temperature scale and Fahrenheit temperature scale.
Ideal (or perfect) Gas Law (always absolute temperature)	$pV = Nk_B T$ (10.5) or $\frac{p_1 V_1}{T_1} = \frac{p_2 V_2}{T_2}$ (10.6) or $pV = nRT$ (10.7)	Relates pressure, volume, and absolute temperature. $k_B = 1.38 \times 10^{-23}$ J/K $R = 8.31$ J/(mol·K) Avogadro's number: $N_A = 6.02 \times 10^{23}$ molecules/mole
Kelvin—Celsius Conversion	$T_K = T_C + 273.15$ (10.8) or $T_K = T_C + 273$	Converts between Celsius temperature scale and Kelvin temperature scale.
Thermal Expansion of Solids: Linear	$\frac{\Delta L}{L_o} = \alpha \Delta T$ (10.9) or $L = L_o(1 + \alpha \Delta T)$ (10.10)	Calculates the fractional change in length in terms of the coefficient of linear expansion and change in temperature.
Thermal Expansion of Solids: Area	$\frac{\Delta A}{A_o} = 2\alpha \Delta T$ (10.11) or $A = A_o(1 + 2\alpha \Delta T)$	Calculates the fractional change in area in terms of the coefficient of linear expansion and change in temperature.
Thermal Expansion of Solids: Volume	$\frac{\Delta V}{V_o} = 3\alpha \Delta T$ (10.12) or $V = V_o(1 + 3\alpha \Delta T)$	Calculates the fractional change in volume in terms of the coefficient of linear expansion and change in temperature.
Thermal Volume Expansion of Fluids	$\frac{\Delta V}{V_o} = \beta \Delta T$ (10.13)	Calculates the fractional change in volume in terms of the coefficient of volume expansion and change in temperature.
Results of Kinetic Theory of Gases	$pV = \frac{1}{3}Nmv_{rms}^2$ (10.14) $\frac{1}{2}mv_{rms}^2 = \frac{3}{2}k_B T$ (10.15) $U = \frac{3}{2}Nk_B T = \frac{3}{2}nRT$ (10.16) $U = \frac{5}{2}Nk_B T = \frac{5}{2}nRT$ (10.17)	Gives the results of the kinetic theory of gases. Relate absolute temperature to kinetic energy. For ideal monatomic gas only. For diatomic gas only.

V. Solutions of Selected Exercises and Paired/Trio Exercises

8. $T_F = \frac{9}{5} T_C + 32 = \frac{9}{5}(39.4) + 32 = \boxed{103°F}$.

10. (a) $\boxed{245°F}$ is lower. (b) $\boxed{375°F}$ is lower.

17. (a) If pressure is held constant, the volume will decrease as temperature decreases, according to the ideal gas law. So the density $\boxed{\text{increases}}$.

(b) If the volume is held constant, the density is also $\boxed{\text{constant}}$.

22. (a) $T_K = T_C + 273.15 = 0 + 273.15 = \boxed{273 \text{ K}}$. (b) $T_K = 100 + 273.15 = \boxed{373 \text{ K}}$.

(c) $T_K = 20 + 273.15 = \boxed{293 \text{ K}}$. (d) $T_K = -35 + 273.15 = \boxed{238 \text{ K}}$.

29. From $\frac{p_1 V_1}{T_1} = \frac{p_2 V_2}{T_2}$ and since $T_1 = T_2$,

we have $p_2 = \frac{V_1}{V_2} \times p_1 = \frac{0.10 \text{ m}^3}{0.12 \text{ m}^3} \times (1.4 \times 10^5 \text{ Pa}) = \boxed{1.2 \times 10^5 \text{ Pa}}$.

30. From $pV = nRT$, we have

$$V = \frac{nRT}{p} = \frac{(1 \text{ mol})[8.31 \text{ /(mol·K)}](273 \text{ K})}{1.01 \times 10^5 \text{ Pa}} = \boxed{0.0224 \text{ m}^3 = 22.4 \text{ L}}.$$

32. (a) $\boxed{2.68 \times 10^{22}}$.

(b) $\boxed{2.68 \times 10^{19}}$.

34. $T_1 = 92°\text{F} = \frac{5}{9}(92 - 32)\ °\text{C} = 33.3°\text{C} = 306.3 \text{ K}$, $T_2 = 32°\text{F} = 0°\text{C} = 273 \text{ K}$.

From $\frac{p_1 V_1}{T_1} = \frac{p_2 V_2}{T_2}$, we have

$$V_2 = \frac{p_1 V_1 T_2}{T_1 p_2} = \frac{(20.0 \text{ lb/in}^2)(0.20 \text{ m}^3)(273 \text{ K})}{(306.3 \text{ K})(14.7 \text{ lb/in}^2)} = \boxed{0.24 \text{ m}^3}.$$

Here we do not have to use pascal as the unit for pressure and can use lb/in^2 because pressure is involved in a ratio.

37. (a) The gas $\boxed{\text{expands}}$ according to ideal gas law.

(b) From $\frac{p_o V_o}{T_o} = \frac{pV}{T}$, we have $\frac{V}{V_o} = \frac{Tp_o}{T_o p} = \frac{T}{T_o} = \frac{313\text{ K}}{283\text{ K}} = 1.106$.

So the fractional change is $\frac{V - V_o}{V_o} = \frac{V}{V_o} - 1 = 0.106 = \boxed{10.6\%}$.

43. Water expands when cooled from 4°C to 2°C as it exhibits abnormal expansion between 0°C and 4°C.

48. Only the higher temperature needs to be considered because the slabs will not touch under the lower temperature $\Delta L = \alpha L_o \Delta T = (12 \times 10^{-6}\text{ C°}^{-1})(10.0\text{ m})[45°\text{C} - (20°\text{C})] = 3.0 \times 10^{-3}\text{ m} = \boxed{3.0\text{ mm}}$.

52. (a) $\boxed{\text{Larger}}$ due to expansion.

(b) $A_o = \pi r^2 = \pi(4.00\text{ cm})^2 = 50.27\text{ cm}^2$.

$\Delta A = 2\alpha A_o \Delta T = 2(24 \times 10^{-6}\text{ C°}^{-1})(50.27\text{ cm}^2)(150°\text{C} - 20°\text{C}) = 0.314\text{ cm}^2$.

So the final area is $50.27\text{ cm}^2 + 0.314\text{ cm}^2 = \boxed{50.6\text{ cm}^2}$.

57. From the definition of density $\rho = \frac{m}{V}$, we have $\frac{\rho}{\rho_o} = \frac{V_o}{V} = \frac{V_o}{V_o(1 + \beta\Delta T)} = \frac{1}{1 + \beta\Delta T}$.

$$\rho = \frac{1}{1 + \beta\Delta T}\rho_o = \frac{1}{1 + (1.8 \times 10^{-4}\text{ C°}^{-1})(100°\text{C} - 0°\text{C})} \times (13.6 \times 10^3\text{ kg/m}^3) = \boxed{13.4 \times 10^3\text{ kg/m}^3}.$$

60. At 20°C, $V_{ob} = 1000\text{ cm}^3$ and $V_{om} = 990\text{ cm}^3$.

At a temperature T, both the beaker and the mercury have the same volume, $V_b = V_m$.

$V = V_o + \Delta V = V_o(1 + 3\alpha\Delta T) = V_o(1 + \beta\Delta T)$, ☞ $V_{ob}(1 + 3\alpha_b\Delta T) = V_{om}(1 + \beta\Delta T)$.

$$\Delta T = \frac{V_{ob} - V_{om}}{V_{om}\beta_m - 3V_{ob}\alpha_b} = \frac{1000\text{ cm}^3 - 990\text{ cm}^3}{(990\text{ cm}^3)(1.8 \times 10^{-4}\text{ C°}^{-1}) - 3(1000\text{ cm}^3)(3.3 \times 10^{-6}\text{ C°}^{-1})} = 59.4\text{ C°}.$$

So the temperature is $T = 20°\text{C} + 59.4\text{ C°} = \boxed{79.4°\text{C}}$.

66. From $U = \frac{3}{2}nRT$, we have $\Delta U = \frac{3}{2}nR\Delta T = \frac{3}{2}(2.0\text{ mol})[8.31\text{ J/(mol·K)}](50°\text{C} - 20°\text{C}) = \boxed{7.5 \times 10^2\text{ J}}$.

74. For monatomic gas, $U_1 = \frac{3}{2}nRT$. For diatomic gas, $U_2 = \frac{5}{2}nRT$.

So $U_2 = \frac{5}{3}U_1 = \frac{5}{3}(5.0 \times 10^3\text{ J}) = \boxed{8.3 \times 10^3\text{ J}}$.

77. $\Delta V_{\text{gas}} = \beta V_o \Delta T = (9.5 \times 10^{-4}\ \text{C}°^{-1})(25\ \text{gal})(30°\text{C} - 10°\text{C}) = 0.48\ \text{gal}.$

$\Delta V_{\text{tank}} = 3\alpha V_o \Delta T = 3(12 \times 10^{-6}\ \text{C}°^{-1})(25\ \text{gal})(30°\text{C} - 10°\text{C}) = 0.018\ \text{gal}.$

So the spilled volume is $\Delta V_{\text{gas}} - \Delta V_{\text{tank}} = 0.48\ \text{gal} - 0.018\ \text{gal} = \boxed{0.46\ \text{gal}}$.

83. From $\Delta L = \alpha L_o \Delta T$, we have $\frac{\Delta L}{L_o} = \alpha \Delta T$. So $\frac{F}{A} = Y\frac{\Delta L}{L_o} = Y\alpha\Delta T.$

Therefore $\Delta T = \frac{F/A}{Y\alpha} = \frac{8.0 \times 10^7\ \text{N/m}^2}{(20 \times 10^{10}\ \text{N/m}^2)(12 \times 10^{-6}\ \text{C}°^{-1})} = \boxed{33\ \text{C}°}$.

89. From $pV = Nk_B T$, we have $N = \frac{pV}{k_B T} = \frac{(20\ \text{Pa})(0.20\ \text{m}^3)}{(1.38 \times 10^{-23}\ \text{J/K})(293\ \text{K})} = \boxed{9.9 \times 10^{20}}$.

95. From $\frac{p_1 V_1}{T_1} = \frac{p_2 V_2}{T_2}$ and since $T_2 = T_1$,

we have $p_2 = \frac{V_1}{V_2} p_1 = 2(1\ \text{atm}) = 2\ \text{atm} = 2(1.013 \times 10^5\ \text{Pa}) = \boxed{2.026 \times 10^5\ \text{Pa}}$.

VI. Practice Quiz

1. Nitrogen condenses into a liquid at approximately 77 K. What temperature, in degrees Fahrenheit, does this correspond to?

(a) –353°F (b) –321°F (c) –196°F (d) –171°F (e) –139°F

2. An air bubble of volume 1.0 cm^3 was released under water. As it rises to the surface of the water, its volume expands. What will be its new volume if its original temperature and pressure are 5.0°C and 1.2 atm, and its final temperature and pressure are 20°C and 1.0 atm?

(a) 1.1 cm^3 (b) 1.3 cm^3 (c) 3.3 m^3 (d) 4.0 cm^3 (e) 4.8 cm^3

3. A fixed container holds oxygen and hydrogen gases at the same temperature. Which one of the following statements is correct?

(a) The oxygen molecules have the greater kinetic energy.
(b) The hydrogen molecules have the greater kinetic energy.
(c) The oxygen molecules have the greater speed.
(d) The hydrogen molecules have the greater speed.
(e) They have the same speed and kinetic energy.

4. The absolute (Kelvin) temperature of an ideal gas is directly proportional to which of the following properties, when taken as an average, of the molecules of the gas?

(a) speed (b) momentum (c) mass (d) kinetic energy (e) potential energy

5. An aluminum beam is 15.0 m long at a temperature of −15°C. What is its expansion when the temperature is 35°C?

(a) 1.8×10^{-2} m (b) 9.0×10^{-3} m (c) 7.2×10^{-3} m (d) 1.2×10^{-3} m (e) 3.6×10^{-4} m.

6. An ideal gas sample has a pressure of 2.5 atm, a volume of 1.0 L at a temperature of 30°C. How many moles of gas are in the sample?

(a) 9.9×10^{-4} (b) 1.0×10^{-2} (c) 0.10 (d) 1.1 (e) 2.5

7. A brass cube, 10 cm on a side, is heated with a temperature change of 200 C°. By what percentage does its volume change?

(a) 5.7×10^{-3} % (b) 0.57 % (c) 1.1 % (d) 1.1×10^{-3} % (e) 0.10 %

8. When water warms from 0°C to 4°C, the density of the water

(a) increases (b) decreases (c) remains constant (d) becomes zero (e) none of the above

9. A molecule has a rms speed of 500 m/s at 20°C. What is its rms speed at 80°C?

(a) 500 m/s (b) 1,000 m/s (c) 2,000 m/s (d) 550 m/s (e) 600 m/s

10. If one mole of a monatomic gas has a total internal energy of 3.7×10^{3} J, what is the total internal energy of one mole of diatomic gas at the same temperature?

(a) zero (b) 2.2×10^{3} J (c) 6.2×10^{-3} J (d) 1.1×10^{4} J (e) 1.9×10^{4} J

Answers to Practice Quiz:

1. b 2. b 3. d 4. d 5. a 6. c 7. c 8. a 9. d 10. c

CHAPTER 11

Heat

I. Chapter Objectives

Upon completion of this chapter, you should be able to:

1. distinguish the various units of heat and define the mechanical equivalent of heat.
2. describe specific heat and explain how the specific heats of materials are obtained from calorimetry.
3. compare and contrast the three common phases of matter and relate latent heat to phase changes.
4. describe the three methods of heat transfer and give practical and/or environmental examples of each.

II. Key Terms

Upon completion of this chapter, you should be able to define and/or explain the following key terms:

heat	**latent heat**
kilocalorie (kcal)	**latent heat of fusion**
calorie (cal)	**latent heat of vaporization**
British thermal unit (Btu)	**evaporation**
mechanical equivalent of heat	**conduction**
specific heat	**thermal conductors**
solid phase	**thermal insulators**
melting point	**thermal conductivity**
freezing point	**convection**
liquid phase	**radiation**
gaseous (vapor) phase	**infrared radiation**
boiling point	**Stefan's law**
condensation point	**emissivity**
sublimation	**black body**

The definitions and/or explanations of the most important key terms can be found in the following section: **III. Chapter Summary and Discussion**.

III. Chapter Summary and Discussion

1. Units of Heat (Section 11.1)

Heat is the net energy transferred from one object to another because of a temperature difference (Chapter 10). The SI unit of heat is joule (J).

Other units of heat commonly used are the **calorie** (cal) and the **kilocalorie** (kcal, or food Calorie, note the capital C for the "large" food calorie). A kilocalorie is the amount of heat required to raise the temperature of 1 kg of water by 1 C° (from 14.5°C to 15.5°C).

A **British thermal unit (Btu)** is the amount heat needed to raise the temperature of 1 lb of water by 1 F° (from 63°F to 64°F). This definition has its limitations because it is based on the weight of water and weight can change depending on the acceleration due to gravity.

The relationship between unit of heat and the standard SI unit (J) is called the **mechanical equivalent of heat**: 1 kcal = 4186 J = 4.186 kJ, or 1 cal = 4.186 J.

2. Specific Heat (Section 11.2)

Specific heat is the amount of heat required to change the temperature of 1 kg of substance by 1 C°. Among the substances known to us, water has a relatively large specific heat (more heat required per kg per C°) value of 1 cal/(g·C°), or 1 kcal/(kg·C°), or 4186 J/(kg·C°). The 4186 J/(kg·C°) value simply means that it takes 4186 J of heat to change t1 kg of =water by a temperature difference of 1 C°. The high specific heat of water explains why the climate doesn't vary much with season in places near a large body of water.

The heat needed to change the temperature of a mass m by ΔT is then $Q = cm\Delta T$, where Q is heat and c is the specific heat. When an object gains heat, ($\Delta T > 0$), $Q > 0$. However, if an object loses heat ($\Delta T < 0$), $Q < 0$.

Within an isolated system, the heat lost by an object will be gained by other objects within the system. According to the conservation of energy, $\Sigma Q = 0$ or the absolute value of heat lost = heat gained. (The absolute value of heat lost has to be used because heat lost is a negative quantity.) This is the basis of **calorimetry** (the method of mixing).

Note: Since heat lost is a negative quantity, when applying calorimetry, you should write $-Q_{\text{lost}} = Q_{\text{gained}}$, (that is, equate magnitude).

Example 11.1 A 2.0-kilogram steel block is originally at 10°C. If 140 kJ of heat energy are added to the block, what is its final temperature?

Solution: Given: $m = 2.0$ kg, $c = 460$ J/(kg·C°) (Table 11.1), $Q = 140$ kJ $= 140 \times 10^3$ J, $T_i = 10$°C.

Find: T_f.

From $Q = cm\Delta T$, we have $\Delta T = \dfrac{Q}{cm} = \dfrac{140 \times 10^3 \text{ J}}{[460 \text{ J/(kg·C°)}](2.0 \text{ kg})} = 152 \text{ C°}$.

So $T_f = T_i + \Delta T = 10°\text{C} + 152 \text{ C°} = 162°\text{C}$.

Example 11.2 A 0.600-kilogram piece of a pure metal is heated to 100°C and placed in an aluminum can of mass 0.200 kg which contains 0.500 kg of water initially at 17.3°C. The final equilibrium temperature of the mixture is 20.2°C. What kind of metal is it?

Solution: Use the following subscripts:

u = unknown metal, w = water, a = aluminum, i = initial, and f = final.

Given: $m_u = 0.600$ kg, m_a 0.200 kg, $m_w = 0.500$ kg, $t_{iu} = 100$°C, $t_{fu} = 20.2$°C,

$t_{ia} = t_{iw} = 17.3$°C, $T_{fa} = T_{fw} = 20.2$°C, $c_w = 4186$ J/(kg·C°), $c_a = 920$ J/(kg·C°).

Find: c_u.

Here we want to identify the metal. If we can find its specific heat (remember it is specific to the substance), we can identify the metal by looking up Table 11.1.

In the mixing process, the metal loses heat, and aluminum and the water gain heat.

The heat lost by metal is $Q_{\text{lost}} = c_u m_u \Delta T_u = c_u (0.600 \text{ kg})(20.2°\text{C} - 100°\text{C}) = -(47.9 \text{ kg·C°})c_u$.

The heat gained by aluminum and water is

$Q_{\text{gained}} = c_a m_a \Delta T_a + c_w m_w \Delta T_w = [920 \text{ J/(kg·C°)}](0.200 \text{ kg})(20.2°\text{C} - 17.3°\text{C})$

$+ [4186 \text{ J/(kg·C°)}](0.500 \text{ kg})(20.2°\text{C} - 17.3°\text{C}) = 6.60 \times 10^3 \text{ J}$.

From calorimetry, $\Sigma Q = 0$, or the absolute value of heat lost = heat gained ($-Q_{\text{lost}} = Q_{\text{gained}}$),

we have $-[-(47.9 \text{ kg·C°})c_u] = 6.60 \times 10^3 \text{ J}$. Solving, $c_u = 138$ J/(kg·C°).

Looking up Table 11.1, we conclude that the metal is lead.

---

3. Phase Changes and Latent Heat (Section 11.3)

Matter normally exists in three phases: solid, liquid, and gas. **Latent heat** is the heat involved in a phase change such as from solid to liquid or from liquid to gas, and does not go into changing the temperature, but in breaking or forming molecular bonds.

The latent heat for a solid-liquid phase change is called the **latent heat of fusion** (L_f), which is the heat required to change 1 kg of solid to liquid while the temperature remains constant at the **freezing point**. The latent heat for a liquid-gas phase change is called the **latent heat of vaporization** (L_v), which is the heat required to change 1 kg of liquid to gas while the temperature remains constant at the **boiling point**. Therefore, the heat involved for a mass m is given by $Q = mL$, where L is the latent heat.

Example 11.3 How much heat energy is needed to change 10 kg of ice at −20°C to steam at 120°C?

Solution: Use the following subscripts: i = ice, w = water, and s = steam.

Given: $m = 10$ kg, $c_i = 2100$ J/(kg·C°), $c_w = 4186$ J/(kg·C°), $c_s = 2010$ J/(kg·C°), $L_f = 3.33 \times 10^5$ J/kg, $L_v = 22.6 \times 10^5$ J/kg.

Find: Q_{tot} (total heat).

Ice at −20°C first needs to be raised to 0°C, and then melted to 0°C liquid water. The water at 0°C needs to be raised to 100°C, where it is vaporized to steam. Finally, the temperature of steam is raised to 120°C.

The heat required to raise the temperature of ice from −20°C to 0°C is

$$Q_1 = c_i\, m_i\, \Delta T_i = [2100 \text{ J/(kg·C°)}](10 \text{ kg})[0°\text{C} - (-20°\text{C})] = 4.2 \times 10^5 \text{ J}.$$

The heat required to melt ice at 0°C to water at 0°C is

$$Q_2 = mL_f = (10 \text{ kg})(3.33 \times 10^5 \text{ J/kg}) = 3.33 \times 10^6 \text{ J}.$$

The heat required to raise the temperature of water from 0°C to 100°C is

$$Q_3 = c_w\, m_w\, \Delta T_w = [4186 \text{ J/(kg·C°)}](10 \text{ kg})(100°\text{C} - 0°\text{C}) = 4.186 \times 10^6 \text{ J}.$$

The heat required to vaporize water at 100°C to steam at 100°C is

$$Q_4 = mL_v = (10 \text{ kg})(22.6 \times 10^5 \text{ J/kg}) = 22.6 \times 10^6 \text{ J}.$$

The heat required to raise the temperature of steam from 100°C to 120°C is

$$Q_5 = c_s\, m_s\, \Delta T_s = [2010 \text{ J/(kg·C°)}](10 \text{ kg})(120°\text{C} - 100°\text{C}) = 4.02 \times 10^5 \text{ J}.$$

So the total heat required is $Q_{tot} = \Sigma Q_i = Q_1 + Q_2 + Q_3 + Q_4 + Q_5 = 3.1 \times 10^7$ J.

Note: Q_4 (liquid to gas) is by far the largest heat required in the above five processes. That is why our bodies cool after perspiration evaporates.

---

4. Heat Transfer (Section 11.4)

There are three mechanisms of heat transfer: **conduction, convection**, and **radiation**.

The **thermal conductivity** (k) characterizes the heat-conducting ability of a material. Its SI unit is J/(m·s·C °). Materials with large k values are called **thermal conductors** while materials with small k values are called **thermal insulators**. **Conduction** is the transfer of energy through a process of molecular collision. The heat conduction (flow) rate is given by $\frac{\Delta Q}{\Delta t} = \frac{kA\Delta T}{d}$, where A is the cross-sectional area, d the thickness, and ΔT is the temperature difference.

Convection involves mass transfer (conduction does not). For example, when cold water is in contact with a hot object, such as the bottom of a pot on a stove, the object transfers heat to the water by conduction, and the warmer water carries the heat away with it by convection as it rises (warmer water is less dense than cold water at the top).

Radiation is the transfer of energy by electromagnetic waves and requires no transfer medium (conduction and convection require a transfer medium). The rate at which an object radiates energy is given by $P = \sigma A e T^4$, where P is the power radiated in watts (W) or joules/s (J/s), e is the **emissivity** which characterizes the radiating property of the material and has dimensionless value between 0 and 1, A is the surface area of the object, T is the absolute (Kelvin) temperature of the object, and $\sigma = 5.67 \times 10^{-8}$ W/(m^2·K^4) is called the *Stefan-Boltzmann constant.* A good emitter of radiation is also a good absorber. A **black body** is a perfect emitter and absorber ($e = 1$).

If an object is at temperature T and its surroundings are at a temperature of T_s, then the net rate of energy loss or gain due to radiation alone is given by $P_{net} = \sigma Ae(T_s^4 - T^4)$. The temperatures used in the radiation equations *must* be in Kelvin.

Example 11.4 A window glass 0.50-centimeter thick has dimensions of 2.0 m by 1.0 m. If the outside temperature is −10°C and the inside temperature 20°C,

(a) what is the rate of heat conduction through the window?

(b) How much heat flows through the window in 1.0 h due to conduction only?

Solution: Given: $d = 0.50$ cm, $A = LW = (2.0\text{ m})(1.0\text{ m}) = 2.0\text{ m}^2$, $\Delta T = 20°\text{C} - (-10°\text{C}) = 30\text{ C}°$, $k = 0.84$ J/(m·s·C°) (Table 11.3).

Find: (a) $\Delta Q/\Delta t$ (b) ΔQ.

(a) $\frac{\Delta Q}{\Delta t} = \frac{kA\Delta T}{d} = \frac{[0.84 \text{ J/(m·s·C°)}](2.0 \text{ m}^2)(30 \text{ C°})}{0.50 \times 10^{-2} \text{ m}} = 1.0 \times 10^4 \text{ J/s} = 1.0 \times 10^4 \text{ W} = 10 \text{ kW}.$

(b) $\Delta Q = \frac{\Delta Q}{\Delta t}\Delta t = (1.0 \times 10^4 \text{ J/s})(1.0 \text{ h})(3600 \text{ s/h}) = 3.6 \times 10^7 \text{ J}.$

Example 11.5 A radiator has an emissivity of 0.70 and its exposed area is 1.50 m^2. The temperature of the radiator is 100°C and the surrounding temperature is 20°C. What is the net heat flow rate from the body?

Solution: Given: $e = 0.70$, $A = 1.50 \text{ m}^2$, $T = 100°\text{C} = 273 + 100 = 373 \text{ K}$,

$T_s = 20°\text{C} = 273 + 20 = 293 \text{ K}$.

Find: P_{net}.

$P_{net} = \sigma Ae(T_s^4 - T^4) = [5.67 \times 10^{-8} \text{ W/(m}^2\text{·K}^4)](1.50 \text{ m}^2)(0.70)[(293 \text{ K})^4 - (373 \text{ K})^4]$

$= -7.1 \times 10^2 \text{ J/s} = -7.1 \times 10^2 \text{ W}.$

The negative sign indicates that the radiator is losing energy.

IV. Mathematical Summary

Mechanical Equivalent of Heat	1 kcal = 4186 J = 4.186 kJ 1 cal = 4.186 J	Gives the conversion between calorie and joules.
Specific Heat (specific heat capacity)	$Q = mc\Delta T$ (11.1)	Relates heat with mass, specific heat, and change in temperature.
Latent Heat	$L = mL$ (11.2)	Relates heat with latent heat and mass. (for water) $L_f = 3.3 \times 10^5$ J/kg (80 kcal/kg) $L_v = 22.6 \times 10^5$ J/kg (540 kcal/kg)
Thermal Conduction	$\frac{\Delta Q}{\Delta t} = \frac{kA\Delta T}{d}$ (11.3)	Calculates the heat conduction rate.
Stefan's Law	$P = \frac{\Delta Q}{\Delta t} = \sigma A e T^4$ (11.5)	Computes the heat power.
Net Radiant Power (Loss or Gain)	$P_{net} = \sigma A e(T_s^4 - T^4)$ (11.6)	Computes the net heat power.

V. Solutions of Selected Exercises and Paired/Trio Exercises

7. (a) The work done in each lift is $W = Fd = (20 \text{ kg})(9.80 \text{ m/s}^2)(1.0 \text{ m}) = 196 \text{ J}$.

The energy input is $E = 2800 \text{ Cal} = 2800 \times 10^3 \text{ cal} = (2800 \times 10^3 \text{ cal})(4.186 \text{ J/cal}) = 1.17 \times 10^7 \text{ J}$.

So the number of lifts required is $\dfrac{1.17 \times 10^7 \text{ J}}{196 \text{ J}} = \boxed{60\,000 \text{ times}}$.

(b) $t = 60\,000(5.0 \text{ s}) = 3.0 \times 10^5 \text{ s} = \boxed{83 \text{ h}}$.

10. $\boxed{\text{No}}$. A negative specific heat corresponds to an increase in temperature when heat is removed.

16. From $Q = mc\Delta T$, we have $\Delta T = \dfrac{Q}{cm} = \dfrac{(200 \text{ J})}{[920 \text{ J/(kg}\cdot\text{C°)}](5.0 \times 10^{-3} \text{ kg})} = 43\text{°C}$.

So the final temperature is $43\text{°C} + 20\text{°C} = \boxed{63\text{°C}}$.

18. The heat gained by the cup is $Q_c = c_c m_c \Delta T_c = c_c(0.250 \text{ kg})(80\text{°C} - 20\text{°C}) = (15 \text{ kg}\cdot\text{C°})c_c$,

The heat lost by the coffee is $Q_{cof} = [4186 \text{ J/(kg}\cdot\text{C°)}](0.250 \text{ kg})(80\text{°C} - 100\text{°C}) = -2.093 \times 10^4 \text{ J}$.

From calorimetry, $-Q_{lost} = Q_{gained}$, we have $2.093 \times 10^4 \text{ J} = (15 \text{ kg}\cdot\text{C°})c_c$.

Solving, $c_c = \boxed{1.40 \times 10^3 \text{ J/(kg}\cdot\text{C°)}}$.

20. $\boxed{1.27 \text{ kg}}$

24. The metal loses heat and the water and the cup gain heat.

The heat lost by the metal is $Q_m = cm\Delta T = c(0.150 \text{ kg})(30.5\text{°C} - 400\text{°C}) = -(55.43 \text{ kg}\cdot\text{C°})c$.

The heat gained by the water and the cup is

$Q_G = [4186 \text{ J/(kg}\cdot\text{C°)}](0.400 \text{ kg})(30.5\text{°C} - 10.0\text{°C}) + [920 \text{ J/(kg.C°)}](0.200 \text{ kg})(30.5\text{°C} - 10.0\text{°C})$

$= 3.810 \times 10^4 \text{ J}$.

From calorimetry, $-Q_{lost} = Q_{gained}$, we have $(55.43 \text{ kg}\cdot\text{C°})c = 3.810 \times 10^4 \text{ J}$.

Solving, $c = \boxed{687 \text{ J/(kg}\cdot\text{C°)}}$.

27. Assume the final temperature is T. $Q = cm\Delta T$.

The heat lost by aluminum is $Q_a = [920 \text{ J/(kg}\cdot\text{C°)}](0.100 \text{ kg})(T - 90.0\text{°C}) = (92 \text{ J/C°})(T - 90.0\text{°C})$,

The heat gained by water is $Q_w = [4186 \text{ J/(kg}\cdot\text{C°)}](1.00 \text{ kg})(T - 20\text{°C}) = (4186 \text{ J/C°})(T - 20\text{°C})$.

From calorimetry, $-Q_{lost} = Q_{gained}$, we have $-92(T - 90.0\text{°C}) = 4186(T - 20\text{°C})$.

Solving, $T = \boxed{21.5\text{°C}}$.

33. This is due to the $\boxed{\text{high value of the latent heat of vaporization}}$. When steam condenses, it releases 2.26×10^6 J/kg of heat. When 100°C water drops its temperature by 1 C°, it releases only 4186 J/kg.

36. The melting point of lead is 328°C. So the temperature of the lead has to be increased to 328°C first. The total heat required is then

$Q = cm\Delta T + mL_f = [130 \text{ J/(kg.C°)}](0.75 \text{ kg})(328°\text{C} - 20°\text{C}) + (0.75 \text{ kg})(0.25 \times 10^5 \text{ J/kg})$

$= \boxed{4.9 \times 10^4 \text{ J}}$.

42. To completely melt the ice to water at 0°C it requires

$Q_1 = cm\Delta T + mL_f = [2100 \text{ J/(kg·C°)}](0.60 \text{ kg})[0°\text{C} - (-10°\text{C})] + (0.60 \text{ kg})(3.3 \times 10^5 \text{ J/kg}) = 2.11 \times 10^5 \text{ J}$.

For 0.30 kg of water not to freeze into ice, it can only release

$Q_2 = [4186 \text{ J/(kg)}](0.30 \text{ kg})(0°\text{C} - 50°\text{C}) = -6.28 \times 10^4 \text{ J} < Q_1$.

So the temperature of the ice will increase to 0°C and then a portion of it will be melted.

Let the amount of ice melted be M. From calorimetry, $-Q_{\text{lost}} = Q_{\text{gained}}$,

we have $6.28 \times 10^4 \text{ J} = [2100 \text{ J/(kg·C°)}](0.60 \text{ kg})[0°\text{C} - (-10°\text{C})] + M(3.3 \times 10^5 \text{ J/kg})$,

solving, $M = 0.15$ kg. Hence the total amount of water is $0.30 \text{ kg} + 0.15 \text{ kg} = \boxed{0.45 \text{ kg}}$.

45. If enough ice is added, the equilibrium temperature is 0°C.

Note 1 Liter of water has a mass of 1 kg.

The heat lost by the tea is $Q_{\text{lost}} = cm\Delta T = [4186 \text{ J/(kg·C°)}](0.75 \text{ kg})(0°\text{C} - 20°\text{C}) = 6.279 \times 10^4 \text{ J}$.

Let the mass of ice melted be M. $Q_{\text{gained}} = ML_f = (3.3 \times 10^5\, M)$ J/kg.

From calorimetry, $-Q_{\text{lost}} = Q_{\text{gained}}$, we have $M = \dfrac{6.279 \times 10^4 \text{ J}}{3.3 \times 10^5 \text{ J/kg}} = 0.190 \text{ kg}$.

So the total amount of liquid is $0.75 \text{ kg} + 0.19 \text{ kg} = \boxed{0.94 \text{ kg or } 0.94 \text{ L}}$.

49. The heat lost by the ceramic is

$Q_{\text{lost}} = cm\Delta T = [840 \text{ J/(kg·C°)}](0.150 \text{ kg})(-196°\text{C} - 20°\text{C}) = 2.72 \times 10^4 \text{ J}$.

Let the mass of nitrogen boiled be M. $Q_{\text{gained}} = ML_v = (2.0 \times 10^5\, M)$ J/kg.

From calorimetry, $-Q_{\text{lost}} = Q_{\text{gained}}$, we have $M = \dfrac{2.72 \times 10^4 \text{ J}}{2.0 \times 10^5 \text{ J/kg}} = 0.136 \text{ kg}$.

Note that 1 liter of liquid nitrogen has a mass of 0.80 kg (the density of liquid nitrogen is 0.80 kg/L).

From $\rho = \dfrac{m}{V}$, we have $V = \dfrac{m}{\rho} = \dfrac{0.136 \text{ kg}}{0.80 \text{ kg/L}} = \boxed{0.17 \text{ L}}$.

54. The bridge is exposed to the cold air above and below while the road is exposed only above. So more heat is removed from the bridge than the road. This results in a fast freeze of the water on the bridge.

59. From $\dfrac{\Delta Q}{\Delta t} = \dfrac{kA\Delta T}{d}$, we have $\dfrac{(\Delta Q/\Delta t)_t}{(\Delta Q/\Delta t)_o} = \dfrac{k_t}{k_o} = \dfrac{0.67\ \text{J/(m·s·C°)}}{0.15\ \text{J/(m·s·C°)}} = \boxed{4.5\ \text{times}}$.

62. The normal body temperature is 37°C.

$$\frac{\Delta Q}{\Delta t} = \frac{kA\Delta T}{d} = \frac{[0.20\ \text{J/(m·s·C°)}](1.5\ \text{m}^2)(37°\text{C} - 33°\text{C})}{0.040\ \text{m}} = \boxed{30\ \text{J/s}}.$$

64. $\boxed{d_{Cu} = 1.6\ d_{Al}}$.

66. (a) The greater the R-value, the greater the insulation value.

(b) (1) $R = \dfrac{L}{k}$, ☞ $L = R\,k$.

So: $\dfrac{L_{\text{fiberboard}}}{L_{\text{foam plastic}}} = \dfrac{k_{\text{fiberboard}}}{k_{\text{foam plastic}}} = \dfrac{0.059\ \text{J/(m·s·C°)}}{0.042\ \text{J/(m·s·C°)}} = 1.40.$

Therefore $L_{\text{fiberboard}} = (1.40)(3.0\ \text{in}) = \boxed{4.2\ \text{in}}$.

(2) $\dfrac{L_{\text{brick}}}{L_{\text{foam plastic}}} = \dfrac{0.71\ \text{J/(m·s·C°)}}{0.042\ \text{J/(m·s·C°)}} = 16.9.$ So $L_{\text{brick}} = 16.9(3.0\ \text{in}) = \boxed{51\ \text{in}}$.

71. $\dfrac{\Delta Q}{\Delta t} = \dfrac{949\ \text{H/s}}{2} = 474.5\ \text{J/s} =$

$$\frac{(3.5\ \text{m})(5.0\ \text{m})[20°\text{C}-(-10°\text{C})]}{(0.020\ \text{m})/[0.059\ \text{J/(m·s·C°)}]+d/[0.042\ \text{J/(m·s·C°)}]+(0.150\ \text{m})/[1.3\ \text{J/(m·s·C°)}]+(0.070\ \text{m})/[0.71\ \text{J/(m·s·C°)}]}$$

Solving for $d = 0.023\ \text{m} = \boxed{2.3\ \text{cm}}$.

79. Let the initial temperature of the shot be T.

The heat lost by the shot is

$Q_{\text{copper}} = cm\Delta T = [390\ \text{J/(kg·C°)}](0.150\ \text{kg})(28°\text{C} - T) = (58.5\ \text{J/C°})(28°\text{C} - T)$,

the heat gained by water is

$Q_{\text{water}} = [4186\ \text{J/(kg·C°)}](0.200\ \text{kg})(28°\text{C} - 25°\text{C}) = 2512\ \text{J}$,

the heat gained by the cup is

$Q_{\text{cup}} = [920\ \text{J/(kg·C°)}](0.375\ \text{kg})(28°\text{C} - 25°\text{C}) = 1035\ \text{J}$.

From calorimetry, $-Q_{\text{lost}} = Q_{\text{gained}}$, we have $-(58.5\ \text{J/C°})(28°\text{C} - T) = 2512\ \text{J} + 1035\ \text{J}$.

Solving, $T = \boxed{88.7°\text{C}}$.

81. 25 km/h = 6.95 m/s. The kinetic energy is $K = \frac{1}{2}mv^2 = \frac{1}{2}(65 \text{ kg})(6.95 \text{ m/s})^2 = 1.57 \times 10^3$ J.

So $Q = 0.40K = 627$ J.

From $Q = mL_f$, we have $m = \dfrac{Q}{L_f} = \dfrac{627 \text{ J}}{3.3 \times 10^5 \text{ J/kg}} = 1.9 \times 10^{-3} \text{ kg} = \boxed{1.9 \text{ g}}$.

The rest of the energy goes to heating the skates and losing to the environment.

VI. Practice Quiz

1. The physiological process of body cooling by perspiration is based on
(a) specific heat. (b) latent heat of fusion. (c) latent heat of vaporization. (d) heat capacity.

2. A machine gear consists of 0.10 kg of iron and 0.16 kg of copper. How much heat is added to the gear if its temperature increases by 35 C°. [The specific heats for iron and copper are 460 and 390 J/(kg·C°).]
(a) 9.1×10^2 J (b) 3.8×10^3 J (c) 4.0×10^3 J (d) 4.4×10^3 J (e) none of the above

3. How much heat is required to change 0.500 kg of ice at 0°C to water at 50°C?
(a) 1.05×10^5 J (b) 1.67×10^5 J (c) 2.71×10^5 J (d) 4.38×10^5 J (e) 1.13×10^6 J

4. A 0.10 kg piece of cooper, initially at 95°C, is dropped into 0.20 kg of water contained in a 0.28-kg aluminum calorimeter; the water and calorimeter are initially at 15°C. What is the final temperature of the system?
(a) 17.8 °C (b) 18.3°C (c) 19.2°C (d) 23.7°C (e) 25.0°C

5. If the absolute temperature of a radiator is doubled, by what factor does the radiating power change?
(a) 2 (b) 4 (c) 8 (d) 16 (e) 32

6. The reason large lake temperatures do not vary drastically is that
(a) water has a relatively high rate of conduction. (b) water is a good radiator.
(c) water is a poor heat conductor. (d) water has a lower specific heat.
(e) water has a relatively high specific heat.

7. You are designing a water heater so it can heat 20 kg of water from 20°C to 100°C in 20 minutes. What should be the power of the heating element? (Assume no heat loss.)
(a) 2.8×10^2 J/s (b) 1.2×10^3 J/s (c) 5.6×10^3 J/s (d) 3.3×10^5 J/s (e) 6.7×10^6 J/s

8. On a cold day, a piece of metal feels much colder to the touch than a piece of wood. This is due to the difference in which of the following physical properties?

(a) density (b) specific heat (c) latent heat (d) thermal conductivity (e) temperature

9. Equal masses of water at 20°C and 80°C are mixed. What is the final temperature of the mixture?

(a) 65°C (b) 50°C (c) 40°C (d) 30°C (e) 25°C

10. A person makes ice tea by adding ice to 1.8 kg of hot tea (water), initially at 80°C. How many kilograms of ice, initially at 0°C, are required to bring the mixture to 10°C?

(a) 0.78 kg (b) 1.0 kg (c) 1.2 kg (d) 1.5 kg (e) 1.8 kg

Answers to Practice Quiz:

1. c 2. b 3. c 4. a 5. d 6. e 7. c 8. d 9. b 10. d

CHAPTER 12

Vibrations and Waves

I. Chapter Objectives

Upon completion of this chapter, you should be able to:

1. describe simple harmonic motion and relate energy and speed in such motion.
2. understand the equation of motion for SHM and explain what is meant by phase and phase differences.
3. describe wave motion in terms of various parameters and identify different types of waves.
4. explain various wave properties and resulting phenomena.
5. describe the formation and characteristics of standing waves and explain the phenomenon of resonance.

II. Key Terms

Upon completion of this chapter, you should be able to define and/or explain the following key terms:

Hooke's law
simple harmonic motion (SHM)
displacement
amplitude
period
frequency
hertz (Hz)
equation of motion
phase constant
damped harmonic motion
wave
wave motion
wavelength
wave speed
transverse wave
longitudinal wave
principle of superposition
interference
constructive interference
destructive interference
total constructive interference
total destructive interference
reflection
refraction
dispersion
diffraction
standing wave
node
antinode
natural (resonant) frequencies
fundamental frequency
harmonic series
resonance

III. Chapter Summary and Discussion

1. Simple Harmonic Motion (Section 12.1)

The motion of an oscillating object depends on the restoring forces that make it go back and forth. The simplest type of restoring force is a spring force described by Hooke's law, $F_s = -kx$, where k is the spring constant, and the negative sign indicates that the force is opposite to the displacement from the spring's relaxed position.

Motion under the influence of the type of force described by Hooke's law is called **simple harmonic motion (SHM)**, because this force is the simplest restoring force and because the motion can be described by harmonic functions (sines and cosines). SHM is described by the following parameters:

amplitude (A): the magnitude of the maximum displacement of a mass from its equilibrium position,
period (T): the time needed to complete one cycle of oscillation,
frequency (f): the number of cycles per second.

The frequency and period are related by $f = \frac{1}{T}$. The SI unit of frequency is 1/s, or hertz (Hz). We sometimes descriptively say cycles/s (cycles per second, cps).

The total mechanical energy of an object in SHM is directly proportional to the square of its amplitude. For example, for a mass m oscillating on a spring of spring constant k, $E = \frac{1}{2}kA^2$. The maximum speed of the mass is directly proportional to the amplitude, $v_{max} = \sqrt{\frac{k}{m}}\,A$, because $E = \frac{1}{2}kA^2 = \frac{1}{2}mv_{max}^2$.

Example 12.1 A 0.50-kilogram object is attached to a spring of spring constant 20 N/m along a horizontal, frictionless surface. The object oscillates in simple harmonic motion and has a speed of 1.5 m/s at the equilibrium position.
(a) What is the total energy of the system?
(b) What is the amplitude?
(c) At what location are the values for the potential and kinetic energies the same?

Solution: Given: $m = 0.50$ kg, $v_{max} = 1.5$ m/s, $k = 20$ N/m.
Find: (a) E (b) A (c) x when $K = U$.

(a) At the equilibrium position, $x = 0$, so the potential energy is zero. Therefore, the total energy is equal to kinetic energy. $E = K = \frac{1}{2}mv_{max}^2 = \frac{1}{2}(0.50\text{ kg})(1.5\text{ m/s})^2 = 0.56\text{ J}$.

(b) At the amplitude ($x = \pm A$), $v = 0$, so the total energy is all in the form of potential energy.

Thus at $x = \pm A$, we have $E = U = \frac{1}{2}kx^2 = \frac{1}{2}kA^2$,

therefore $A = \sqrt{\frac{2E}{k}} = \sqrt{\frac{2(0.56\text{ J})}{20\text{ N/m}}} = 0.24\text{ m}.$

(c) When $K = U$, $E = K + U = U + U = 2U = 2\frac{1}{2}kx^2 = kx^2$,

so $x = \sqrt{\frac{E}{k}} = \sqrt{\frac{0.56\text{ J}}{20\text{ N/m}}} = 0.17\text{ m}.$

Example 12.2 An object is attached to a spring of spring constant 60 N/m along a horizontal, frictionless surface. The spring is initially stretched by a force of 5.0 N on the object and let go. It takes the object 0.50 s first get back to its equilibrium position after its release.

(a) What is the amplitude?

(b) What is the period?

(c) What is the frequency?

Solution: Given: $k = 60$ N/m, $F = 5.0$ N, $t = 0.50$ s.

Find: (a) A (b) T (c) f.

(a) The initial stretch is also the maximum distance from the equilibrium position. (The spring force is the reaction force of the stretching force and thus equal in magnitude to it.) From Hooke's law,

$F_s = -kx$, we have $A = |x_{max}| = \frac{F_s}{k} = \frac{5.0\text{ N}}{60\text{ N/m}} = 0.083\text{ m}.$

(b) The motion from the amplitude to the equilibrium position is only 1/4 of a complete oscillation. So the period is $T = 4t = 4(0.50\text{ s}) = 2.0\text{ s}$.

(c) $f = \frac{1}{T} = \frac{1}{2.0\text{ s}} = 0.50\text{ Hz}.$

---

2. Equation of Motion (Section 12.2)

The **equation of motion** of an object in SHM has the general form $y = A\sin(\omega t + \delta)$, where A is the amplitude, ω is the *angular* frequency of the motion ($\omega = 2\pi f = \frac{2\pi}{T}$), and δ is the **phase constant**. The amplitude and the phase constant depend on the initial conditions of the motion. The frequency f depends on the intrinsic properties of the system (for example, the stiffness and the inertia). From this equation of motion, we can express the velocity and acceleration of an object in SHM as

$$v = \omega A\cos(\omega t + \delta) \quad \text{and} \quad a = -\omega^2 A\sin(\omega t + \delta) = -\omega^2 y.$$

For a mass-spring system, $T = 2\pi\sqrt{\frac{m}{k}}$, and $f = \frac{1}{2\pi}\sqrt{\frac{k}{m}}$, or $\omega = \sqrt{\frac{k}{m}}$, where m is the mass of the object and k is the spring constant.

For a simple pendulum, $T = 2\pi\sqrt{\frac{L}{g}}$, and $f = \frac{1}{2\pi}\sqrt{\frac{g}{L}}$, where L is the length of the pendulum and g is the acceleration due to gravity. (**Note**: the mass of the pendulum is not in the equation so the period is independent of mass.)

Without a driving force and with frictional losses, the amplitude and the energy of an oscillator will decrease with time, giving rise to **damped harmonic motion**.

Example 12.3 An object with a mass of 1.0 kg is attached to a spring with a spring constant of 10 N/m. The object is displaced by 3.0 cm from the equilibrium position and let go.

(a) What is the amplitude A?

(b) What is the period T?

(c) What is the frequency f?

Solution: Given: $m = 1.0$ kg, $k = 10$ N/m, initial $x = 3.0$ cm.

Find: (a) A (b) T (c) f.

(a) The initial stretch is the maximum displacement. So $A = 3.0$ cm.

(b) $T = 2\pi\sqrt{\frac{m}{k}} = 2\pi\sqrt{\frac{1.0\text{ kg}}{10\text{ N/m}}} = 2.0\text{ s.}$

(c) $f = \frac{1}{T} = \frac{1}{2.0\text{ s}} = 0.50\text{ Hz.}$

Example 12.4 The pendulum of a grandfather clock is 1.0 m long.

(a) What is its period on the Earth?

(b) What would its period be on the Moon where the acceleration due to gravity is 1.7 m/s^2?

Solution: Given: $L = 1.0$ m, $g_E = 9.8$ m/s^2, $g_M = 1.7$ m/s^2.

Find: (a) T_E (b) T_M.

(a) $T_E = 2\pi\sqrt{\frac{L}{g}} = 2\pi\sqrt{\frac{1.0\text{ m}}{9.8\text{ m/s}^2}} = 2.0\text{ s.}$

(b) $T_M = 2\pi\sqrt{\frac{1.0\text{ m}}{1.7\text{ m/s}^2}} = 4.8\text{ s.}$

Example 12.5 The position of an object in simple harmonic motion is described by $y = (0.25 \text{ m}) \sin\left(\frac{\pi}{2} t\right)$. Find (a) the amplitude A, (b) the period T, (c) the maximum speed.

Solution: Given: $y = (0.25 \text{ m}) \sin\left(\frac{\pi}{2} t\right)$.

Find: (a) A (b) T (c) v_{max}.

(a) Comparing the equation of motion $y = (0.25 \text{ m}) \sin\left(\frac{\pi}{2} t\right)$ with the general form $y = A \sin(\omega t + \delta)$, we see that $A = 0.25$ m.

(b) Again, comparing the equation of motion with the general form, $\omega t = 2\pi f t = \frac{\pi}{2} t$.

So $2\pi f = \pi/2$, or $f = 1/4$ 1/s = 0.25 Hz. Therefore $T = \frac{1}{f} = \frac{1}{0.25 \text{ Hz}} = 4.0$ s.

(c) From the equation of velocity as a function of time $v = A\omega \cos(\omega t + \delta)$, we know that the maximum speed is $v_{max} = \omega A = (2\pi f)A = 2\pi(1/4.0 \text{ Hz})(0.25 \text{ m}) = 0.39$ m/s.

3. Wave Motion (Section 12.3)

Wave motion is the propagation of a disturbance (energy and momentum) through a material. The medium though which the wave propagates is *not* transferred in wave motion. It simply support the wave's passage. A periodic (as opposed to a pulse) wave can be characterized by the following quantities:

amplitude: the magnitude of the maximum displacement of the particles of the material from their equilibrium positions,

wavelength: the distance between two successive crests or troughs, (see note below),

frequency: the number of wavelengths that passes by a given point in a second,

wave speed: the speed of the wave motion (speed of a crest or trough) given by $v = \lambda f$.

Note: The wavelength is actually the distance between any two successive particles that are in phase (that is, at identical points on the wave form). Crests are used just for convenience.

In a wave, there are two motions, the motion of the particle of the medium (medium motion) and the motion of the travelling disturbance (wave motion). **Waves** are divided into two types based on the direction of the medium motion relative to the wave motion. For a **transverse wave** (sometimes called a *shear wave*) the particle motion is *perpendicular* to the direction of the wave velocity. A wave on a rope is an example of a transverse wave. For a **longitudinal wave** (or sometimes called a *compressional wave*) the particle motion is *parallel* to the direction of the wave velocity. Sound waves are examples of longitudinal waves.

Some waves are, however, combinations of transverse waves and longitudinal waves. Two good examples of this are water waves and seismic waves.

Example 12.6 The diagram shown is a "snapshot" of a wave on a rope at a given time. The frequency of the wave is 60 Hz.
(a) What is the amplitude?
(b) What is the wavelength?
(c) What is the wave speed?

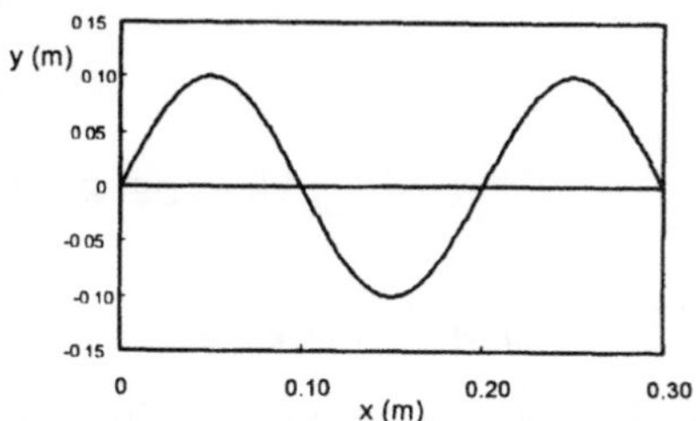

Solution: Given: $f = 60$ Hz and information in the diagram.

Find: (a) A (b) λ (c) v.

(a) Amplitude is the maximum distance from the equilibrium position.

From the diagram, $A = 0.10$ m.

(b) Wavelength is the distance between successive crests.

From the diagram, $\lambda = 0.20$ m.

(c) $v = \lambda f = (0.20 \text{ m})(60 \text{ Hz}) = 12$ m/s.

---

4. Wave Phenomena (Section 12.4)

Interference occurs when waves meet or overlap. The **principle of superposition** states: *at any time, the combined waveform of two or more interfering waves is given by the sum of the displacements of the individual waves at each point in the medium.* If the amplitude of the combined wave is greater than that of any of the individual waves, we have what is called **constructive interference**. If the amplitude of the combined wave is smaller than that of any of the individual waves, it is called **destructive interference**. **Total constructive interference** occurs when two waves of the same frequency and amplitude are exactly in phase (the crest of one wave is aligned with the crest of the other) and **total destructive interference** takes place if two waves of the same frequency and amplitude are completely 180° out of phase (the crest of one wave is aligned with the trough of the other and vice versa).

Reflection occurs when a wave strikes an object or comes to a boundary of another medium and is at least partly bounced back. **Refraction** occurs when a wave crosses a boundary into another medium and the transmitted wave moves in a different direction. Generally, when a wave strikes the boundary, both reflection and refraction occur. **Dispersion** is exhibited when the wave speed depends on the wavelength or frequency. Waves of different wavelength or frequency travel at different speeds so if they start together they spread apart from one another. The rainbow we sometimes see is an excellent example of wave dispersion for light. **Diffraction** refers to the bending of waves around an edge of an object. A person in a room with an open door can hear sound from outside the room, which is partially due to diffraction (there may be some reflection).

5. Standing Waves and Resonance (Section 12.5)

Interfering waves of the same frequency and amplitude traveling in opposite directions in a rope or other conditions can produce a **standing wave**. In this case, some points on the rope are always stationary (destructive interference) and they are called **nodes**. The points of maximum amplitude, where constructive interference is greatest, are called **antinodes**.

The frequencies at which large-amplitude standing waves are produced are called **natural frequencies**, or **resonant frequencies**. The lowest frequency f_1 is called the **fundamental frequency**. In a stretched string fixed at both ends, all of the other natural frequencies are integral multiples of the fundamental frequency $f_n = nf_1$, where $n = 1, 2, 3, \ldots$, is an integer. The set of frequencies $f_1, f_2 = 2f_1, f_3 = 3f_1$, and so on, is called a **harmonic series**: f_1 is the *first harmonic*, f_2 the *second harmonic*, and so on.

Note: The names fundamental frequency and first harmonic frequency are interchangeably used.

The speed of a wave in a stretched string is given by $v = \sqrt{\frac{F_T}{\mu}}$, where F_T is the tension in the string, and μ the linear mass density (mass per unit length, $\mu = m/L$). Therefore, the frequencies of the harmonic series *in a stretched string* is given by $f_n = n\frac{v}{2L} = \frac{n}{2L}\sqrt{\frac{F_T}{\mu}}$ (for $n = 1, 2, 3, \ldots$).

Resonance is a phenomena in which the vibrational amplitude of a system is greatly enhanced. It happens when the driving frequency of an external source matches a natural frequency of the system.

Example 12.7 A 50-meter long string has a mass of 0.010 kg. A 2.0-meter segment of the string is fixed at both ends and when a tension of 20 N is applied to the string, three loops are produced. What is the frequency of the standing wave?

Solution: Three loops correspond to the 3rd harmonic.

Given: $L_o = 50$ m, $m = 0.010$ kg, $L = 2.0$ m, $F_T = 20$ N.

Find: f_3.

$$\mu = \frac{m}{L_o} = \frac{0.010 \text{ kg}}{50 \text{ m}} = 2.0 \times 10^{-4} \text{ kg/m}. \quad v = \sqrt{\frac{F_T}{\mu}} = \sqrt{\frac{20 \text{ N}}{2.0 \times 10^{-4} \text{ kg/m}}} = 3.2 \times 10^2 \text{ m/s}.$$

$$f_3 = 3f_1 = 3\frac{v}{\lambda_1} = 3\frac{v}{2L} = \frac{3(3.2 \times 10^2 \text{ m/s})}{2(2.0 \text{ m})} = 2.4 \times 10^2 \text{ Hz}.$$

IV. Mathematical Summary

Hooke's Law	$F_s = -kx$ (12.1)	Relates spring force to displacement of spring from equilibrium.
Frequency and Period for SHM	$f = \frac{1}{T}$ (12.2)	Relates frequency and period for simpler harmonic motion.
Total Energy of a Spring-Mass in SHM	$E = \frac{1}{2}kA^2 = \frac{1}{2}mv^2 + \frac{1}{2}kx^2$ (12.4-5)	Gives the total energy of a spring-mass system in simple harmonic motion.
Velocity of Oscillating Mass on a Spring	$v = \pm\sqrt{\frac{k}{m}(A^2 - x^2)}$ (12.6)	Gives the velocity of an oscillating mass on a spring as a function of position.
Period of a Mass Oscillating on a Spring	$T = 2\pi\sqrt{\frac{m}{k}}$ (12.11)	Computes the period of a mass on a spring in simple harmonic motion.
Angular Frequency of a Mass Oscillating in a Spring	$\omega = 2\pi f = \sqrt{\frac{k}{m}}$ (12.13)	Calculates the angular frequency of a mass on a spring in simple harmonic motion.
Period of a Simple Pendulum	$T = 2\pi\sqrt{\frac{L}{g}}$ (12.14)	Computes the period of a simple pendulum at small-angle approximation.
Displacement of a Mass in SHM	$y = A \sin(\omega t + \delta)$ (12.15) (with $\delta = 0$) $y = A \sin \omega t$ $= A \sin 2\pi ft = A \sin \frac{2\pi t}{T}$	Defines the equation of motion for a simple harmonic oscillator.
Velocity of a Mass in SHM ($\delta = 0$)	$v = \omega A \cos \omega t$ (12.16)	Calculates the velocity of a simple harmonic oscillator as a function of time.

Acceleration of a Mass in SHM ($\delta = 0$)	$a = -\omega^2 A \sin \omega t$ $= -\omega^2 y$ (12.17)	Calculates the acceleration of a simple harmonic oscillator as a function of time.
Wave Speed	$v = \frac{\lambda}{T} = \lambda f$ (12.18)	Relates wave speed to wavelength and frequency.
Natural Frequencies in a Stretched String	$f_n = n\frac{v}{2L} = \frac{n}{2L}\sqrt{\frac{F_T}{\mu}}$ $(n = 1,2,3,\ldots)$ (12.21)	Gives the natural frequencies in a stretched string as a harmonic series.

V. Solutions of Selected Exercises and Paired/Trio Exercises

3. (a) $E = \frac{1}{2}kA^2$, so $\boxed{\text{four times as large}}$.

(b) $v_{max} = \sqrt{\frac{k}{m}}\, A$, so $\boxed{\text{twice as large}}$.

10. From $T = \frac{1}{f}$, we have $\Delta T = \frac{1}{f_2} - \frac{1}{f_1} = \frac{1}{0.50\text{ s}} - \frac{1}{0.25\text{ s}} = -2.0\text{ s}$.

That is a $\boxed{\text{decrease of 2.0 s}}$.

14. (a) $F = kx = (150\text{ N/m})(0.150\text{ m}) = \boxed{22.5\text{ N}}$; $a = \frac{F}{m} = \frac{22.5\text{ N}}{0.500\text{ kg}} = \boxed{45.0\text{ m/s}^2}$.

(b) $F = (150\text{ N/m})(0.050\text{ m}) = \boxed{7.50\text{ N}}$; $a = \frac{7.50\text{ N}}{0.500\text{ kg}} = \boxed{15.0\text{ m/s}^2}$.

(c) $F = \boxed{0}$; $a = \boxed{0}$.

18. $T = 2\pi\sqrt{\frac{m}{k}} \propto \sqrt{m}$, so the ratio is $\boxed{\sqrt{2}}$.

20. Since $f = \frac{1}{2\pi}\sqrt{\frac{k}{m}}$, $\frac{f_2}{f_1} = \sqrt{\frac{m_1}{m_2}} = \sqrt{\frac{0.25\text{ kg}}{0.50\text{ kg}}} = 0.707$.

So $f_2 = (0.707)(1.0\text{ Hz}) = \boxed{0.71\text{ Hz}}$.

22. (a) $\boxed{0.90\text{ J}}$.

(b) $\boxed{\text{No}}$.

25. (a) From conservation of energy (choose the position of the object when the spring is compressed as $U_g = 0$), $E = \frac{1}{2}kA^2 = U = mgh$, we have $\frac{1}{2}(60.0 \text{ N/m}) A^2 = (0.250 \text{ kg})(9.80 \text{ m/s}^2)(0.100 \text{ m} + A)$.

Reduce to a quadratic equation: $30.0A^2 - 2.45A - 0.245 = 0$.

Solving, $A = \boxed{0.14 \text{ m}}$ or -0.058 m, which is discarded.

(b) From energy conservation, the object will go to a height of $\boxed{10.0 \text{ cm}}$ (original position).

32. (a) $T = 2\pi\sqrt{\frac{m}{k}} = 2\pi\sqrt{\frac{0.50 \text{ kg}}{200 \text{ N/m}}} = \boxed{0.31 \text{ s}}$.

(b) $f = \frac{1}{T} = \frac{1}{0.31 \text{ s}} = \boxed{3.2 \text{ Hz}}$.

36. (a) Compare to $y = A \sin\omega t$. $A = \boxed{0.10 \text{ m}}$.

(b) $\omega = 2\pi f = 100$ rad/s, so $f = \frac{100}{2\pi} = \boxed{16 \text{ Hz}}$.

(c) $T = \frac{1}{f} = \frac{1}{16 \text{ Hz}} = \boxed{0.063 \text{ s}}$.

41. From $T = 2\pi\sqrt{\frac{L}{g}}$, we have $g = \frac{4\pi^2 L}{T^2} = \frac{4\pi^2 (0.3690 \text{ m})}{(1.220 \text{ s})^2} = \boxed{9.787 \text{ m/s}^2}$.

44. From $T = 2\pi\sqrt{\frac{m}{k}}$, we have $\frac{T_1}{T_2} = \sqrt{\frac{k_2}{k_1}} = \sqrt{2}$. So $\boxed{\text{the first one by } \sqrt{2} \text{ times}}$.

46. $\boxed{2.5 \text{ N/m}}$.

50. (a) Since $T = 2\pi\sqrt{\frac{L}{g}}$ and the length is shorter, T is also shorter.

So the clock runs faster or $\boxed{\text{gains time}}$.

(b) $\Delta T = 2\pi\sqrt{\frac{0.7500 \text{ m}}{9.80 \text{ m/s}^2}} - 2\pi\sqrt{\frac{0.7480 \text{ m}}{9.80 \text{ m/s}^2}} = 2.32 \times 10^{-3}$ s.

So in 24 hours = 86 400 s (or 43 200 periods), the time difference is

$43\,200(2.32 \times 10^{-3} \text{ s}) = 100 \text{ s} = \boxed{1.7 \text{ min}}$.

(c) $\boxed{\text{Yes}}$. Because of linear thermal expansion, the length depends on the temperature.

54. (a) $\boxed{\text{Transverse}}$. (b) $\boxed{\text{Longitudinal}}$.

60. $\lambda_{max} = \dfrac{v}{f} = \dfrac{345 \text{ m/s}}{20 \text{ Hz}} = \boxed{17 \text{ m}}$, $\lambda_{min} = \dfrac{345 \text{ m/s}}{20 \times 10^3 \text{ Hz}} = \boxed{0.017 \text{ m}}$.

65. (a) 90° latitude represents one quarter of the Earth's circonference. The straight line distance between the locations is

$d = \sqrt{R^2 + R^2} = \sqrt{2}\, R = \sqrt{2}\, (6.4 \times 10^3 \text{ km}) = 9.05 \times 10^3 \text{ km}$.

$\Delta t = \dfrac{d}{v_S} - \dfrac{d}{v_P} = \dfrac{9.05 \times 10^3 \text{ km}}{6.0 \text{ km/s}} - \dfrac{9.05 \times 10^3 \text{ km}}{8.0 \text{ km/s}} = \boxed{3.8 \times 10^2 \text{ s}}$.

R

r

R 45°

d

(b) $r = R \cos 45°$. So the depth under the surface is

$R - r = R(1 - \cos 45°) = (6.4 \times 10^3 \text{ km})(1 - \cos 45°) = 1.9 \times 10^3 \text{ km} > 30 \text{ km}$.

Therefore, $\boxed{\text{yes}}$, the waves do cross the boundary of the mantle.

(c) $t = \dfrac{2(6.4 \times 10^3 \text{ km})}{8.0 \text{ km/s}} = \boxed{1.6 \times 10^3 \text{ s; S waves do not go through the liquid core}}$.

66. (a) $v = \sqrt{\dfrac{Y}{\rho}} = \sqrt{\dfrac{7.0 \times 10^{10} \text{ N/m}^2}{2.7 \times 10^3 \text{ kg/m}^3}} = 5091 \text{ m/s}$. $\lambda = \dfrac{v}{f} = \dfrac{5091 \text{ m/s}}{40 \text{ Hz}} = \boxed{1.3 \times 10^2 \text{ m}}$.

(b) $v = \sqrt{\dfrac{11 \times 10^{10} \text{ N/m}^2}{8.9 \times 10^3 \text{ kg/m}^3}} = 3516 \text{ m/s}$. $\lambda = \dfrac{3516 \text{ m/s}}{40 \text{ Hz}} = \boxed{88 \text{ m}}$.

76. $\boxed{5}$ nodes.

78. From $f_3 = 3f_1$, we have $f_1 = \dfrac{f_3}{3} = \dfrac{450 \text{ Hz}}{3} = \boxed{150 \text{ Hz}}$.

80. (a) $f_1 = \dfrac{v}{2L} = \dfrac{12 \text{ m/s}}{2(4.0 \text{ m})} = 1.5 \text{ Hz}$. So $\boxed{\text{yes}}$, 15 Hz is the 10th harmonic.

(b) $\boxed{\text{No}}$, 20 Hz is not a harmonic.

83. $v = \sqrt{\dfrac{F_T}{\mu}} = \sqrt{\dfrac{40 \text{ N}}{2.5 \times 10^{-2} \text{ kg/m}}} = 40 \text{ m/s}$. $f_n = \dfrac{nv}{2L} = \dfrac{40 \text{ m/s}}{2(2.0 \text{ m})}\, n = 10n \text{ Hz}$.

So the frequencies of the first four harmonics are $\boxed{10 \text{ Hz, 20 Hz, 30 Hz, and 40 Hz}}$.

86. The first harmonic, $\lambda_1 = 4L$. $f_1 = \frac{v}{\lambda} = \frac{v}{4L} = 1 \times \frac{v}{4L}$;

the next harmonic (3rd), $\lambda_3 = \frac{4L}{3}$, $f_3 = \frac{3\,v}{4L} = 3 \times \frac{v}{4L}$;

the next harmonic (5th), $\lambda_5 = \frac{4L}{5}$, $f_5 = \frac{5\,v}{4L} = 5 \times \frac{v}{4L}$.

Therefore $f_m = \frac{mv}{4L} = m\frac{3.5 \times 10^3 \text{ m/s}}{4(1.0 \text{ m})} = \boxed{m(8.8 \times 10^2 \text{ Hz}),\ m = 1, 3, 5, \ldots}$.

91. $x = A\cos\omega t = A\sin(\omega t + 90°)$.

So $v = \omega A\cos(\omega t + 90°) = -\omega A\sin\omega t$

and $a = -\omega^2 x = -\omega^2 A\cos\omega t$.

$v_{max} = \omega A = (50 \text{ rad/s})(0.10 \text{ m}) = \boxed{5.0 \text{ m/s}}$.

$a_{max} = \omega^2 A = (50 \text{ rad/s})^2(0.10 \text{ m}) = \boxed{2.5 \times 10^2 \text{ m/s}^2}$.

95. Since $v = \sqrt{\frac{F_T}{\mu}}$, doubling the tension will make the speed $\sqrt{2}$ times larger.

The wavelength is unchanged since it is determined by the length of the string and the mode of vibration. However, the frequency is increased by a factor of $\sqrt{2}$ due to the speed increase.

VI. Practice Quiz

1. A 2.0-kilogram object is attached to a spring of spring constant 1.8 N/m. If the object is displaced slightly from its equilibrium position and released. What is the period of vibration?
(a) zero (b) 0.90 s (c) 0.95 s (d) 1.9 s (e) 6.0 s.

2. An object attached to the free end of a spring executes simple harmonic motion according to the equation $y = (0.50 \text{ m})\sin(18\pi t)$ where y is in meters and t in seconds. What is the frequency of the vibration?
(a) 0 (b) 3.0 Hz (c) 9.0 Hz (d) 18 Hz (e) 18π Hz

3. The wave speed on a string is 12 m/s. What is the wavelength of a wave of frequency 3.0 Hz traveling on the string?
(a) 3.0 m (b) 4.0 m (c) 9.0 m (d) 15 m (e) 36 m

4. Resonance in a system, such as a string fixed at both ends or a suspension bridge, occurs when

(a) it is oscillating in simple harmonic motion.

(b) it is oscillating in damped simple harmonic motion.

(c) a natural frequency of the system is the same as the external driving frequency.

(d) a natural frequency of the system is smaller than the external driving frequency.

(e) a natural frequency of the system is larger than the external driving frequency.

5. In seismology, the S wave is a transverse wave. As an S wave travels through the Earth, the relative motion between the S wave and the particles of the Earth's interior is

(a) perpendicular. (b) first perpendicular, then parallel.

(c) not at any particular angle to each other. (d) parallel. (e) antiparallel.

6. The mass of a simple pendulum is doubled. By what factor does the frequency change?

(a) It does not change. (b) It doubles. (c) It quadruples.

(d) It becomes half as large. (e) It becomes 1/4 as large.

7. When an object of mass m oscillates on a spring, its frequency is f. A mass $2m$ is now placed on the same spring and it again oscillates in SHM. What is its frequency?

(a) $0.25f$ (b) $0.50f$ (c) $0.71f$ (d) $1.4f$ (e) $2f$

8. A piano string of linear mass density 0.0050 kg/m is under a tension of 1350 N. What is the wave speed?

(a) 130 m/s (b) 260 m/s (c) 520 m/s (d) 1040 m/s (e) 2080 m/s

9. If a guitar string has a third harmonic frequency of 1500 Hz, which of the following frequencies can set the string into resonant vibration?

(a) 125 Hz (b) 250 Hz (c) 500 Hz (d) 625 Hz (e) 750 Hz

10. An object on a spring oscillates in simple harmonic motion with a frequency of 1.00 Hz and an amplitude of 5.00 cm. If a timer is started when the mass is at the equilibrium position, what is its distance from its equilibrium position at $t = 2.25$ s?

(a) 7.50 cm (b) 5.00 cm (c) 2.50 cm (d) 1.25 cm (e) zero

Answers to Practice Quiz:

1. e 2. c 3. b 4. c 5. a 6. a 7. c 8. c 9. c 10. b

CHAPTER 13

Geometrical Optics: Reflection and Refraction of Light

I. Chapter Objectives

Upon completion of this chapter, you should be able to:

1. define and explain the concept of wave fronts and rays.
2. explain the law of reflection and distinguish between regular (specular) and irregular (diffuse) reflections.
3. explain refraction in terms of Snell's law and the index of refraction, and give examples of refractive phenomena.
4. describe internal reflection and give examples of fiber optic applications.
5. explain dispersion and some of its effects.

II. Key Terms

Upon completion of this chapter, you should be able to define and/or explain the following key terms:

wave front
plane wave front
ray
geometrical optics
reflection
angle of incidence
angle of reflection
law of reflection
regular (specular) reflection
irregular (diffuse) reflection
refraction
Huygen's principle
angle of refraction
Snell's law
index of refraction
critical angle
total internal reflection
fiber optics
dispersion

The definitions and/or explanations of the most important key terms can be found in the following section: **III. Chapter Summary and Discussion.**

III. Chapter Summary and Discussion

1. Wave Fronts and Rays (Section 13.1)

A **wave front** is the line (in two dimensions) or surface (in three dimensions) defined by adjacent portions of a wave that are in phase. For example, a point light source emits spherical wave fronts because the points having the same phase angle are on the surface of a sphere. For a parallel beam of light, the wave front is a **plane wave front**. The distance between adjacent wave fronts is the wavelength.

A **ray** is a line drawn perpendicular to a series of wave fronts and pointing in the direction of propagation. For a spherical wave, the rays are radially outward, and for a plane wave, they are parallel to each other. The use of wave fronts and rays in describing optical phenomena such as reflection and refraction is called **geometrical optics**.

2. Reflection (Section 13.2)

The **law of reflection** states that the **angle of incidence** (the angle between the incident ray and the normal) equals the **angle of reflection** (the angle between the reflected ray and the normal), $\theta_i = \theta_r$, where θ_i is the angle of incidence and θ_r the angle of reflection. The incident ray, the normal, and the reflected ray are always in the same plane.

Note: All angles are measured *from the normal (line perpendicular) to the reflecting surface.*

Regular (specular) reflection occurs from smooth surfaces, with the reflected rays parallel to each other. **Irregular (diffuse) reflection** occurs from rough surfaces, with the reflected rays being at different angles.

Example 13.1 Two mirrors make an angle of 90° with each other. A ray is incident on mirror M_1 at an angle of 30° to the normal. Find the direction of the ray after it is reflected from mirror M_1 and M_2.

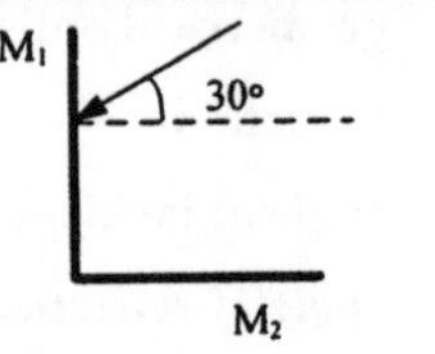

Solution:

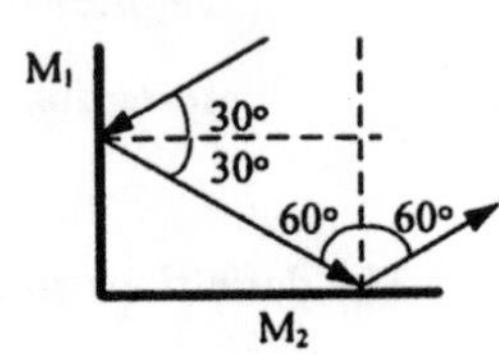

All angles should be measured from the normal to the reflecting surface. The angle of incidence of the ray at M_1 is 30°. According to the law of reflection, the angle of reflection at M_1 is also 30°. From geometry, the angle of incidence at M_2 is $90° - 30° = 60°$. Therefore, the angle of reflection at M_2 is also 60°, and the ray emerges parallel to the original incident ray.

---

3. **Refraction** (Section 13.3)

Refraction refers to the change in direction of a wave at a boundary where it passes from one medium into another as a result of different wave speeds in different media. This phenomenon can be geometrically explained by **Huygens' principle**: every point on an advancing wave front can be considered to be a source of secondary waves, or wavelets, and the line or surface tangent to all these wavelets defines a new position of the wave front.

Snell's law relates the angle of incidence, θ_1, and angle of refraction θ_2, (the angle between the refracted ray and the normal to the boundary) to the wave speeds in the respective media: $\frac{\sin \theta_1}{\sin \theta_2} = \frac{v_1}{v_2}$. The **index of refraction** of a medium is defined as the ratio of the speed of light in vacuum to its speed in that medium, $n = \frac{c}{v}$. Snell's law can be conveniently expressed in terms of the indices of refraction, $n_1 \sin \theta_1 = n_2 \sin \theta_2$. If the second medium is more optically dense ($n_2 > n_1$), then $\theta_1 > \theta_2$, or the refracted ray is bent toward the normal; if less dense ($n_2 < n_1$), then $\theta_2 > \theta_1$ and bending is away from the normal.

When light travels from one medium to another, the frequency remains constant, but the speed and wavelength change. In terms of wavelength, the index of refraction can be rewritten as $n = \frac{\lambda}{\lambda_m}$, where λ is the wavelength in vacuum and λ_m the wavelength in the medium.

Note: Since the geometrical representation of light is used here, a diagram is very helpful (if not necessary) in solving problems. Again, all angles are measured from the normal to the interface boundary.

Example 13.2 A light ray travels through an air–fused quartz interface at an angle of 30° to the normal. Find the speed of light in the quartz and the angle of refraction.

Solution: Given: $n_2 = 1.46$ (fused quartz, from Table 22.1),

$n_1 \approx 1.00$ (air), $\theta_1 = 30°$.

Find: v and θ_2.

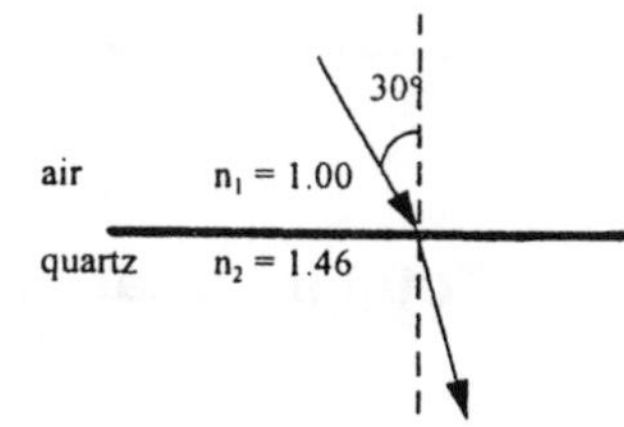

From $n = \frac{c}{v}$, we have $v_2 = \frac{c}{n_2} = \frac{3.00 \times 10^8 \text{ m/s}}{1.46} = 2.05 \times 10^8$ m/s.

From Snell's law, $n_1 \sin \theta_1 = n_2 \sin \theta_2$,

$\sin \theta_2 = \frac{n_1 \sin \theta_1}{n_2} = \frac{(1.00) \sin 30°}{1.46} = 0.342.$ So $\theta_2 = 20.0°$

Example 13.3 A beam of light traveling in air is incident on a slab of transparent material. The incident beam and the refracted beam make angles of 40° and 26° to the normal, respectively. Find the speed of light in the transparent material.

Solution: Given: $n_1 \approx 1.00$ (air), $\theta_1 = 40°$, $\theta_2 = 26°$.

Find: v_2.

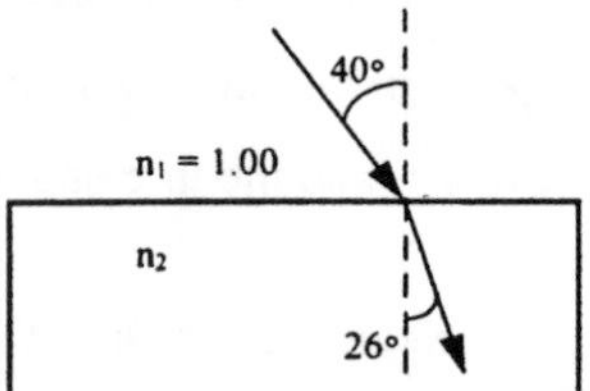

We first find the index of refraction of the transparent material.

From Snell's law, $n_1 \sin\theta_1 = n_2 \sin\theta_2$,

we have $n_2 = \dfrac{n_1 \sin\theta_1}{\sin\theta_2} = \dfrac{(1.00)\sin 40°}{\sin 26°} = 1.47$.

Therefore, from $n = \dfrac{c}{v}$, the speed of light in the material is

$$v_2 = \frac{c}{n_2} = \frac{3.00 \times 10^8 \text{ m/s}}{1.47} = 2.04 \times 10^8 \text{ m/s}.$$

Example 13.4 A light ray from a He-Ne laser has a wavelength of 632.8 nm and travels from air to crown glass.

(a) What is the frequency of the light in air?

(b) What is the frequency of the light in glass?

(c) What is the wavelength of light in glass?

Solution: Given: $n_2 = 1.52$ (crown glass from Table 22.1)

$n_1 = 1.00$ (air), $\lambda = 632.8 \text{ nm} = 632.8 \times 10^{-9}$ m.

Find: (a) f (b) f_m (c) λ_m.

(a) From $c = \lambda f$, we have $f = \dfrac{c}{\lambda} = \dfrac{3.00 \times 10^8 \text{ m/s}}{632.8 \times 10^{-9} \text{ m}} = 4.74 \times 10^{14}$ Hz.

(b) The frequency is a constant (same for all media). So $f_m = f = 4.74 \times 10^{14}$ Hz.

(c) From $n = \dfrac{\lambda}{\lambda_m}$, $\lambda_m = \dfrac{\lambda}{n} = \dfrac{632.8 \text{ nm}}{1.52} = 416$ nm.

4. Total Internal Reflection and Fiber Optics (Section 13.4)

At a certain **critical angle** (θ_c), the angle of refraction for a ray going from a medium of greater optical density to a medium of lesser optical density ($n_1 > n_2$) is 90° and the refracted ray is along the media boundary. For any angle of incidence $\theta_1 > \theta_c$, the **total internal reflection** (no refracted light) occurs and the surface acts like a mirror. By Snell's law, the critical angle can be calculated in terms of the indices of refraction of the two media,

$\sin\theta_c = \dfrac{n_2}{n_1}$ (for $n_1 > n_2$). If the second medium is air, then $\sin\theta_c = \dfrac{1}{n}$. **Fiber optics** uses the principle of total internal reflection. Signals can travel a long distance without losing much intensity due to the lack of refraction.

Note: Total internal reflection occurs only if the second medium is less dense than the first *and* if the angle of incidence exceeds the critical angle.

Example 13.5 A diver is 1.5 m beneath the surface of a still pond of water. At what angle must the diver shine a beam of light toward the surface in order for a person on a distant bank to see it?

Solution: Given: $\theta_2 = 90°$, $n_2 = 1.00$ (air), $n_1 = 1.33$ (water).

$n_2 = 1.00$

$n_1 = 1.33$

θ_1

Find: θ_1.

When the refracted light is along the boundary, the angle in water is equal to the critical angle. $\theta_1 = \theta_c = \sin^{-1}\dfrac{n_2}{n_1} = \sin^{-1}\dfrac{1.00}{1.33} = \sin^{-1} 0.752 = 48.8°$.

Or from Snell's law, $n_1 \sin\theta_1 = n_2 \sin\theta_2$, we have $\sin\theta_1 = \dfrac{n_2 \sin\theta_2}{n_1} = \dfrac{(1.00)\sin 90°}{1.33} = 0.752$,

so $\theta_1 = 48.8°$.

For the light to reach the distant person, it has to shine at or below 48.8°, so there is no total internal reflection. Do you know why some fish-preying birds like pelicans stay very low before they try to catch fish?

Example 13.6 A 45°–45° prism is a wedge-shaped object in which the two acute angles are 45°. It is very useful for changing the direction of light rays in optical devices. If a light ray is traveling through a glass prism according to the diagram shown, what is the minimum index of refraction of the glass?

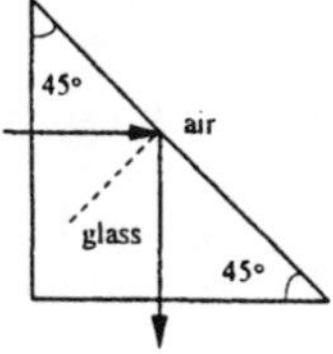

Solution: Given: $n_2 = 1.00$ (air), $\theta_c = 45°$. Find: n_1 (minimum).

There is no refracted ray beyond the glass–air boundary, so the light must be internally reflected. For total internal reflection to occur, the index of reflection n_1 must be greater than that of air. The minimum index of reflection corresponds to an angle of incidence of 45°.

$\sin\theta_c = \dfrac{n_2}{n_1}$, so the minimum n_1 is $\dfrac{n_2}{\sin\theta_c} = \dfrac{1.00}{\sin 45°} = 1.41$.

---

5. **Dispersion** (Section 13.5)

Dispersion is the separation of multi-wavelength light into its component wavelengths when the light is refracted. This is caused by the fact that different wavelengths have slightly different indices of refraction and therefore different speeds. In most materials (so called normal dispersion), longer wavelengths have smaller indices of refraction. According to Snell's law, different wavelengths will have different angles of refraction and are therefore separated. A rainbow is produced by refraction, dispersion, and total internal reflection within water droplets.

Example 13.7 A beam of white light strikes a piece of glass at a 70° angle (measured from the normal). A red light of wavelength 680 nm and a blue light of wavelength 430 nm emerge from the boundary after being dispersed. The index of refraction for the red light is 1.4505 and the index of refraction for the blue light is 1.4693.

(a) Which color of light is refracted more?

(b) What is the angle of refraction for each color?

(c) What is the angular separation between the two colors?

Solution: Given: $n_1 = 1.0000$ (air), $n_{2r} = 1.4505$, $n_{2b} = 1.4693$, $\theta_1 = 70°$.

Find: (b) θ_{2r} and θ_{2b} (c) $\Delta\theta$.

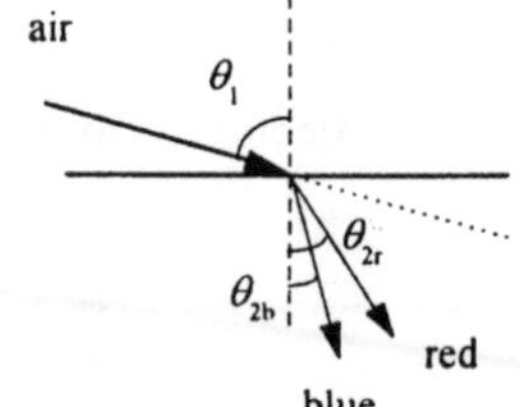

(a) Since the index of refraction of the blue light is greater, its angle of refraction is smaller (bent more toward the normal), and therefore it is refracted more.

(b) We use Snell's law, $n_1 \sin\theta_1 = n_2 \sin\theta_2$,

for red: $$\sin\theta_{2r} = \frac{n_1 \sin\theta_1}{n_{2r}} = \frac{(1.0000)\sin 70°}{1.4505} = 0.64784, \text{ so } \theta_{2r} = 40.379°;$$

for blue: $$\sin\theta_{2b} = \frac{(1.0000)\sin 70°}{1.4693} = 0.63955, \text{ so } \theta_{2b} = 39.758°.$$

(c) $\Delta\theta = \theta_{2r} - \theta_{2b} = 40.379° - 39.758° = 0.621°$.

IV. Mathematical Summary

Law of Reflection	$\theta_1 = \theta_r$ (13.1)	Relates the angles of incidence and reflection.
Snell's Law	$\frac{\sin\theta_1}{\sin\theta_2} = \frac{v_1}{v_2}$ (13.2) or $n_1 \sin\theta_1 = n_2 \sin\theta_2$ (13.3)	Relates the angles of incidence and refraction, and the speeds of light in the media (or indices of refraction).

Index of Refraction	$n = \frac{c}{v} = \frac{\lambda}{\lambda_m}$ (13.3,4)	Defines the index of refraction of a material.
Critical Angle at Boundary between Two Materials	$\sin \theta_c = \frac{n_2}{n_1}$ (13.6) where $n_1 > n_2$	Computes the critical angle between two materials for total internal reflection.
Critical Angle at Material–Air Boundary	$\sin \theta_c = \frac{1}{n}$ (13.7)	Computes the critical angle between material–air boundary for total internal reflection.

V. Solutions of Selected Exercises and Paired/Trio Exercises

5. They are visible because of the diffuse reflections by the particulate matter in the air.

9. $\theta_r = \theta_i = 90° - 43° = \boxed{47°}$

so $\theta_i = \theta_r = \tan^{-1} 0.833 = \boxed{40°}$.

12. According to the law of reflection, the angle of reflection from the second mirror is $\boxed{20°}$.

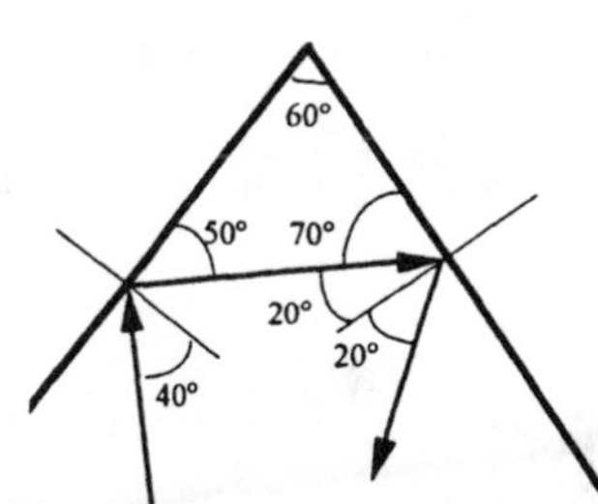

16. According to the law of reflection,

$\beta = 180° - [\alpha + (90° - \theta_{i_1})] = 90° - \alpha + \theta_{i_1}$.

So the angle of reflection from the second mirror is

$\theta_{r_2} = 90° - \beta = \alpha - \theta_{i_1}$.

(a) $\theta_{r_2} = 70° - 35° = \boxed{35°}$.

(b) $\theta_{r_2} = 115° - 60° = \boxed{55°}$.

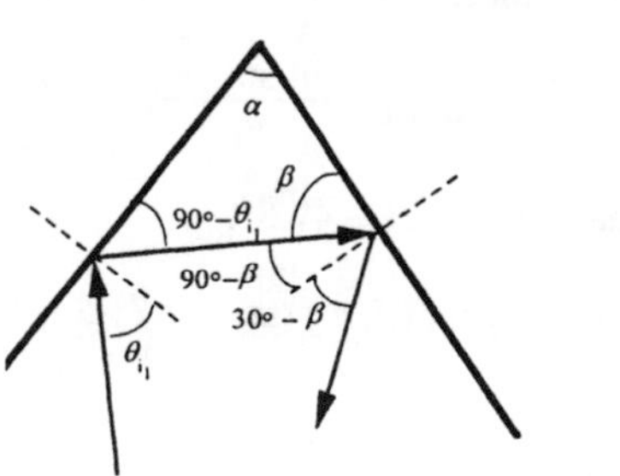

25. The laser has a better chance to hit the fish. The fish appears to the hunter at a location different from its true location due to refraction. The laser beam obeys the same law of refraction and retraces the light the hunter sees the fish. The arrow goes into the water in a near-straight line path.

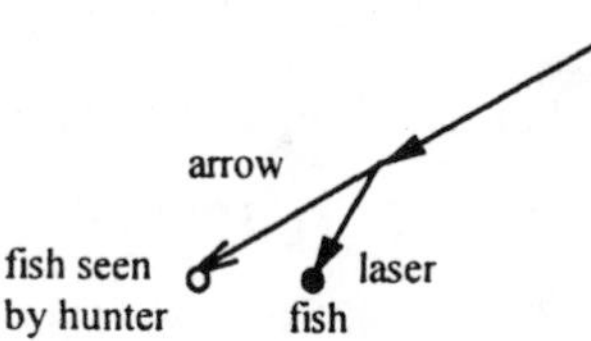

28. $n_1 \sin \theta_1 = n_2 \sin \theta_2$, ☞ $\sin\theta_2 = \dfrac{n_1 \sin\theta_1}{n_2} = \dfrac{(1)\sin 60°}{1.33} = 0.651$. So $\theta_2 = \boxed{41°}$.

30. $\boxed{1.34}$.

36. $\dfrac{v_B}{v_A} = \dfrac{c/n_B}{c/n_A} = \dfrac{n_A}{n_B} = \dfrac{4/3}{5/4} = \boxed{\dfrac{16}{15}}$.

40. The first refraction is at the air-glass interface and the second refraction is at the glass-water interface.

From Snell's law, $n_1 \sin \theta_1 = n_2 \sin \theta_2$, we have $\sin \theta_2 = \dfrac{n_1 \sin \theta_1}{n_2} = \dfrac{(1) \sin 40°}{1.50} = 0.429$.

So $\theta_2 = 25.4°$.

The critical angle at the glass-water interface is $\theta_c = \sin^{-1} \dfrac{n_3}{n_2} = \sin^{-1} \dfrac{1.33}{1.50} = \sin^{-1} 0.887 = 62.5°$.

Therefore the angle of incidence at the glass-water interface is smaller than the critical angle and thus there is no total internal reflection and $\boxed{\text{yes}}$, the fish is illuminated.

46. The setting is at zero altitude or 90° from the normal, so the angle should equal to the critical angle of

$\theta_c = \sin^{-1} \dfrac{1}{n} = \sin^{-1} \dfrac{1}{1.33} = \sin^{-1} 0.752 = \boxed{48.8°}$.

53. $\theta_2 = \tan^{-1} \dfrac{0.50 \text{ m}}{0.75 \text{ m}} = \tan^{-1} 0.667 = 33.7°$.

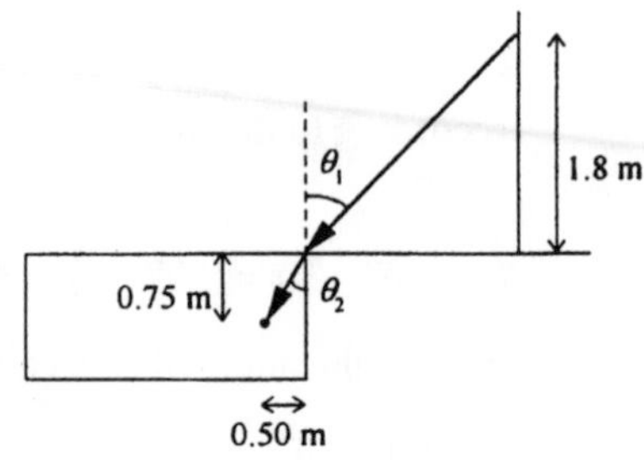

From Snell's law, $n_1 \sin \theta_1 = n_2 \sin \theta_2$,

we have $\sin \theta_1 = \dfrac{n_2 \sin \theta_2}{n_1} = \dfrac{(1.33) \sin 33.7°}{1} = 0.738$.

Therefore $\theta_1 = 47.5°$.

Thus $d = (1.8 \text{ m}) \tan \theta_1 = (1.8 \text{ m}) \tan 47.5° = \boxed{2.0 \text{ m}}$.

55. (a) We use Snell's law, $n_1 \sin \theta_1 = n_2 \sin \theta_2$.

For refraction at the prism-prism interface, $(1.60) \sin 45° = (1.40) \sin \theta_2$,

so $\theta_2 = \sin^{-1} 0.808 = 53.9°$.

For the prism-air interface,

$\theta_3 = 180° - [135° + (90° - \theta_2)] = \theta_2 - 45° = 53.9° - 45° = 8.9°$.

So $(1.40) \sin 8.9° = (1) \sin \theta$,

therefore $\theta = \sin^{-1} 0.217 = \boxed{12.5°}$.

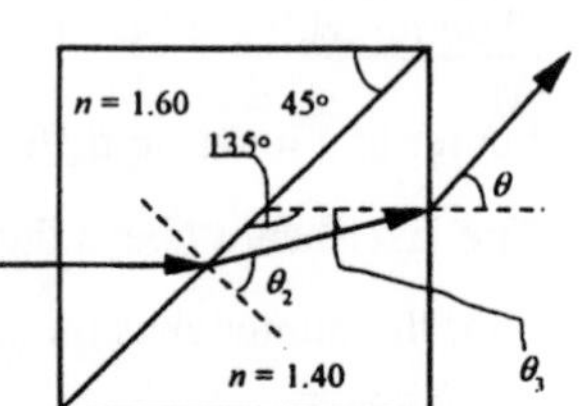

(b) $\theta_c = \sin^{-1}\dfrac{n_2}{n_1} = \sin^{-1}\dfrac{1.40}{1.60} = 61.0°$.

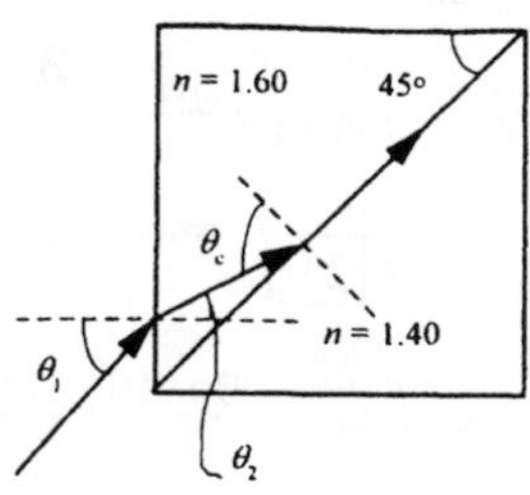

This is the angle required at the interface.

For the air-prism interface,

$\theta_2 = 180° - [135° + (90° - \theta_c)] = \theta_c - 45° = 61.0° - 45° = 16.0°$.

So (1) $\sin\theta_1 = (1.60)\sin 16°$,

therefore $\theta_1 = \sin^{-1} 0.441 = \boxed{26.2°}$

58. It is due to the $\boxed{\text{different speeds of different frequencies in the material}}$. This, in turn, causes the different indices of refraction, therefore the different angles of refraction.

62. From Snell's law, $n_1 \sin\theta_1 = n_R \sin\theta_R = n_B \sin\theta_B$, so $\sin\theta_R = \dfrac{n_1 \sin\theta_1}{n_R} = \dfrac{(1)\sin 37°}{1.515} = 0.3972$.

Therefore $\theta_R = 23.406°$. $\sin\theta_B = \dfrac{(1)\sin 37°}{1.523} = 0.3952$. Thus $\theta_B = 23.275°$.

Finally $\Delta\theta = 23.406° - 23.275° = \boxed{0.131°}$.

65. (a) We use Snell's law, $n_1 \sin\theta_1 = n_2 \sin\theta_2$.

For the first air-prism interface, (1) $\sin 80.0° = (1.400)\sin\theta_2$,

So $\theta_2 = \sin^{-1} 0.7034$. Therefore $\theta_2 = 44.70°$.

For the second prism-air interface,

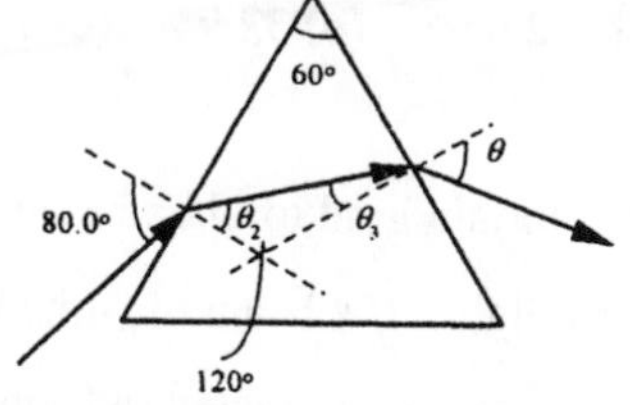

$\theta_3 = 180° - (120° + \theta_2) = 60° - \theta_2 = 60° - 44.70° = 15.30°$.

So $(1.400)\sin 15.30° = (1)\sin\theta$,

therefore $\theta = \sin^{-1} 0.3693 = \boxed{21.7°}$.

(b) For blue light, $\theta_2 = \sin^{-1}\dfrac{\sin 80.0°}{1.403} = 44.58°$. $\theta_3 = 60° - 44.58° = 15.42°$.

So $\theta = \sin^{-1}[(1.403)\sin 15.42°] = 21.90°$.

Therefore $\Delta\theta = 21.90° - 21.68° = \boxed{0.22°}$.

(c) For blue light, $\theta_2 = \sin^{-1}\dfrac{\sin 80.0°}{1.405} = 44.50°$. $\theta_3 = 60° - 44.50° = 15.50°$.

So $\theta = \sin^{-1}[(1.405)\sin 15.50°] = 22.05°$.

Therefore $\Delta\theta = 22.05° - 21.68° = \boxed{0.37°}$.

70. (a) From Snell's law, $n_1 \sin\theta_1 = n_2 \sin\theta_2$,

we have $\sin\theta_2 = \dfrac{n_1 \sin\theta_1}{n_2} = \dfrac{(1)\sin 40°}{1.52} = 0.423.$

So $\theta_2 = \boxed{25°}$.

(b) $v = \dfrac{c}{n} = \dfrac{3.00 \times 10^8 \text{ m/s}}{1.52} = \boxed{1.97 \times 10^8 \text{ m/s}}$.

(c) $\lambda_m = \dfrac{\lambda}{n} = \dfrac{550 \text{ nm}}{1.52} = \boxed{362 \text{ nm}}$.

VI. Practice Quiz

1. If a material has a speed of light of 2.13×10^8 m/s, what is its index of refraction?

(a) 0.710 (b) 1.07 (c) 1.41 (d) 2.13 (e) 5.13

2. A light ray in air is incident on an air to glass interface boundary at an angle of 45° and is refracted in the glass at an angle of 27° with the normal. What is the index of refraction of the glass?

(a) 0.642 (b) 1.16 (c) 1.41 (d) 1.56 (e) 2.20

3. An optical fiber is made of clear plastic with index of refraction of $n = 1.50$. What is the minimum angle of incidence so total internal reflection can occur?

(a) 23.4° (b) 32.9° (c) 38.3° (d) 40.3° (e) 41.8°

4. A certain kind of glass has an index of refraction of 1.65 for blue light and an index of refraction of 1.61 for red light. If a beam of white light (containing all colors) is incident at an angle of 30°, what is the angle between the refracted red and blue light?

(a) 0.22° (b) 0.35° (c) 0.45° (d) 1.90° (e) 1.81°

5. A ray of white light, incident upon a glass prism, is dispersed into its various color components. Which one of the following colors experiences the least refraction?

(a) orange (b) yellow (c) red (d) blue (e) green

6. Which one of the following describes what will generally happen to a light ray incident on a glass-to-air boundary?

(a) total reflection (b) total refraction (c) partial reflection, partial refraction

(d) either (a) or (c) (e) either (b) or (c)

7. Light enters water from air. The angle of refraction will be

(a) greater than or equal to the angle of incidence. (b) less than or equal to the angle of incidence.

(c) equal to the angle of incidence. (d) greater than the angle of incidence.

(e) less than the angle of incidence.

8. A monochromatic light source emits a wavelength of 633 nm in air. When passing through a liquid, the wavelength reduces to 487 nm. What is the index of refraction of the liquid?

(a) 0.769 (b) 1.30 (c) 1.41 (d) 1.62 (e) 2.11

9. A fiber optic cable ($n = 1.50$) is submerged in water. What is the critical angle for light to stay inside the cable?

(a) 27.6° (b) 41.8° (c) 45.0° (d) 62.5° (e) 83.1°

10. An oil film ($n = 1.47$) floats on a water ($n = 1.33$) surface. If a ray of light is incident on the air–oil boundary at an angle of 37° to the normal, what is the angle of refraction at the oil–water boundary?

(a) 17.9° (b) 24.2° (c) 26.9° (d) 33.0° (e) 37.0°

Answers to Practice Quiz:

1. c 2. d 3. e 4. c 5. c 6. d 7. e 8. b 9. d 10. c

CHAPTER 14

Physical Optics: The Wave Nature of Light

I. Chapter Objectives

Upon completion of this chapter, you should be able to:

1. explain how Young's experiment demonstrates the wave nature of light and compute the wavelength of light from experimental results.
2. describe how thin films produce colorful displays and give some examples of practical applications of thin-film interference.
3. define diffraction and give examples of diffractive effects.
4. explain light polarization and give examples of polarization, both in the environment and in commercial applications.
5. define scattering and explain why the sky is blue and sunsets are red.

II. Key Terms

Upon completion of this chapter, you should be able to define and/or explain the following key terms:

physical (wave) optics
Young's double-slit experiment
thin-film interference
optical flats
Newton's rings
diffraction
diffraction grating
Bragg's law
polarization
polarizing (Brewster) angle
birefringence
dichroism
transmission axis (polarization direction)
optical activity
LCD (liquid crystal display)
scattering
Rayleigh scattering

The definitions and/or explanations of the most important key terms can be found in the following section: **III. Chapter Summary and Discussion**.

III. Chapter Summary and Discussion

1. Young's Double-Slit Experiment (Section 14.1)

Physical (wave) optics treats light as a wave in the study of some light phenomena, such as interference, diffraction, and polarization. These effects can not be successfully explained with geometric optics, in which light is treated as several rays that follow straight line paths.

Young's double-slit experiment not only demonstrates the wave nature of light, but also allows the measurement of the wavelength of light. In this experiment, a light source is incident on two closely spaced narrow slits. The light waves emanating from these two slits can be considered as two in-phase spherical sources and they interfere when they arrive at a screen. On the screen, the interference pattern consists of equally spaced bright fringes separated by equally spaced dark fringes.

As for sound waves , the condition for interference is determined by the *path-length difference* (ΔL) of the two waves, or the difference in distance traveled. If $\Delta L = n\lambda$ for $n = 0, 1, 2, 3, \ldots$, the interference is constructive (bright fringe); if $\Delta L = \frac{m\lambda}{2}$ for $m = 1, 3, 5, \ldots$, the interference is destructive (dark fringe). For two slits separated by a distance d, the path difference is $\Delta L = d \sin\theta$, so the condition for constructive interference in Young's double-slit experiment is $d \sin\theta = n\lambda$ for $n = 0, 1, 2, 3, \ldots$, where n is called the order number. The zeroth-order fringe ($n = 0$) corresponds to the central maximum, the first-order fringe ($n = 1$) is the first bright fringe on either side of the central maximum (there are two first-order fringes), and so on.

For a small angle θ, we have $\sin\theta \approx \tan\theta \approx \frac{y}{L}$, where y is the distance from the central maximum on the screen and L is the distance from the slits to the screen. The distance of the nth bright fringe (y_n) from the central maximum on either side is $y_n \approx \frac{nL\lambda}{d}$, the wavelength of light is then $\lambda \approx \frac{y_n d}{nL}$ for $n = 1, 2, 3, \ldots$, and the separation between adjacent bright fringes is $y_{n+1} - y_n = \frac{L\lambda}{d}$. (The dark fringes are separated by this distance also.)

Example 14.1 Light of wavelength 632.8 nm falls on a double-slit and the third-order bright fringe is seen at an angle of 6.5°. Find the separation between the double slits.

Solution: Given: $\lambda = 632.8\text{ nm} = 632.8 \times 10^{-9}\text{ m}$, $n = 3$, $\theta_3 = 6.5°$. Find: d.

From $d \sin\theta = n\lambda$, we have $d = \frac{n\lambda}{\sin\theta} = \frac{(3)\,\lambda}{\sin\theta_3} = \frac{(3)(632.8 \times 10^{-9}\text{ m})}{\sin 6.5°} = 1.7 \times 10^{-5}\text{ m} = 17\ \mu\text{m}$.

Example 14.2 In a Young's double-slit experiment, if the separation between the two slits is 0.10 mm and the distance from the slits to a screen is 2.5 m, find the spacing between the first-order and second-order bright fringes for light with wavelength of 550 nm.

Solution: Given: $d = 0.10$ mm $= 0.10 \times 10^{-3}$ m, $L = 2.5$ m, $\lambda = 550$ nm $= 550 \times 10^{-9}$ m.

Find: $y_2 - y_1$.

From $y_n = \frac{nL\lambda}{d}$, $y_2 - y_1 = \frac{(2)L\lambda}{d} - \frac{(1)L\lambda}{d} = \frac{L\lambda}{d} = \frac{(2.5\text{ m})(550 \times 10^{-9}\text{ m})}{0.10 \times 10^{-3}\text{ m}} = 1.4 \times 10^{-2}\text{ m} = 1.4\text{ cm}$.

2. Thin-Film Interference (Section 14.2)

The waves reflected from the two surfaces of a thin-film can interfere, and this **thin-film interference** depends on the reflective phases of the two reflected waves. Light reflected off a material whose index of refraction is greater than that of the one it is in ($n_2 > n_1$) undergoes a *180° phase change*. If $n_2 < n_1$, there is *no phase change* on reflection. For a particular film, light reflected from the film surfaces may interfere constructively and destructively, depending on the film thickness and any additional phase changes. A practical application of thin-film interference is the nonreflecting coatings for lenses (destructive interference for reflection of certain wavelengths). In a nonreflecting coating, the index of refraction of the film is usually between those of air and glass, so there are 180° phase changes for each reflection off the two surfaces of the film. The minimum thickness of the film is given by $t = \frac{\lambda}{4n}$, where n is the index of refraction of the film.

When a perfect spherical lens is placed on an **optical flat**, a very flat (usually as smooth as $\lambda/20$) piece of glass, circular fringes are observed. These fringes are called **Newton's rings**. If a lens has irregularities, the fringes are distorted. This is a simple, yet effective, method to check the quality of lenses in optical industries.

Example 14.3 A transparent material with an index of refraction 1.30 is used to coat a piece of glass with an index of refraction 1.52. What is the minimum thickness of the film in order to minimize the reflected light with a wavelength of 550 nm if the light is incident perpendicularly?

Solution: Given: $\lambda = 550$ nm, n (film) $= 1.30$. Find: t (minimum).

The index of refraction of the film is between those of air and glass, so both reflections from the two surfaces of the film have 180° phase shifts. We can use Equation (24.8).

The minimum film thickness is $t = \frac{\lambda}{4n} = \frac{550\text{ nm}}{4(1.30)} = 106$ nm.

3. Diffraction (Section 14.3)

Diffraction is the deviation or bending of light around objects, edges or corners. Generally, the smaller the size of the opening or object compared to the wavelength of light, the greater the diffraction. The diffraction pattern from a single slit of width w consists of a broader central maximum and some narrower side maxima (the width of the central maximum is twice that of the side maxima). Between two maxima, there is a region of destructive interference (dark fringes). In diffraction, the dark fringes rather than the bright fringes are analyzed.

The condition for the dark fringes is given by $w \sin \theta = m\lambda$ for $m = 1, 2, 3, \ldots$, where θ is the angle for a particular minimum designated by $m = 1, 2, 3, \ldots$ on either side of the central bright fringe (there is no dark fringe corresponding to $n = 0$. Why?) For a small angle approximation, the position of the dark fringes from the center of the central bright fringe on a screen can be calculated from $y_m = \frac{mL\lambda}{w}$, where L is the distance from the single slit to the screen. The width of the mth side maximum is the distance between the mth dark and the (m+1)th dark, or $y_{m+1} - y_m$. It is evident from this equation that

- for a given slit width (w), the greater the wavelength (λ), the wider the diffraction pattern (y_m);
- for a given wavelength (λ), the narrower the slit width (w), the wider the diffraction pattern (y_m);
- the width of the central maximum is twice the width of the side maxima.

Example 14.4 Light of wavelength 832.8 nm is incident on a slit of width 0.200 mm. An observing screen is placed 2.50 m from the slit. Find the width of the central maximum and the positions of the third-order dark fringe.

Solution: Given: $\lambda = 632.8 \text{ nm} = 632.8 \times 10^{-9}$ m, $w = 0.200 \text{ mm} = 0.200 \times 10^{-3}$ m, $L = 2.50$ m,

Find: $2y_1$ and y_3.

The central maximum is the region between the first-order dark fringes on either side of this maximum, so its width is simply $2y_1$.

From $y_m = \frac{mL\lambda}{w}$, we have $y_1 = \frac{(1)L\lambda}{w} = \frac{(1)(2.50 \text{ m})(632.8 \times 10^{-9} \text{ m})}{0.200 \times 10^{-3} \text{ m}} = 7.91 \times 10^{-3} \text{ m} = 7.91 \text{ mm}.$

So the width of the central maximum is $2y_1 = 2(7.91 \text{ mm}) = 15.8$ mm.

$$y_3 = \frac{(3)L\lambda}{w} = \frac{(3)(2.50 \text{ m})(632.8 \times 10^{-9} \text{ m})}{0.200 \times 10^{-3} \text{ m}} = 23.7 \text{ mm}.$$

Example 14.5 Light of wavelength 550 nm is incident on a single slit 0.75 mm wide. At what distance from the slit should a screen be placed if the second dark fringe in the diffraction pattern is to be 1.7 mm from the center of the screen?

Solution: Given: $\lambda = 550\text{ nm} = 550 \times 10^{-9}\text{ m}$, $w = 0.75\text{ mm} = 0.75 \times 10^{-3}\text{ m}$, $m = 2$,

$y_2 = 1.7\text{ mm} = 1.7 \times 10^{-3}\text{ m}$.

Find: L.

From $y_m = \dfrac{mL\lambda}{w}$, we have $L = \dfrac{y_m w}{m\lambda} = \dfrac{(1.7 \times 10^{-3}\text{ m})(0.75 \times 10^{-3}\text{ m})}{(2)(550 \times 10^{-9}\text{ m})} = 1.2\text{ m}$.

A **diffraction grating** consists of a larger number of closely spaced narrow slits. The diffraction pattern of a diffraction grating is a combination of multiple slit interference and single slit diffraction. It is very useful for dispersing different wavelengths or colors. (In general, it gives a larger dispersion than a prism.) The sharp (narrow, or well defined) bright fringes for a diffraction grating are given by $d \sin \theta = n\lambda$ for $n = 0, 1, 2, 3, \ldots$, where d is the spacing (or grating's spacing) between adjacent grating slits, which can be obtained from the number of lines per unit length of the grating, $d = \dfrac{1}{N}$. The number of spectral orders produced by a grating depends on the wavelength and on the grating's spacing d. Since $\sin \theta$ cannot be greater than 1, $\sin \theta = \dfrac{n\lambda}{d} \leq 1$, so the order number is therefore limited as follows: $n \leq \dfrac{d}{\lambda}$.

Note: In general, the small angle approximation cannot be used in a diffraction grating because of the grating's larger dispersion power. The bright fringes are usually separated by bigger distances here and, therefore, the angles do not satisfy the small angle approximation.

Example 14.6 Monochromatic light is incident on a grating that is 10.0 cm wide and ruled with 50 000 lines. The third-order maximum is seen at 46.3°. What is the wavelength of the incident light?

Solution: Given: $n = 3$, $\theta_2 = 46.3°$, $N = \dfrac{50\,000\text{ lines}}{10\text{ cm}} = 5000\text{ lines/cm}$.

Find: λ.

The grating spacing is $d = \dfrac{1}{N} = \dfrac{1}{5000\text{ lines/cm}} = 2.00 \times 10^{-4}\text{ cm} = 2.00 \times 10^{-6}\text{ m}$.

From $d \sin \theta = n\lambda$, we have $\lambda = \dfrac{d \sin \theta}{n} = \dfrac{(2.00 \times 10^{-6}\text{ m}) \sin 46.3°}{3} = 4.82 \times 10^{-7}\text{ m} = 482\text{ nm}$.

Example 14.7 Monochromatic light of wavelength 632.8 nm is incident normally on a diffraction grating. If the third-order maximum of the diffraction pattern is observed at 32.0°,

(a) what is the grating's spacing?

(b) how many total number of visible maxima can be seen?

Solution: Given: $\lambda = 632.8 \text{ nm} = 632.8 \times 10^{-9} \text{ m}$, $n = 3$, $\theta_3 = 32.0°$.

Find: (a) d (b) total number of visible maxima.

(a) From $d \sin\theta = n\lambda$, we have $d = \dfrac{n\lambda}{\sin\theta} = \dfrac{(3)(632.8 \times 10^{-9} \text{ m})}{\sin 32.0°} = 3.58 \times 10^{-6} \text{ m}$.

(b) The maximum value of the angle θ is 90° (sin 90° = 1), so the maximum order number is

$n_{max} = \dfrac{d}{\lambda} = \dfrac{3.58 \times 10^{-6} \text{ m}}{632.8 \times 10^{-9} \text{ m}} = 5.66.$ Since n is an integer, $n_{max} = 5$.

Therefore, 11 maxima are seen including the center one ($n = 0$, two for $n = 1$, two for $n = 2$, two for $n = 3$, two for $n = 4$, and two for $n = 5$).

The regular atomic spacing in a crystalline solid acts as a diffraction grating for light of much shorter wavelength than visible light such as X-rays. By measuring the diffraction angle, which is equal to the incidence angle also, of an X-ray beam with known wavelength, the distance between the crystal's internal planes (d) can be determined from **Bragg's law**, $2d\sin\theta = n\lambda$ for $n = 1, 2, 3, \ldots$.

4. Polarization (Section 14.4)

Polarization is the preferential orientation of the electromagnetic field vectors that make up a light wave, and is evidence that light is a transverse wave. Light with some partial preferential orientation of the electromagnetic field vectors is said to be *partially polarized.* If the electromagnetic field vectors oscillate in *one* plane (or *one* direction), the light is then *plane (linearly) polarized.* Light can be polarized by reflection, double refraction (**birefringence**), selective absorption (**dichroism**), and scattering.

Light that is partially reflected and partially refracted is partially polarized. However, when the reflected and the refracted rays form a 90° angle, the reflected ray is linearly polarized or maximum polarization occurs. The angle of incidence for this maximum polarization is called the **polarizing** or **Brewster angle**. The polarizing angle for a material of index of refraction n in air is given by $\tan\theta_p = n$ or $\theta_p = \tan^{-1} n$.

In some materials, the anisotropy of the speed of light with direction (speed of light is different in different directions) gives rise to different indices of refraction in different directions. This property is called birefringence, and such materials are said to be *birefringent* or *double refracting*. When a beam of unpolarized light is incident on a birefringent crystal, it is doubly refracted and separated into two components, or rays. These two rays are linearly polarized with the electromagnetic field vectors in mutually perpendicular directions.

Some crystals, such as tourmaline and herapathite, exhibit the interesting property of absorbing one of the polarized components more than the other. This property is called **dichroism**. If the dichroic material is sufficiently thick, the more strongly absorbed component may be completely absorbed, resulting in a linearly polarized beam with the unabsorbed component. Polaroid films (used in sunglasses) are synthetic polymer materials, which allow light of one polarization direction to pass. This direction is called the **transmission axis**, or **polarization direction**. If two films (the first one is called the polarizer and the second one is called the analyzer) are placed with their transmission axes parallel to each other, light can pass through both films. If the two transmission axes are perpendicular to each other, little or no light can pass. In general, the intensity of the transmitted light is given by $I = I_o \cos^2 \theta$, where θ is the angle between the transmission axes of the polarizer and analyzer, I_o the original intensity, and I the intensity after the analyzer. This expression is known as *Malus's law*.

Some transparent materials have the ability to rotate the polarization direction of the linearly polarized light. This is called the **optical activity** and is due to the molecular structure of the material. Some liquid crystals are optically active, and this property forms the basis of the common **liquid crystal display (LCD)**.

Example 14.8 How far above the horizon is the Moon when its image reflected in calm water is completely polarized?

Solution: Given: $n = 1.33$ (water). Find: $90° - \theta_p$.

The polarizing angle is the angle of incidence (measured from the normal) when the reflected ray is linearly polarized. The angle above the horizon is the angle measured from the surface ($90° - \theta_p$).

From $\tan \theta_p = n$, we have $\theta_p = \tan^{-1} n = \tan^{-1} 1.33 = 53.1°$.

So the angle above the horizon is $90° - 53.1° = 36.9°$.

Example 14.9 Unpolarized light is passed through a polarizer-analyzer combination. The transmission axes of the polarizer and analyzer are at 45° to each other. What percentage of the light gets through the filters?

Solution:

When unpolarized light is incident on the polarizer, only one of the two components can pass; that is, only 50% of the intensity gets through the polarizer. So before the light reaches the analyzer, the intensity is already reduced to half.

From Malus's law, $I = I_o \cos^2 \theta$, $\frac{I}{I_o} = \cos^2 \theta = \cos^2 45° = 0.50$ or 50%.

Therefore, only $\frac{50\%}{2} = 25\%$ of the original intensity passes through the polarizer-analyzer.

---

5. Atmospheric Scattering of Light (Section 14.5)

Scattering is the process of particles (like air molecules or dust particles) absorbing light and re-radiating polarized light. The scattering of sunlight by air molecules causes the sky to look blue and sunsets to look red because the shorter wavelength (blue) is scattered more efficiently than long wavelength (red). This is called **Rayleigh scattering** and the scattering intensity is found to be proportional to $\frac{1}{\lambda^4}$.

Blue scatters more efficiently than red. In the morning and evening, the blue component of the light from the Sun is scattered more in the denser atmosphere near the Earth, so we see red when we look in the direction of the rising or setting Sun. During the day, we mainly see the blue component from overhead scattering.

IV. Mathematical Summary

Bright Fringe Condition (double-slit interference)	$d\sin\theta = n\lambda$ for $n = 0, 1, 2, \ldots$ (14.3)	Gives the positions of the bright fringes in double-slit interference experiment.
Wavelength Measurement (double-slit interference for small θ only)	$\lambda = \frac{y_n d}{nL}$ for $n = 1, 2, 3, \ldots$ (14.7)	Determines the wavelength in double-slit interference experiment.
Nonreflecting Film Thickness (minimum)	$t = \frac{\lambda}{4n}$ (for $n_2 > n_1 > n_o$) (14.8)	Gives the minimum thickness of a thin film coating to minimize reflection.
Dark Fringe Condition (single-slit diffraction)	$w\sin\theta = m\lambda$ for $m = 1, 2, 3, \ldots$ (14.9)	Gives the positions of the dark fringes in single slit diffraction experiment.

Lateral Displacement of Dark Fringes (single-slit diffraction)	$y_m = \frac{mL\lambda}{w}$ for $m = 1, 2, 3, \ldots$ (14.10)	Gives the lateral position of the mth dark fringe in single-slit diffraction experiment.
Interference Maxima for a Diffraction Grating	$d \sin\theta = n\lambda$ for $n = 0, 1, 2, \ldots$ (14.13) where $d = \frac{1}{N}$ and N is the number of lines per unit length	Determines the positions of the bright fringes for a diffraction grating.
Limit of Order Number	$n \le \frac{d}{\lambda}$ (14.14)	Gives the highest order number for a diffraction grating.
Brewster (polarizing) Angle	$\tan\theta_p = n$ (14.16)	Calculates the polarizing or Brewster angle in a medium to air boundary.

V. Solutions of Selected Exercises and Paired/Trio Exercises

5. The path-length difference will change because of the airplane. This change in path-length difference results in a change in the condition of interference, i.e., constructive is no longer constructive and destructive is no longer destructive, etc. Therefore the pictures flutter.

8. $0.75 \text{ m} = 0.50 \text{ m} + 0.25 \text{ m} = 1.5(0.50 \text{ m}) = 1.5\lambda$.

So the waves will interfere $\boxed{\text{destructively}}$.

12. The distance is equal to $y_3 - y_o = 3\Delta y = \frac{3L\lambda}{d} = \frac{3(1.5 \text{ m})(680 \times 10^{-9} \text{ m})}{0.25 \times 10^{-3} \text{ m}} = \boxed{1.2 \text{ cm}}$.

14. $\boxed{\text{600 nm (orange-yellow)}}$.

20. (a) because only the reflection at n_o–n_1 interface has 180° phase shift.

25. (a) $\lambda_n = \frac{\lambda}{n} = \frac{550 \text{ nm}}{1.5} = 367 \text{ nm}$. $t = 1.1 \times 10^{-5} \text{ m} = 30(367 \times 10^{-9} \text{ m}) = \boxed{30\lambda}$.

(b) The path length difference $\Delta L = 2t = 2(30\lambda) = 60\lambda$.

However, the first reflection has a 180° phase shift. So they will interfere $\boxed{\text{destructively}}$.

26. $t = \frac{\lambda}{4n} = \frac{700 \text{ nm}}{4(1.4)} = 125 \text{ nm} = \boxed{1.3 \times 10^{-7} \text{ m}}$.

31. (a) The two rays for interference are the reflections from the bottom surface of the top plate and the top surface from the bottom plate. The reflection from the top surface of the bottom plate has 180° phase shifts, so the condition for constructive interference for reflection is $\Delta L = 2t = \frac{\lambda}{2}$,

so $t = \frac{\lambda}{4} = \frac{632.8 \text{ nm}}{4} = \boxed{158.2 \text{ nm}}$.

(b) Constructive for transmission is the same as destructive for reflection.

So $\Delta L = 2t = \lambda$, ☞ $t = \frac{\lambda}{2} = \frac{632.8 \text{ nm}}{2} = \boxed{316.4 \text{ nm}}$.

38. (a) The width of the central maximum is

$y_1 - y_{-1} = 2\Delta y = \frac{2L\lambda}{w} = \frac{2(1.0 \text{ m})(480 \times 10^{-9} \text{ m})}{0.20 \times 10^{-3} \text{ m}} = \boxed{4.8 \text{ mm}}$.

(b) $y_3 - y_2 = y_4 - y_3 = \Delta y = \frac{L\lambda}{w} = \boxed{2.4 \text{ mm}}$.

41. (a) From $d \sin\theta = m\lambda$, we have $\lambda = \frac{d \sin\theta}{m} = (0.025 \text{ m}) \sin 10° = \boxed{4.3 \text{ mm}}$.

(b) $f = \frac{c}{\lambda} = \frac{3.00 \times 10^8 \text{ m/s}}{4.34 \times 10^{-3} \text{ m}} = 6.9 \times 10^{10} \text{ Hz}$, $\boxed{\text{microwave}}$.

46. $d = \frac{1}{10\,000 \text{ lines/cm}} = 1.0 \times 10^{-4} \text{ cm} = 1.0 \times 10^{-6} \text{ m}$.

From $d \sin\theta = m\lambda$, we have $m_{\text{max}} = \frac{d \sin 90°}{\lambda} = \frac{d}{\lambda} = \frac{1.0 \times 10^{-6} \text{ m}}{560 \times 10^{-9} \text{ m}} = 1.8$.

So there are $\boxed{3}$ orders of maxima corresponding to $m = 0$ or ± 1.

48. $\boxed{\text{They do not overlap}}$.

51. Since $d \sin\theta = m\lambda$, $\theta = \sin^{-1} \frac{m\lambda}{d}$.

For violet, $\theta_{3\text{v}} = \sin^{-1} \frac{(3)(400 \text{ nm})}{d} = \sin^{-1} \frac{1200 \text{ nm}}{d}$.

For yellow-orange, $\theta_{2\text{y}} = \sin^{-1} \frac{(2)(600 \text{ nm})}{d} = \sin^{-1} \frac{1200 \text{ nm}}{d}$.

So $\theta_{3\text{v}} = \theta_{2\text{y}}$, i.e., they overlap.

56. We see the rainbow by the scattering of light from the water droplets. The light is partially polarized in the horizontal direction, so the axis of the analyzer should be in the horizontal direction. We can never block out the polarized light completely because it is only partially polarized.

60. $n = \tan\theta_p = \tan 58° = \boxed{1.6}$.

69. Blue scatters more efficiently than red. In the morning and evening, the blue component of the light from the Sun is scattered more in the denser atmosphere near the Earth, so we see red when we look in the direction of the rising or setting Sun. During the day, we mainly see the blue component from overhead scattering.

73. From $n = \tan\theta_p$, we have $\theta_p = \tan^{-1} n = \tan^{-1} 1.5 = \boxed{56°}$.

77. Since $\Delta y = \dfrac{\lambda L}{d}$, $\Delta\theta = \dfrac{\Delta y}{L} = \dfrac{\lambda}{d} = \dfrac{480 \times 10^{-9}\text{ m}}{0.75 \times 10^{-3}\text{ m}} = \boxed{6.4 \times 10^{-4}\text{ rad}}$.

80. $d = \dfrac{1}{9000\text{ lines/cm}} = 1.11 \times 10^{-4}\text{ cm} = 1.11 \times 10^{-6}\text{ m}$.

From $d \sin\theta = m\lambda$, we have $m_{max} = \dfrac{d \sin 90°}{\lambda} = \dfrac{d}{\lambda}$.

For red, $m_{max} = \dfrac{1.11 \times 10^{-6}\text{ m}}{700 \times 10^{-9}\text{ m}} = 1.6$. So $m_{max} = \boxed{1\text{ for red}}$.

For violet, $m_{max} = \dfrac{1.11 \times 10^{-6}\text{ m}}{400 \times 10^{-9}\text{ m}} = 2.8$. So $m_{max} = \boxed{2\text{ for violet}}$.

VI. Practice Quiz

1. If a wave from one slit of a Young's double-slit experiment arrives at a point on the screen two wavelengths behind the wave from the other slit, what is observed at that point?
(a) bright fringe (b) dark fringe (c) gray fringe (d) multi-colored fringe (e) none of the above

2. A monochromatic light is incident on a Young's double-slit separated by 3.00×10^{-5} m. The resultant bright fringe separation is 2.15×10^{-2} m on a screen 1.20 m from the double slit. What is the separation between the third order bright fringe and the zeroth order fringe?
(a) 8.60×10^{-2} m (b) 7.35×10^{-2} m (c) 6.45×10^{-2} m (d) 4.30×10^{-2} m (e) 2.15×10^{-2} m

3. What is the minimum thickness of a nonreflecting coating ($n = 1.35$) on a glass lens ($n = 1.52$) for wavelength 550 nm?

(a) zero (b) 102 nm (c) 204 nm (d) 90.5 nm (e) 181 nm

4. What will happen to the width of the central maximum if the width of the slit decreases in a single slit experiment?

(a) decrease (b) increase (c) remain unchanged (d) does not depend on the separation
(e) cannot be determined because not enough information is given

5. Light of wavelength 610 nm is incident on a slit 0.20-millimeter wide and the diffraction pattern is produced on a screen that is 1.5 m from the slit. What is the width of the central maximum?

(a) 0.34 cm (b) 0.68 cm (c) 0.92 cm (d) 1.22 cm (e) 1.35 cm

6. A beam of unpolarized light in air strikes a flat piece of glass at an angle of incidence of 57.0°. If the reflected beam is completely polarized, what is the index of refraction of the glass?

(a) 0.54 (b) 0.84 (c) 1.12 (d) 1.54 (e) 1.84

7. What is the process to obtain polarized light in a dichroic material like Polaroid film?

(a) reflection (b) refraction (c) double refraction (d) selective absorption (e) scattering

8. When the transmission axes (polarization directions) of two Polaroid sheets are parallel to each other, what is the percentage of the incident light which will pass the two sheets?

(a) 0% (b) 25% (c) 50% (d) 75% (e) 100%

9. White light is spread out into spectral hues by a diffraction grating. If the grating has 2000 lines per centimeter, at what angle will red light ($\lambda = 640$ nm) appear in the first-order?

(a) 0° (b) 3.57° (c) 7.35° (d) 11.2° (e) 13.4°

10. A helium–neon laser ($\lambda = 632.8$ nm) is used to calibrate a diffraction grating. If the first-order maximum occurs at 20.5°, how many lines are there in a millimeter?

(a) 138 (b) 185 (c) 276 (d) 455 (e) 552

Answers to Practice Quiz:

1. a 2. c 3. b 4. b 5. c 6. d 7. d 8. c 9. c 10. e